MY NAME IS SAROYAN

William Saroyan 1908-1981

MY NAME IS SAROYAN

Compiled with a Commentary by
James H. Tashjian

Coward-McCann, Inc.
New York

Endpaper Linoleum Cuts by Dertad P. Boyajian
Library of Congress Cataloging in Publication Data

Saroyan, William, date.
  My name is Saroyan.

  I. Tashjian, James H.   II. Title.
PS3537.A826A6   1983   818'.5209   82-22136
ISBN 0-698-11229-6

Printed in the United States of America

First Edition

to
William Saroyan
August 31, 1908–May 18, 1981

> My writing will be discovered
> again and again. It will speak
> to the begatters.
>   —WILLIAM SAROYAN

This work was proffered to The Putnam Publishing Group, in tribute to Putnam's late brilliant head, George Haven Putnam (1844–1930) who, in his lifetime, was a tireless advocate of the rights of the Armenian nation, a cause to which William Saroyan was himself devoted.

EDITOR'S NOTE

The 103 Saroyan pieces found in the present anthology were earliest and originally published in one or another of the three organs of the Hairenik publishers, of Boston, Massachusetts: the *Hairenik Daily, Hairenik Weekly* (now *Armenian Weekly*), and *The Armenian Review*. On understandings arrived at between Mr. Saroyan and the Haireniks, all Saroyan works published in the Haireniks were to be the sure property of the Haireniks; while the right of any media other than the Haireniks to republish such pieces was contingent on the issuance by the Haireniks of written permission to republish, and/or the unencumbered will of Mr. Saroyan to select pieces submitted to and published in the Haireniks for republication in other media denoted by him. Accordingly, 32 of the concomitant Saroyan writings were later republished in media other than the Haireniks, whence they were borrowed; but no Saroyan work included in this anthology has been republished from other media or sources.

Although the republication history of these 32 pieces republished elsewhere after their earliest appearance in the Haireniks is clearly spelled out in the Notes appended to this anthology, separate acknowledgment is here made. *This listing includes titles of works by William Saroyan or others from which important quotations have been taken.*

Avon Books, NY: *31 Selected Stories from Inhale and Exhale* (1958); George Braziller, NY: *The William Saroyan Reader* (1958); Creative Arts Book Company, Berkeley, CA: *Obituaries* (1979); Dell Publishing Company, Inc., NY: *The Man With the Heart in the Highlands* (1968); George Fields, San Francisco, CA: *A Native American* (1938); Harcourt Brace and Company, NY: *The Assyrian and Other Stories* (1949), *Dear Baby* (1944), *Little Children* (1937), *My Name Is Aram* (1940), *Saroyan's Fables* (1941), *The Time of Your Life and Miscellaneous Essays* (1939), *The Trouble With Tigers* (1938); Harcourt Brace and World, Inc., NY: *My Kind of Crazy, Wonderful People: Seventeen Stories and a Play* (1964); Harcourt Brace Jovanovich, Inc., NY: *The Saroyan Special* (1948); Little, Brown and Company, Boston, MA: *The Whole Voyald and Other Stories* (1956); McGraw-Hill Book Company, NY: *Sons Come and Go, Mothers Hang In Forever* (1976); Modern Age Books, Inc., NY: *Love, Here is My Hat* (1938), *Peace, It's Wonderful* (1939); Modern Library (Random House), NY: *Inhale and Exhale* (1936); Pocket Books, NY: *Short Drive, Sweet Chariot* (1967); Praeger Publishers, NY: *Places Where I've Done Time* (1972); Simon and Schuster, NY: *Here Comes / There Goes You Know Who* (1961); World Publishing Company, NY: *Letters from 74 rue Taitbout or Don't Go But If You Must Say Hello to Everybody* (1969); and, Random House, Inc., NY: Karen Kennedy (ed.), *Hesitant Wolf and Scrupulous Fox: Fables Selected from World Literature* (1973); Twayne-G. K. Hall and Company, Boston, MA: Howard R. Floan, *William Saroyan* (imprinted "New York," 1966).

APPRECIATIONS

To the staffs of the Main Branch, Boston Public Library; the Widener Library, Harvard University, Cambridge; the Free Library of the City of Newton, Massachusetts, for having patiently endured the insistent harassment of the editor.

To Lemyel Amirian, Palo Alto, California, an intimate and early associate of William Saroyan, for his encouragement; John Kallenberg, The Librarian, Fresno, California, County Library, who dug out for us important statistical biographics of the Saroyan family; our friend, the bibliophile Mark A. Kalustian, Arlington, Massachusetts, for permitting us to avail ourselves of the wonders found in his important collection of Saroyana; Dickran Kouymjian, Professor of Armenian Studies, California State University, Fresno; Thomas Vartabedian, Haverhill, Massachusetts, for photography gracing these pages; Armenne Kechichian Derderian, Watertown, Massachusetts, for retyping certain manuscript pages.

To the administration of the Hairenik Publications, Boston, who without reserve threw open to us the files of *Hairenik Daily*, *Hairenik Weekly*, and *The Armenian Review*, where we located the Saroyan pieces found in this anthology; the Armenian Research Foundation, which enthusiastically urged this publication; reverently, to the memory of the late Reuben Darbinian who, as editor in chief of Haireniks, earliest gave Saroyan print and who served as his surrogate father; and to the late James Garabed Mandalian, whose understanding of the vagaries of genius allowed William Saroyan to test freely his fledgling wings.

J. H. T.

Contents

A Preface (and Other Things)

The dusty files of the three remarkable publications of the Armenian Hairenik (Fatherland) Association of Boston—the *Hairenik Daily*, the *Hairenik Weekly* (now the *Armenian Weekly*), and *The Armenian Review*, a quarterly journal—are the home of a large body of works of the late American author and playwright, William Saroyan (August 11, 1908–May 8, 1981). Many of these Saroyan short stories, plays, and verses are today little, if at all, known even to the most devoted zealots of the international Saroyan cult.

The present Saroyan anthology is meant to provide access to these neglected works, most of which date back to the most brilliant period of his literary career—the years immediately preceding the Second World War, when his popularity was at its height. We hope at the same time to press a firmer understanding than now prevails of the man and his work through an exposition of the influences and motivations which spurred Saroyan—a matter of some confusion.

We submit that this disorder exists precisely because the significance of Saroyan's career-long collaboration with the Haireniks—his unique empathy with them—is undiscussed and unappreciated, and that the key to an understanding of what William Saroyan was all about is found in the Haireniks phase of his career.

The neglect of Saroyan's works in the Haireniks and the meaning of his persistence in contributing *sans honoraire* to that press is all the more confounding in that Saroyan's literary career received its fair start there. In fact, as this anthology shows, Saroyan's Haireniks input represents the largest body of Saroyan works to appear in any one unitarian source.

From his earliest contribution to the *Hairenik Daily* (January 14, 1933) to his last literary work in *The Armenian Review* (late 1963), Saroyan published 97 short stories, most in the *Hairenik Weekly*, 4 plays, and 5 verses, that is, 106 pieces falling into the creative category. In all, at least 117 Saroyan contributions appeared in these three Hairenik publications, but this anthology does not contain 11 of these pieces since they are commentaries, letters, messages, book reviews, and other miscellany which fall out of the creative-literary purview.

Of the 97 short stories, only 32 are known to have been republished in Saroyan's better-known anthologies. These include seven brief fables republished in 1941 under one title. None of his four concomitant plays and five verses has ever been republished. Every piece here included received its maiden print in the Haireniks. Unfortunately, comparatively few Saroyan anthologies containing material borrowed from the Haireniks have given clear and proper credit to the original source publication, a matter of distress to Saroyan. Such omissions of credit lines have, of course, contributed to the dearth of public knowledge of Saroyan's collaboration with the Haireniks.

Nevertheless, one must question the authority of those Saroyan bibliographies which, for whatever reason, pass dumbly over the existence of this enormous company of Saroyan works; for definitive studies of the life and works of William Saroyan can hardly be produced without extensive notices of the author's Haireniks writings and his relations with that press, reflective of the all-pervasive "Armenian phase" of his career, an influence readily apparent in most of his total output, both in the Haireniks and elsewhere.

Working with this anthology and the "Saroyan Memorial Issue: 105 Unpublished Letters of William Saroyan: Ethnic Motivations of an American writer"[1] the researcher will have available most of the tools he will need to correct the serious lacunae, to which reference has been made, that plague existing Saroyan biographies, bibliographies, and critical studies. As for general readership, we think there will be agreement that the Saroyan specimens published herewith are representative of the highest genius of this extraordinary talent.

It is a matter of record that by 1933, when Saroyan was twenty-five years of age, he had only two publications, two stories appearing in 1928 issues of *California Overland Monthly and Outwest Magazine*, which were disregarded universally. In a letter to the *Hairenik Weekly* (printed May 9, 1974) in which Saroyan mourns the passing of that organ's editor, James G. Mandalian, Saroyan relates how it was that he found his way to the Haireniks in early 1933:

> In San Francisco right now is the man who ran into me sometime in 1933 and suggested that I might send some "news" to *Hairenik Daily* which was running half a page in English every issue—Armen Bardizian, or Bardizbanian . . . Well, it was not possible for me to send the English-language page of *Hairenik Daily* "news" but it seemed to me that I had better send that page a piece of my own

writing, a sketch, a short story, or even a poem, and so I did, and the writing appeared on that page and I began to hear from the editor . . . Now, it is very useful for a new writer to see his stuff in print because this is apt to bring home to him the responsibility he must accept about making his writing worthy of being put into print. There are other, more subtle, reasons for apprentice writers to find a place for their early writings, and I am glad to be able to say again that the English-language page at the *Hairenik* became established at just the right time for me, and that I was quick to see the good sense of sending my efforts first to the *Hairenik Daily*, and soon after to the newly-founded *Hairenik Weekly*. . . .[2]

Valuable though this confessional might be, it neglects to report that what followed on his early printings in the *Hairenik Daily* and *Hairenik Weekly* proved of crucial consequence to the launching of his career—to his meteoric rise and establishment as an internationally honored writer.

After his first three appearances in the *Daily*—in the form of three poems (*HD*, January 14, 21, and April 7, 1933)—writing as "Sirak Goryan," Saroyan contributed his two earliest short stories to the *Daily*: "A Fist Fight for Armenia" (May 9 and 10, 1933), and "The Broken Wheel" (June 3, 4, and 5, 1933). A third, "The Barber's Apprentice," followed (October 5 and 6, 1933).

According to the accepted versions, Saroyan then sent another short story, his "Daring Young Man on the Flying Trapeze," to Whit Burnett and Martha Foley, the editors of *Story* magazine, who accepted it and published it in their February 1934 issue. It was an instant sensation. According to one source, Burnett and Foley thought they "had discovered the most significant talent since Jack London and Frank Norris. They had never known a more instantaneous response to a newcomer. . . . The reception of his first story [they said] brought him dozens of letters from other writers . . ." (Howard R. Floan, *William Saroyan*. New York: Twayne, 1966).

During a 1975 chat with this editor, Saroyan cast important new light on the story of his "discovery":[3]

It is important we straighten that one out. My letter on James' [Mandalian] death, and most other accounts, simply do not tell the whole story. I have always had the greatest gratitude to Whit and Martha, but it seems to me that they simply planted their story of my discovery in *Story* in the interests of gilding the image of their magazine, and their story is true as far as it goes, and here is the full story. Now, when "The Barber's Apprentice" appeared in *Hairenik Daily*, I clipped it out of the paper and then, on second thought, I clipped out my other two *Daily* stories ["A Fist Fight for Armenia" and "The Broken Wheel"] and sent them to *Story* with a covering letter of a sort, using my real name and not "Sirak Goryan," the presumed author who was of course William Saroyan. At the same time, I had a third thought. I clipped out another set of the three stories and sent it to Edward J. O'Brien, but I did not tell O'Brien that the Sirak Goryan who was supposed to be the author of the three pieces was really a guy named William Saroyan. Shortly, Martha and Whit wrote back and said they were impressed with my stories and suggested that I send them a fresh piece for their reading. Now, I had just banged out a crazy type of novel called "Trapeze Over the Universe," so I just made a short story out of it, called it "The Daring Young Man on the Flying Trapeze," and sent it to them. They accepted it and there we were. But I found I had a problem. Shortly after *Story* published "Trapeze" under my real name, O'Brien wrote me, as "Sirak Goryan" of course, informing me that he had selected "The Broken Wheel" for appearance in his *Best American Stories of 1934*. There I was, two stories written by the same author—and two authors—and each being published in different sources. But no harm done—I wrote O'Brien and told him that Sirak Goryan was really the William Saroyan of *Story*, and that was that. What we have then is this: I sent the first three *Hairenik* stories to Whit and Martha, and then another set to Edward O'Brien. Whit and Martha liked them and asked for something fresh, and you couldn't ask for a fresher story than "Trapeze." Meanwhile, O'Brien chose "The Broken Wheel" which originally appeared in *Hairenik*, for his 1934 anthology. Now, you must say the *Hairenik* gave me my start. That is all . . .[4]

For Saroyan and the Haireniks it was the start of an extraordinary relationship, and there never really was an end.

Saroyan gave a fuller account of his discovery of the *Hairenik Daily* in private conversations with me:

In 1932, Armen Bardizian was an editor of Hairenik, in Boston and, if I recall, he was visiting in Fresno. I met him at my uncle Aram's office which I often visited to pass the time of day and enjoy a lively argument. Aram's office was often a gathering place for Armenian dignitaries, and I always enjoyed listening in on their discussions. Years before, I had met the great [General] Antranik there, as I have related in one of my stories. This time, it was Armen Bardizian. There were certainly others there too but I cannot remember them. When Aram saw me, tilting his head in my general direction, my uncle said in Armenian to Bardizian, "Here now, here's my nephew

Willie, the crazy son of the Saroyans, and the Lord forgive them for
begetting such a son. Only crazy boys try to be writers. But he is a
good *lagod* [kid] and somehow manages to stay out of trouble,
although his pockets have holes. Bardizian, talk to him. Advise him
to stop trying to be a writer and to go to work, get married, have
children, buy land, study, become a lawyer, and join me in this
office." Bardizian was a short and rather wiry man, with deepset
eyes, and I warmed to him when he started talking quietly to me,
while the others conducted their *bartkam [avor] akan dzoghov* [conven-
tion]. He asked about my writing, and I told him I was always
writing, but no one seemed to want to read what I wrote. He said,
do *you think* you *can* write? I said, I write great stuff. In that case, he
said, "keep writing. A man is his own best critic." He asked if I knew
that his paper in Boston had just started several columns of English-
language stuff in each issue, and I told him that I had observed this
arrangement in *Hairenik* issues I had seen at the *Asbarez* club. Well,
he said, why don't you write something to the *Hairenik* yourself? I
said, what something? Well, news of Fresno Armenian activities. I
said, I write literature, not news, but let me think about it. He said,
well, send your stuff to Reuben Darbinian, the editor, and I'll talk to
him about it.[5]

And continuing:

You're making me think back and that is good for a writer because
the only thing a writer can really *write* about is the past *he* has
experienced, because then he can be sure it's real life. You ask, did I
have any knowledge of *Hairenik* before I met Bardizian? Well the
Asbarez of Fresno, published by the same people who produced
Hairenik [the Armenian Revolutionary Federation] first came out in
the same year I was born [1908] and before that almost everyone
read the *Hairenik*, which came by mail. My father died when I was
three years of age and I later found a number of issues of *Hairenik* in
his belongings which he had chosen to save, for one reason or
another. When *Asbarez* came out, I have been told, my folks
switched to that paper, probably because they couldn't afford to buy
both. But they were the same, and we grew up within the *Asbarez-
Hairenik* circle. My father even worked for a short while at the
Asbarez, as a custodian or something like that. Later, whenever I
would drop in at the Asbarez *surjaran* [coffee-house, club] to play
scambil [a boisterous Armenian card game], or *tavloo* [backgammon],
I would see copies of the *Hairenik* on the reading table and would
often fondly handle them, wondering what treasures they told, for I
couldn't read a word of Armenian. When I discovered the English-

language columns in *Hairenik*, I took to reading them, but it never occurred to me to write to them until Bardizian put the bee in my bonnet, so to speak. Say, it was an act of providence that I did. It often occurs to me that I might never have made it if the *Hairenik* had not been there . . .[6]

What emerges from this is that Saroyan's decision to "write something" for *Hairenik* was taken not merely because it represented an avenue toward publication, but also because of the position the *Hairenik* enjoyed in the rapidly growing Armenian community in America. It was the Armenian *Times*. The step Saroyan took in the direction of Boston's *Hairenik* was a natural gravitation to a beckoning hearth.

Although by 1982 the *Hairenik Daily* was in its eighty-third year of uninterrupted publication—the oldest and largest Armenian-language newspaper in the Armenian dispersion and, in that year, at least the seventh oldest ethnic organ in the United States—it could not claim to have been the first Armenian journalistic venture in America.[7]

Before Hairenik's conception in 1899 out of an editorial facility located in the rear of one of the ubiquitous Armenian tailor shops in downtown New York City, short-lived Armenian "newspapers" had been published in Jersey City Heights, New Jersey; New York City, and Lynn and Worcester, Massachusetts; but all examples of this pioneer press had been initiated as personal enterprises and were hardly more than local community news sheets, crudely done and lacking the stuff of longevity. Similarly, *Hairenik*'s founder and first editor, Tovmas Charshafjian, had no supporting company or organization behind him, but his weekly paper boldly espoused the cause of the Armenian Revolutionary Federation (A.R.F.), a growingly popular Armenian political party. This gave him a sort of built-in readership and the tools for national distribution.

In 1900, the A.R.F. acquired outright Charshafjian's *Hairenik* and moved its offices to Boston, the center of an immense industrial area the Armenian population of which was steadily multiplying as Armenian immigrants continued to arrive in Boston, Worcester, Lowell, Lawrence, Providence, and their general contiguity, seeking employment in the New England factories and mills. Charshafjian yielded his editorship to Arshag Vramian, who had had considerable editorial experience abroad. Under Vramian's guidance, the organ flourished and, when he left his *Hairenik* desk seven years later for other assignments abroad, *Hairenik* enjoyed a surprising financial stability and a considerable national stature, and had, under public demand, converted to a biweekly.

Vramian was followed by a brilliant succession of editors: H. H. Chakmakjian, a Harvard man who later was to serve as professor of biochemistry at Tufts Medical; N. D. S. Tashjian, a Harvard-graduate dental surgeon; Adom Yorjanian who, as "Siamanto," was one of the

more widely read Armenian poets of his day; Manoog Hampartzou-
mian, a Yale graduate and later an attorney; Nishan Desdegule, a Brown
University Ph.D.; and others, who preserved in *Hairenik* not only the
virtues inculcated by Vramian, but also, through their American experience, helped the organ define its role as a medium serving an ethnic
community which was rapidly becoming the largest concentration of
Armenians in any nation outside the bounds of historical Armenia.

It should be clearly noted that *Hairenik* became established firmly
during that period (1899–1915) when, because of political, economic, and
social developments in the Armenian homeland, the influx of Armenian
migrants to the United States mounted from an estimated 55 in all of
America in the early 1870s to 55,000 by 1914, or during that span of years
just preceding the Armenian massacres in Turkey that opened in 1915—a
dread event which temporarily staunched the flow of Armenian migra-
tion to America. This simply means that *Hairenik's* early career bracketed
that era when the present Armenian community, now about 600,000
strong, had its most immediate beginnings. Following the cessation of
World War I, the prewar Armenian American demography of 55,000 was
augmented by the arrival of another block of about 150,000 immigrants, a
group almost entirely composed of survivors of the massacres. During
this age of Armenian displacement and survival, the *Hairenik* served as
the voice of the Armenian conscience in America, assisted the adjustment of the newcomers to their new surroundings, imparted hope and
inspiration to them, and became for them a fixture and a tradition on the
Armenian American scene. In Saroyan's day, *Hairenik's* influence on the
developing character and institutions of the Armenian community in
America was already pervasive.

But the *Hairenik Daily* took real shape in 1922, with the assumption of
its editorial reins by Dr. Reuben Darbinian (1883–1968), a graduate of
Heidelberg and Moscow universities, who had served as Minister of
Justice in the cabinet of the Independent Republic of Armenia (1918–
1920). Darbinian quickly took the organ past the bounds of a simple
news publication and gave it breadth and substance. Soon perceiving
that a mongrelization of news, community affairs, and other public
services, with a smattering of intellectual writings, simply was a mixture
of oil and water, Darbinian provided the learned community with a
vehicle of expression upon the initiation of *Hairenik Daily's* companion
journal, the *Hairenik Monthly* (1923).

Similarly in the early thirties, Darbinian and his sponsors felt the
growing need for an English-language organ for the service of a swiftly
multiplying generation of American-born Armenians versed in English
and unhappily only somewhat, if at all, in Armenian.

To search out public response, in 1932 Darbinian opened a series of
English-language columns in the otherwise wholly Armenian-language

pages of *Hairenik*. The reaction to this experiment was positively stunning. The Armenian community in America had successfully endured its period of settlement here and could now turn from its domestic retrenchment to Armenian national considerations. Contrary to the gloomy predictions of those Armenian leaders—Darbinian was not among the Jeremiahs—the American-born Armenian had not been lost in the warp and woof of the American tapestry. The public response to the English-language materials in the *Hairenik* was a vindication of those who swore that all had not been lost in the American maelstrom; further, it demonstrated that the atavistically enthusiastic young Armenian in America had to be given tools that would encourage him to understand and preserve his heritage. One of these tools would be a separate *Hairenik* published in English. Thus, on March 1, 1934, the *Hairenik Weekly*, still another Hairenik component inseparable from the Saroyan story, was born.

A decade later, Darbinian and his friends noted the necessity of still another publication, an English-language journal which would be to the *Weekly* what the *Hairenik Monthly* was to the *Daily* in Armenian—a vehicle that would allow the *Weekly* to follow its chosen path of news and community reporting, while the new journal invited the contributions of creative writers and historians, and of allied disciplinarians in the Armenian studies field. And so, in the winter of 1948, the fourth member of the Hairenik family was born—*The Armenian Review*. This newest addition to the *Hairenik*s was also to play an important role in the Saroyan saga.

In a word, as we shall see in the Saroyan materials that follow, William Saroyan's career was intimately connected to three milestones in the history of the Haireniks: the English-language columns of *Hairenik Daily*, the founding and firming of *Hairenik Weekly*, and the establishment and course of *The Armenian Review*—the present Hairenik trinity.[8]

It is disgraceful—and the word is carefully chosen—that for whatever reasons or considerations, the significant Haireniks syndrome in the life and career of William Saroyan is today buried under layers of "intellectual" debris laid down by those who have pretended to be authorities on this "complex" and "enigmatic" man; but the truth is that William Saroyan is "enigmatic" only to those who cannot or do not bother to understand what his Armenian heritage meant to him—how large a role the practice of that heritage played in his success. That ethnic motivation is best typified by the Haireniks phase of Saroyan's life and career.

For William Saroyan was a restless man torn between two worlds—the world of Armenia, his overseas heritage into which, through the accidents of fate, he had not been born but which he felt welling within him; and the world of America, into which he had been born, and in whose opportunities he exulted. Saroyan's life was spent synthesizing and mediating this "immigrant" dichotomy, a phenomenon present in those blessed with undying and compulsive pride in their parental heritage; and this he was able to do brilliantly in a manner more poignant and graphic, but with less homily and maudlin eloquence, than any other American author of avowed ethnic persuasion and inspiration.

William Saroyan was born August 31, 1908, in Fresno, California, to Armenak and Takoohi Saroyan, both natives of the important city of Bitlis (Baghesh), west of Lake Van, in historical Armenia. His father was a lay Armenian Presbyterian preacher who had, in his native city, enjoyed the patronage of a local American missionary, the Reverend William Stonehill, after whom Armenak named his younger son.

When her husband passed away in 1911, William was three years of age. Mrs. Saroyan placed her four children—Cosette (who was later to marry the Reverend Stonehill's son), Zabel, and Henry, all born in the old country, and William—in the Fred Finch Orphanage in Oakland, while she worked as a domestic in the Bay area. William's impressions of his five years at Finch, limited of course by the uncertainties of childhood memory, were later only sketchily, but in some strikingly bittersweet prose, described in his writings.[9]

In 1916 the family moved back to Fresno, where William entered the public schools. He proved at best to be a troublesome and unsuccessful pupil, but his primary educational years were not a loss; what he did not learn in school he made up for in the streets of the colorful "Armenian town" ward, which William was to immortalize in his magical *My Name is Aram* and recurrently in other works, notably in a number of other, neglected "Aram" stories which originally appeared in the Haireniks.

His reluctant, tumultuous years of formal education ended with his second year at high school. To supplement the family income, Saroyan took on odd jobs, including a disastrous stint as a factotum in his uncle Aram's law office. By nature a maverick, a rebellious nonconformist and the utter despair of his family, Saroyan had early conceived the ambition to be a writer. For Saroyan it would seem a quite natural determination; for that profession, above all others, is peculiarly attractive to the iconoclastic, creative, and eccentric mind. This purpose was fortified by Saroyan's early discovery of the works of other writers at the Fresno public library, "where I read everything that struck my eye."

In 1925 Saroyan broke away from what he regarded as the constrictive atmosphere of Fresno and fled to Los Angeles, where for a short time he worked as a stock boy at Bullock's Department Store and lived in a rented room "near the public library." Los Angeles, he said, "did nothing to me," so he hitched a ride to San Francisco where he became first a clerk, then key operator, and finally manager of a Postal Telegraph Company office, an experience on which he was to draw heavily later on, especially in his early movie scenario *The Human Comedy* and his still later novel of the same title.

The appearance in 1928 (when Saroyan was twenty) of his first story in *Overland Monthly* encouraged him to take up writing full time; he left Postal Telegraph and, after a long and memorable bus trip to New York—an odyssey sometime the subject of his Haireniks stories—he took a room, bought a used typewriter, found a job at the Postal Telegraph office then on Warren Street, and "tried to crack New York wide open with my great stuff." Unfortunately, New York was not ready for Saroyan, and it would follow that Saroyan was not ready for New York. Running out of patience, Saroyan left for San Francisco where he returned to the Postal Telegraph facility and continued to write and get "mountains of rejection slips, which simply fueled my fire."

Finally, late in 1932, after his fateful meetings with Bardizian of the Haireniks, Saroyan mailed his three poems to *Hairenik Daily*; in May of 1933, his first short story, "A Fist Fight for Armenia," appeared in the same publication, followed in June by "The Broken Wheel," and in October by "The Barber's Apprentice." These he sent to Burnett and Foley of *Story*, with the notable results already cited.

The Saroyan riot was on . . . .

Most critical acknowledgments of the indebtedness of William Saroyan to his Armenian heritage bear within themselves flavors of hesitancy and uncertainty because they disclose little understanding that the immigrant Saroyan family, into which Saroyan was born, represents a nationality, a culture, and a case unique in itself.

Saroyan's ethnicity and its impact on his work have eluded Saroyan scholars, because they have failed to understand that each American immigrant is the product of centuries of his own peculiar national history, evolution, customs, and experience.

What is very real is that the family of the Armenian immigrant Armenak Saroyan was possessed of deeply rooted atavistic traits peculiar to Armenians, and that the household adjusted to America in its own "Armenian way"—a process licensed and governed ineffably by the Saroyans' ancient Armenian heritage, just as the "German way" guided and dictated the evolution of the family of Aram's (William's) German childhood friend, Herman ("Hate"). And the fact is, of course, that each immigrant circle becomes as "American" as quickly, as much, and as distinctively as its own heritage allows, and that that process of adjustment is ground out in as many different machines as there are different nationality stocks.

William Saroyan's writings were of course those of an offspring of an immigrant family and, we suppose, would fall under the heading of "immigrant literature." But Saroyan's work is a radical departure from that "immigrant literature" that pretends a common ethnic personality in America. Saroyan's variations on the theme of his own Armenian ethnicity are perhaps more *literary* than other writings on the early twentieth-century immigrant experience in America since, among other things, he disdains the pompous, homiletic poverty-to-pious approach, or even the Alger bit, which pretends to extol the free-enterprise virtues of the American way of life but simply ends up glorifying the pauper or immigrant who made it. But many immigrants, such as Armenak Saroyan, Saroyan's father, did not.

Saroyan's stories preserve in vivid color the picture of the early Armenian community in Fresno in a way unique in the American literary experience. They may be "immigrant" stories, but are, better, *Armenian* facets of the whole American drama of immigration, and one cannot understand the larger epic of the American immigration without mastering the story of each immigrant group.

It is relevant, here, to properly identify those more personal forces which, within the broader context of his Armenian heritage, profoundly influenced William Saroyan. Specifically, a discussion of Saroyan and the father he lost when he was three years of age is in perfect order.

Now, most Saroyanologists eagerly pass through that door unwittingly left ajar by Saroyan himself to concur that his maternal grandmother, Lucy (Garoghlanian), and his paternal uncle, Aram, were the two family members who more than anyone else influenced William Saroyan.

Almost totally neglected is the figure of Armenak, Saroyan's father, the unpublished poet and preacher without a pulpit, sometime farmhand, custodian of an Armenian publishing house, dreamer and certainly mystic, even though Saroyan's references in his works to his deceased father are greater in quantity and quality than are the allusions to his good grandmother and his often unsympathetic and quarrelsome uncle Aram, on whom see our Notes.

The Saroyan writings in this anthology and elsewhere starkly reveal Saroyan's lifelong quest to find a father he had lost before he could know him—a father who, strangely, found a ghostly dwelling within his son.

This quest, this yearning, to transfer his father's voice within him into a living image is, for example, expressed metaphorically in Saroyan's first contribution to Hairenik, his verse "To the Voice of Shah-Mouradian," which is both a tribute to the great Armenian tenor, and a poem about fathers and sons:

> For when you sing, you sing at least for me.
> And when at last my mortal day is done

> Remember, friend, that I shall leave a son,
> Tutored to seek the glory of his race
> (Wherever he may go, to what strange place) . . .

In this quotation Saroyan's father *is* Shah-Mouradian.

His third Hairenik piece, the poem "To Lake Van," extols that historic and fabled body of water; but equally it pays a tribute to his father:

> Lake Van, O inland sea my father saw
> With stinging eyes and steadfast blurring stare,
> Our hearts unite in race's filial prayer.
> His blood to mine restores that fearful awe
> He felt as he from homeland's shore turned west,
> Smothering harsh and violent farewell. . . .

Having trembled himself at his father's "violent farewell" to his homeland, Saroyan turns to his death:

> He from his spirit's soul took lasting leave,
> From heavens that his legend had sustained,
> And though he left and died, there he remained
> In his young ghost, above thy cool grieve . . .

and of course that "young ghost" was William himself, who was to sense forever the violence and awful meaning of his father's wrenching himself from his homeland, the trauma of the expulsion of the Armenians from Armenia, and the yearning, shared by most Armenians, to return to the bosom of the homeland.

One gets the feeling that Saroyan is somehow aware of the ubiquitous presence of his father as one reads certain stories in which his father plays no apparent role. For instance, in his famous "The Broken Wheel," Saroyan does not mention his father at all while writing of his mother and other relatives and friends; nevertheless, one gets the eerie sense that there is present over the whole thing an unseen force, a powerful ghostliness occupying a visibly vacant chair at the family table and indeed presiding over the affairs of the household.

Two stories later, in "The Moment of Life," Saroyan finally gets down to what he has been trying to say about his father. We find him talking about a father who had cruelly left him when he was an infant, leaving behind some books, some scribblings,

> and a framed photograph of him over the piano in our parlor. He
> was a tall young man with a solemn expression and an old style

moustache with the ends curled up. I knew he was dead and had no remembrance of him, but I did not feel that his being dead had ended his life or at least the meaning of it for me.

What makes this story and its treatment of Saroyan's father so remarkable is its ingenuous simplicity, its lack of literary device, its warmth, its very personal reverence for a dead father, as if Saroyan were not conversing with editor-publisher or even reader, but with himself. It is really not a public short story, but an entry into a family Bible; and this sort of very private respect and cherishing Saroyan accorded no other member of the Saroyan clan.

The celebrated Lucy is invariably written of in love and gratitude tinged with humor, but because she is almost always introduced or identified as an invaluable source of many of Saroyan's "old country" stories, her image somehow comes through not as it should—as the warm and affectionate but gruff guardian and sometime surrogate mother of the Saroyan kids—but simply as a colorful character who would inevitably find her way into her talented grandson's writings; or else Lucy is represented as a person simply being exploited, a fountain of Saroyan stories.

We wonder if in fact Grandmother Lucy ever exerted anything but an occasional literary inspiration on Saroyan, despite Saroyan's repeated affectionate bows to her. Saroyan's references to Lucy appear to lack any real spiritual punch, perhaps because Saroyan may have felt little spiritual rapport with her, although he certainly loved her dearly. On the other hand, there is little question that such a rapport, a bond of great spiritual and uplifting strength, existed between the deceased Armenak Saroyan and his son, William.

The spirit of Armenak Saroyan hovers over the fun and games of "The Broken Wheel," the earliest "Aram Garoghlanian" story to be printed anywhere, and that influence spread itself over all the succeeding stories of that great series, many of which were published exclusively in the Haireniks until their republication here.

The four other most notable and revealing "father syndrome" stories to appear herewith, and which bear special attention, are "Lauri," "My Grandmother Lucy Tells a Story Without a Beginning, a Middle, or an End," "The Man Who Knew My Father as a Boy in Bitlis," and "Hayastan and Charentz."

In "Lauri," Saroyan purports to character-sketch a "giant of a man named Lauri" who came to the United States early this century, and who, despite "his stupidity—which was exalted . . . was not disliked by his relatives" but was spoken of "as being poetic." His grandmother would say "He is a poet, he belongs to no nationality. He is his own nationality," a picture of a maverick not fit to work ("stupidity" here would connote that), a "poetic man." The story concludes with this passage:

> This is, however, all I have to say about him just now. I suppose some rainy day I shall find it impossible not to try to tell the whole story of his quiet, poetic life, which I am sure pleased God, although it irritated some people who had no imagination, and didn't know an immortal when they saw one.

Is this all about Saroyan's poetic father Armenak, all beautifully muscled into the character of a "giant of a man named Lauri"? We know from William himself that certain "unimaginative" members of his mother Takoohi's family (and some of his father's relatives) had showed undisguised irritation that her husband Armenak had difficulty providing for his family. They manifested little appreciation for a poet's life, or even for poet Armenak's repeated efforts somehow to keep house and home together as a laborer.[10] But William's sympathy is with his father, and his chiding is directed at Armenak's crass detractors.

This family skepticism about Armenak's role as father and provider is marked in Saroyan's story "My Grandmother Lucy Tells a Story Without a Beginning, a Middle, or an End." Here, he asks his ubiquitous grandmother to tell him something of his father; and this she apparently proceeds to do, getting absolutely nowhere and revealing nothing that was not generally known about his father. It certainly looks as if Lucy was simply reluctant to say anything salutary about Armenak; since she couldn't be critical of her son-in-law in the face of his son, she said nothing at all, which was saying the whole works.

And so Saroyan's quest to call forth his father's image continued. He talks about his father to one of his father's old friends ("The Man Who Knew My Father as a Boy in Bitlis"):

> Sarkis Janian was born on the last day of the year 1874, this is also the year of my father's birth and to me therefore one of the years of particular interest. I have always felt a closeness to this year, to these four figures, 1874, and each time I have seen them in print I have said to myself, That is the year my father was born; and of the year 1911 I have always said, And that is the year my father died, at the age of 37.
>
> Sarkis Janian knew my father in Bitlis, and then again he knew him in Paterson, N.J. . . . . Every time he steps into [my] house, he turns to me suddenly and says, I knew your father.
>
> Tell me about him, I say.

Well, he says, your father and I were friends. We went swimming together. . . .

and that is about all that is new that Saroyan learns from his father's friend, that apparently Armenak Saroyan knew how to swim and that he and Baron Janian had been accustomed to taking long walks "everywhere" in Bitlis. So Saroyan tries again. Tell me, he asks Janian,

about my father's voice . . . tell me something my father told him in the old country—a few of his words, his exact words. . . . Many things, the carpenter would say, Oh, he said many things. I cannot tell you what he said, but he said many things.

This obvious inability to bring to mind the "many things" Armenak had supposedly told his chum seems to have confirmed an impression Saroyan had that his father had been a taciturn man:

It is very likely that my father scarcely spoke, but it seemed to his friend that he had said many things, and of course in a way he had, although he hadn't spoken. . . .

Here, too, Saroyan encountered that certain reserve on the part of relatives and friends to discuss his father.

In 1954, Saroyan electrified the Armenian scene by publishing in *Hairenik Weekly* his "Hayastan and Charentz," a commentary built around his 1935 meeting in Moscow with Yeghishe Charentz, the most honored Armenian poet of his day, who in 1938 was to be executed in the Stalinist purges.[11] He says flatly that this, his maiden trip to present Armenia, was motivated by the spirit of his father:

In a way I suppose it was just as well that my father was dead, for it is not unlikely that I would have found fault with him, too; but since he was dead, I dwelt in thought on his good qualities, and paid no attention to his bad ones; his inability to prosper in the world, to get along among commonplace men on their own terms, to take the world with a grain of salt, and to make a joke of it,

as, we point out, Armenak's son, William, had learned to do.

By 1954, Saroyan's untiring digging into his father's life and the kind of man he had been brought him to a different conclusion:

. . . my father was simply a good man, dead at the age of thirty-seven. Nobody ever had a critical word to say of him, so that I myself in asking questions about his life and work tried to provoke criticism. In this I was unsuccessful. The worst that anybody was willing to say of my father was that he was too good for this world. I accepted this theory with simultaneous admiration and disbelief, but I made up my mind to go back to where he had come from as soon as possible. . . .

which led him to Armenia and then to Yeghishe Charentz—to a poet he might have felt was the reincarnation of his own poet-father, Armenak Saroyan.

Frequent intriguing references to his father are found in Saroyan's works printed in media other than the Haireniks.

His autobiographical *Here Comes/There Goes You Know Who* is especially rich in such allusions:

I may not die a writer, I'm a cinch to die Saroyan. I have thought all about death all my life, most likely because my father died before I was three. I didn't like that. As the years go by I continue to dislike it, even though I am fifteen years older than my father was when he died. He died in San Jose, California, in 1911, far from his birthplace, Bitlis, in Armenia. He was thirty-seven years of age.

My father was in a vineyard in Sanger, twelve miles east, trying to gather the pieces together of a preacher without a pulpit and a poet without a reader. My mother was hushed and angry in the ramshackle house, because now here was one more, making four, two daughters born in Bitlis, in 1899 and 1902, a son born in Erzeroum in 1905, and now another son, in 1908, myself.

William says that when he was born, his father, Armenak,

came in from Sanger on a bicycle the following day and gave [me] the strange name of William, after his friend, Dr. William Stonehill of New York, also a Presbyterian preacher, deceased three months [d. June, 1908] . . .

and he reports that father Armenak was working in the Sanger vineyards of his mother's sister's boys, the Moradian brothers.

And so, one day, Saroyan, still the child, asks his mother to show him his father's effects:

My mother brought out the bundle of my father's writings when I asked if I might look at them. I was nine or ten and we were back from the San Francisco orphanage in Fresno, in our own rented house on San Benito Avenue . . . "There was more," she said. "He lost some, we lost some, this is all that remains." In Armenian, you understand; English spoken only in the presence of those who were unable to speak Armenian . . . [The bundle of manuscripts consisted of] a stack of homemade notebooks and manuscripts . . . His library was made up of books he had bought in connection with his being a preacher . . .

• I picked up the first notebook and just held it a moment . . . After the name of it came his name, very clearly, in English, with that touch of foreignness which is the handwriting of all men who are not English or American by birth.

The Word, we'll say, *A Poem* by Armenak Saroyan. *The Bowery, New York, June 1905*, we'll say.

I know he lived in the Bowery for some time. I know he reached New York alone . . .

In a sense the writing was my own, and I didn't like it . . . Nothing was finished . . . I loved them. I loved the plain paper . . . the ink . . . the words, the calligraphy . . .

On pages 116 and 117 of the same work Saroyan describes what must have been, at the start anyway, a sort of pilgrimage of respect and curiosity to the Brooklyn home of the late William Stonehill, his father's missionary patron, after whom he had named his son William.

The visit was paid during Saroyan's five-month 1928 stay in New York City. Saroyan recalls that Stonehill's widow opened the door at his summons, and that she said,

You are Armenak Saroyan's son. Please come in.

I was astonished that she knew, and for a moment I wondered *how* she knew, since she had never seen me. I was twenty years old, my father had been dead seventeen years, she hadn't seen him in twenty years . . .

I had seen a photograph of her with her husband and my father since I had been eight years old . . .

Well, why had I gone out there? Was that part of a search for a home, a world, a way?

While they had tea, they talked:

This woman knew my father before I was born, and she knew my mother, and my mother's mother [Lucy], but I gathered that she had been a little let down by the women, because neither of them had cared very much for her good works, and were entirely unwilling to accept and wear the corsets she had given them. They hadn't been at home in the correct atmosphere she and her husband maintained, and they may have even have been a little scornful of it. And until their arrival in New York my father had been entirely at home in that atmosphere and with them, and they had always imagined that he had intended to continue his ministry in New York, as she put it, or in nearby Paterson, where he had given sermons in English and Armenian . . .

Mrs. Stonehill then talked about how things went after the arrival in New York of Takoohi and Lucy:

. . . my father became deeply troubled, for they wanted him to drop everything, a whole career that promised to be brilliant, and move to California. Soon after her husband [Rev. Stonehill] had been called to a better life and world, and a few years later so had Armenak, and so on.

Well, it was informative, but it was depressing, too.

Somewhere during the tea and the conversation she said that in working among the Armenian immigrants she and her husband had received notes from many of them but hadn't heard from them again. This puzzled me. What sort of notes had the Armenian immigrants written? . . .

So Saroyan asked her, what sort of notes?

Well, this was a matter that dismayed her, and she showed it now.

"Why, they were notes for the loans my husband and I made to them. They all promised to repay the loans but not one of them did. Not one of them."

And now I was angry. What the devil was the matter with the Armenians? How could they accept money from such kind, gentle, refined, earnest and helpful people, and send them notes, and not pay them back? And of course I felt deeply ashamed and embarrassed.

"Did my father or mother or grandmother hand you a note?"

If they had I meant to pay it in full, with interest, as soon as possible. But the lady said my father and mother and my grandmother had paid their own way entirely. They had worked for wages, and when they had saved enough for railroad tickets they had gone to California.

Saroyan's passages on his visit to Mrs. Stonehill are of course laced with irony. They may hint at the presence of a severe conflict between Armenak Saroyan and his wife and in-laws which seems to have tinged William's life, even after his father had gone, and of course affected his mother Takoohi's relations with members of the Saroyan clan. Armenak Saroyan may have been a poet and a dreamer, but he was also clearly a God-fearing, genuinely righteous and outwardly puritanical man who had apparently adjusted to the Yankee missionary straitjacket into which he had strapped himself in an ancient country far distant from America.

Over there, then, was Armenak Saroyan, who had chosen to adopt, practice, and preach a way of rigorous worship and living; and over here were his wife and her mother, good Christians as they were in *their own* understanding of the term, who, in their ancestral pride, did not feel that it was the province of religion to require the faithful to accept such used intimates as corsets from the pious women whose husbands sought to preach the pride and glory of the Christian way of life to a nation of people whose Christianity antedated Luther by at least a millennium.

The latent conflict that apparently existed between Armenak and Takoohi was not something unique to the Saroyans; in those days strong religious feelings divided many Armenian households. As Saroyan matured, he must have become increasingly aware of this clash between his mother and father, and it is frightening to imagine what might have taken place between father and son had the father lived, if William Saroyan, the free spirit, the iconoclast, the nonconformist and recalcitrant, had spent his youth under the potentially rigid discipline of his father.

In its own way, however, the pattern of William's life was an acknowledgment of the basic rectitude of his father's philosophy, which both repelled and attracted him. There is little question that Saroyan's personal conduct was in direct contradiction of his father's rigid code—Saroyan gambled and gamboled, he was flaky and notoriously unreliable, he drank heavily on occasion, wenched and was twice divorced—all misvirtues anathema to Christian temperance types and an outrageous personal record for a preacher's son. But he was, at the same time, a dedicated pacifist, a ridiculer of the goosestep, a foe of peonage and patronage. He was impatient of dissimulation, generous and charitable (he never pinned his philanthropies to his sleeve, and gave when he was not broke, which was almost always); and was respectful of all religions. Certainly Armenak Saroyan and his own missioner religious circle could find no faults with these traits; but they would be appalled by Saroyan's "other" personality.

No question: William Saroyan was a battlefield on which Ormuzd and Ahriman fought relentlessly—good versus evil, Christ versus satan. Two contrasting personalities had found lodging within him, and he was powerless to exorcise himself of his demon. After one of his wild escapades—he had just thrown away $50,000 at a racetrack—Saroyan bemoaned the presence of something within him which "drives me to do nutty things; but of course there is nothing I can do about it."

His tendency to be the occasional rake he could not trace back to any known ancestry. "I was just *born* a bit crazy, but what puzzles me is that I have never heard of any other Saroyan or Garoghlanian a bit crazy just like me, so I guess I am an accident, a sort of family freak." On the other hand, Saroyan thought the goodness in him was the handiwork of his father's genes.

When Saroyan was at play, he played hard and loved every moment of it, but these bacchanalian episodes were inevitably succeeded by Tannhaüser's remorse. And so, in the best Christian tradition, he would seek expiation for his sins in pilgrimage—back to his delightful Armenian people, back to the Haireniks, a flight to Armenia, and back to his search for his father, whose stern fundamentalism fascinated him.

There is more than a clear suggestion in all this that Saroyan's early loss of his father, and his adult understanding that his own character was both attendant to and repelled by his father's austerity, had forged in him a basic Oedipal urge—to find the father who had left him. This was to grow into a veritable passion in his manhood. It colored his thoughts and his career.[12]

But this "complex" did not develop into a debilitating neurosis precisely and happily because Saroyan discovered a living surrogate father, a paternal alter ego. He adopted a man who encouraged the temperance within him, brought out the best in him, and gave him in his crucial adult years the comfort and strength that only a father can accord, something that he had been denied during his formative years.

That "stepfather" was Doctor Reuben Darbinian, editor in chief of the Haireniks, who entered Saroyan's life when Saroyan was twenty-five years of age and most needed inspiration, encouragement, guidance, and companionship.

Saroyan's course to success dates back to the beginning of his association with Reuben Darbinian—when Darbinian first published him, or when Saroyan accepted Darbinian in lieu of his deceased father.

The circumstances into which Armenak Saroyan and Reuben Darbinian were born reflect the sharp contrasts imposed on Armenians by the division, early in the nineteenth century, of the historical Armenian homeland into Turkish and Russian spheres of occupation. The quality of life and opportunity of Armenians in the six Armenian provinces held by the Turks was dramatically lower than that enjoyed by their confreres on the other side of the line of demarcation that split Armenia into two parts.

Saroyan's father was born in the city of Bitlis, in the western ("Turkish") section of the Armenian landmass. From what little we know of the early history of the family, the Saroyans were struggling minor craftsmen unable to formally educate their children. The presence of an American Presbyterian mission in Bitlis allowed the precocious Armenak to enter that establishment's free school, and his promise came to the attention of his mentors, especially the Reverend William Stonehill. Armenak adopted the Presbyterian faith and finally was made, under circumstances still unclear, a presbyter preparing for pulpits in America. He married Takoohi Garoghlanian and, by the time he went to the United States in the early 1890s, leaving his family behind to rejoin him later, Armenak had sired two daughters, Cosette and Zabel. William's older brother, Henry—the "Krikor" of his "Aram" stories—was born in Erzurum, Armenia, during the family's trek to America.

Armenak only somewhat practiced his profession while awaiting the arrival of his family. Apparently, on Sundays, he would trolley from New York to preach before a Protestant Armenian congregation in Paterson, New Jersey, but this must have been a part-time occupation, for when his family debarked at New York, they found Armenak working principally at odd jobs in the Bowery. His wife's people had already migrated to California, and it was at their insistence that Armenak finally yielded and led his brood to Fresno where, again, poverty awaited them. So to speak, the Saroyans had jumped from the Turkish frying pan into the American fire.

Reuben Darbinian,[13] born Artasches Tchillingarian (January 23, 1883), was a native of the city of Alkhalkalak in eastern Armenia, in the Russian occupation zone. Like most Armenians residing within the Russian-held area, the Darbinian family was well-off compared to the suppressed Armenians living in Armenak's Turkish sphere. Reuben received a European education and eventually graduated from the University of Moscow in June 1909 as a Doctor of Jurisprudence, with a reputation as a campus liberal and an Armenian political agitator.

Hounded by the Russian authorities, Darbinian made his way to Vienna and finally assumed an editorial post with the Armenian journal *Azadamart*, in Constantinople. In 1913 he transferred to Berlin as the journal's correspondent.

In 1914, with the threat of war hanging over Europe, Darbinian returned to Russia where he became the editor of the Baku *Arev* newspaper. Upon the establishment of the Independent Republic of Armenia (May 28, 1918), Darbinian headed that state's negotiating mission in Moscow and, in January 1920, was appointed the Republic's Minister of Justice.

When the Armenian Republic fell (December 2, 1920) through the complicity of the Turkish and Soviet authorities, Darbinian was able to escape to Teheran, where he accepted an invitation to edit the *Hairenik Daily* in Boston. He arrived in the United States on March 22, 1922, and the first issue of *Hairenik* to appear under his editorship was that of April 1, 1922.

Already a charismatic figure of the Armenian revolution, Darbinian added to his personal prestige by producing the most sought-after

Armenian newspaper of his day. Almost immediately, he initiated the *Hairenik Monthly*, a literary-historical journal and, nine years later, he introduced an English-language section into the *Daily*. It was in these columns, as we have already pointed out, that Saroyan began publishing in the Haireniks, a collaboration which Saroyan continued when the wholly English-language *Hairenik Weekly* appeared in 1934.

Saroyan's relations with Reuben Darbinian soon transcended those that normally exist between author and editor:

> Saroyan revered Reuben Darbinian . . . as an intellectual, a leader, a man—as god and in awe; so solemn was this veneration that Saroyan worshipped his deity at a distance. There was a spiritual bond between the two—the toughest of all fibers—but they infrequently touched hands, for both were private people, despite Saroyan's public image as a brash, outspoken "Peck's bad boy" who often made the news with a vengeance. The truth is the two friends were basically retiring people who learned the hard way that their professions called for treating with people. When Saroyan and Darbinian met, there was the very correct Armenian bear hug, high color in both faces, conversation in halting Armenian countered by as halting English—but an instant air of camaraderie and understanding which brought Saroyan's booming voice down, raised Darbinian's, until both were speaking in the same tone. In all respects, Darbinian, the man of the Old World, and Saroyan, of the New, were clones.
>
> Here, then, were two Armenians transfixed not by hero worship—one for the other—but in that they recognized each other to be kindred souls—a real rarity. We suspect that Saroyan's adoration was that here was a giant of the Armenian revolution, this immensely talented editor, who chose to meet him as an equal; and we suspect that the fact that Darbinian had been the first to recognize Saroyan's talent had really very little to do with Saroyan's admiration of Reuben Darbinian. We suspect further that Darbinian loved Saroyan because in him he had met a phenomenon on the Armenian scene—a successful Armenian American who was a "humble Armenian"—not one of those wind-bag moguls who often would bring the plague to Darbinian's office. If their relations need be characterized further, then Darbinian and Saroyan were sort of gifted father and talented son . . .[14]

While Saroyan had been searching for a father, Darbinian had been searching for a son—a quest fulfilled by his "adoption" of William Saroyan almost immediately after the tragic passing, in 1929, of his stepson, the talented concert pianist Levon (Leon) Vartanian. Levon's passing left a vacuum in Darbinian's life which, he later confided, he sought to fill with his fatherlike sentiments for his protégé, William Saroyan. Darbinian lavished his every fatherly affection on William, advising him, guiding him, chiding him for his moments of folly, but always cherishing him and understanding him, giving William that alter father he so needed during an adulthood in which Saroyan's family affairs were often chaotic, certainly as much his doing as anyone else's.

One may wonder why publication of an anthology of Saroyan's creative pieces in the Haireniks has been deferred to this time. That delay reflects the wishes of the author himself. When the idea of such a compilation was proposed to Saroyan in 1975 ("Conversation with Tashjian"), he willed:

> Now, you can get all that stuff together? There were poems, if you can call them poems, a few plays and a great number of short stories. Is that what we are talking about? I don't have a collection. Have you? Send me your list. Yes, we must do something with those pieces. They were sent to Haireniks, as I explained to Reuben Darbinian, to be their sure property, on the understanding I would be able to use them—one or the other—on occasion in other works. You have of course my O.K. to do an anthology of my stuff, and *you* are the proper person to do that. But I fear that if you were to attempt this work at this time, I would have to become involved in the business, and I can't at this time. Why not wait until I am gone— if that is ever to happen? Yes, I like that: a Saroyan anthology from Haireniks published posthumously. It will be an important book. Let me know how you are making out in this.

And so, this "Saroyan anthology from Haireniks published posthumously."

Without doubt, this preface has passed both its logical bounds and annoyed the spirit of William Saroyan up there; for he often asked, "Who reads introductions and prefaces?" But no apologies to William, the reader, the publisher—or even to the craft of writing. Republication of Saroyan's material in Haireniks is a one-shot thing; there may never be an opportunity for a second. Because most of these pieces are little known (although they represent an important phase of Saroyan's literary career), such an anthology calls for more than the pieces themselves. For instance, there is need for supporting literature, as represented by this preface, which will lend to an understanding of those circumstances and motivations that led Saroyan to contribute so persistently to the Haireniks, and which in turn contributed to Saroyan's development both as a writer and as a personality. Similarly, an attempt must be made to shed light on the history of each piece, to cast salt on the bread. To this end, the Notes appended to this volume, which catalogue in numerical sequence each specimen in order of its appearance in Haireniks, from the first Saroyan writings there, to the last.

—James H. Tashjian

To the Voice of Shah-Mouradian

I. EPISTLE

To the man this humble word:
Great soul, I your voice have heard.
If in this fact I stand alone,
My clamor will the wrong atone.

Before your own my voice is small:
You sing, while my poor words must fall
Like so much sodden clay or mud
Into the rush of thought's swift flood.

Yours is the flowing of the ancient soul.
While mine is but the lisping of the mind.
Yet if music the deaf cannot make whole,
Then print shall give hearing to those not blind.

II. WHILE HE SINGS "MAYR ARAKSIE"

No art is lost and yours shall never be,
For when you sing, you sing at least for me.
And when at last my mortal day is done
Remember, friend, that I shall leave a son,
Tutored to seek the glory of his race
(Wherever he may go, to what strange place)
In your clear voice, which is the very pith
Of our old legend and our deathless myth.

And if the mother of his son shall be
A daughter of our ancient family,
I think she'll teach him in his early years
That when you sing, though he be moved to tears,
He will yet know how once in strength we stood,
And stand forever in her motherhood.

San Francisco, California

To the River Euphrates

Euphrates, which is mine, doth flow or not,
There where its mountains feed its rush and roar.
And through those hills and plains by most forgot,
And by these eyes not seen, for evermore
Euphrates swells and rolls majestically,
Or is now dry, an arid myth, a tale.
If this is so, the truth, so let it be.
In me Euphrates is; nor can it fail

To ride its bed and cool its burning earth
With drink, and mine as well. Of wing no flight
May end in graceless crash. No spirit's mirth
May burn and die by heaven's harshest light.
Euphrates flows, however it may be
That but in dreams these eyes its grace may see.

San Francisco, California

To Lake Van

Lake Van, O inland sea my father saw
With stinging eyes and steadfast blurring stare,
Our hearts unite in race's filial prayer.
His blood to mine restores that fearful awe
He felt as he from homeland's shore turned west,
Smothering harsh and violent farewell.
O lake and symbol of our grief, they spell
With growing strength denies all easy rest.

He from his spirit's soil took lasting leave,
From heavens that his legend had sustained,
And though he left and died, there he remained
In his young ghost, above thy cool grieve,
Lament and weep in mists and pouring rains,
O Lake and pool of all your mortal pains.

San Francisco, California

A Fist Fight for Armenia

BY "SIRAK GORYAN"

It grew slowly, accumulating in distantly removed movements, carrying itself forward from where it had been dropped: to do. To perform. Outwardly. With the body. It was enough, he felt, to be there among them, the howling schoolboys. And it was too much to turn loose with a whoop, to free himself the way the others did, simply because he knew definitely that nothing he might do in that way could possibly have any meaning for him. They ran, they tripped one another, they wrestled, they struck: struck one another in the face. He took the shame. In the latest days of the calendar they were without shame. They struck. Laughed about it.

But it grew, and he began to envy. Why not? Why not run with them? Why not shout? Participate in the animal fun? Why not do? It was the lesser thing, of course, but he could not always isolate himself, watching, could not continue biding inside. They, the boys in motion, were the beginning of an idea alien to him, embarrassing, a scheme of flight, outward, anyway. The movement was physical, a thing into things.

They taunted, teased, called him names: the awkward one, they implied, the frightened, timid one. But he was not frightened. He was ashamed because of the direction they were taking, because they were not aware of the year in which they lived, not aware that all the history of life was accumulated in them. For their use. So that they could be men.

The games that were compulsory he played, baseball and soccer. It wasn't easy, since he hadn't discovered the reason, to catch a flying ball, and though he forced himself to try his best it was only by a stroke of good luck that he sometimes succeeded. The fact was so amazing to him that, instead of throwing the ball straight to another player, he would fling it wild, too high or too low, and he would be malicious with anger at the imperfection of the act. At bat he would be terrified, not out of fear of being struck with the ball—that had happened several times, painfully, swiftly startling—but because he wished to hit the ball with precision, solidly, with art, and send it far. As a result he waved at air while the others laughed or jeered. His knees would wobble and he would grit his teeth, swearing physically with all his body, fulminating with all his spirit. It was no use: he was fanned every time, and if he did succeed in touching the ball it would be a glancing touch, a foul that went straight up, a miscarriage of effort.

No group wanted him as a member of a team. He was impractical, tense, undependable, and an evil influence on other players.

In soccer he did little moving about, stood to one side of the center of action, bewildered, envious of the accuracy of others, and if the ball moved smartly up to his very feet his kick would be ineffectual. Either his foot would travel a greater distance than the ball or he would discover, amid the frantic shouts of his teammates, that he had kicked the ball in the wrong direction. Another boy as clumsy would be established as a comedian; there would be laughter. But no one could enjoy him. He was too solemn, too earnest.

It grew. Alone, he struck out, in fantasy, at night, or dreaming at his desk. I'll hit, he said, I'll throw. It was the idea he despised, the insistence to act that tormented him. He didn't mind the boys themselves, though they were hateful enough: he loathed the notion, the scale of values, the distortion of good and bad.

And suddenly, wholly willfully, he was in a fist fight with the school's biggest bully, a boy no one dared challenge. It was a test, a rehearsal, and though it could have been easily avoided, he stepped into it, alarming everyone. He was not afraid. No one frightened him. The inevitability of getting a bloody nose or a black eye was not horrible. He fought without precision, most of his punches going wild, but, what was worse, when he had a chance to land a solid punch, he avoided it, refused to strike another in the face. He was whipped, of course, but there was a certain gain; he had made a beginning. It did not matter that what he had begun was utterly meaningless and futile. It was an undeniable certainty that this was so, but he continued. He ran with them, shouted, tripped, wrestled and joined their groups.

The idea was to keep moving, and it didn't matter to what end. Do. Always. In every moment and without pause. From one thing to another, continuously. No contemplation or reflection. No summary of the past. No documentation.

He accepted and at seventeen was a member of the high school football team. Not a big fellow, but he was very lithe and could carry the ball through an open field for a long run. He liked the game but did not take it seriously, did not fight. It was game, it was sport. Those who cheered would be sitting in homes or offices in a year or two. If he strained to get an objective he learned that the intensity of his desire defeated his purpose, got him so tangled in scrimmage that he no longer could be amused, and he could not keep from hating the opposing team, which was stupid.

Small boys in the neighborhood looked up to him, and he enjoyed teaching them to box and wrestle. When he observed that a boy was serious and angry he would stop a fight. "Now listen," he would say. "You must stop hating him. This is sport. You've got to have the right attitude." He believed if he could teach the boys to box without becoming bitter they could find it easier living. He was convinced that it was an individual's viewpoint that got him into an abnormal series of events that culminated in a violence of one sort or another.

One evening he and Reuben Paul sat on the porch of his home talking when a group of seven or eight boys came up, running and shouting; they had been insulted. Roy Sommers, who had boxed in the ring of the American Legion, had insulted them.

"He called us dirty Armenians," said Ara George, a boy of eight, who began to tremble and burst into tears. "Stop bawling," an older boy ordered. "Caspar will show him. Caspar will make him take it back."

"Yes," said another, "you don't have to bawl."

Reuben Paul thought it was very amusing: "Said we were dirty, did he? Well, did you boys tell him you were just as clean as he was? Did you say you bathed once a week the same as he?"

"It isn't that," said an older boy, trying to justify their humiliation.

Caspar did not laugh at Reuben's remarks. It was amusing, of course, and absurd to trouble with such a coarse and stupid fellow as Roy Sommers, but Ara George, weeping, cut him deep. The boy, though unable to speak his own tongue, wept with ancient grief, wailing at the outrage of a vulgar hatred.

"Where is Sommers?" he asked.

Reuben remarked with impatience, "We know we're hated, but what of it?"

Sommers, the boys said, was waiting in the lot across the street from California Playground. They said two fellows and a woman were with him, and stood silent and solemn, waiting to see if Caspar would go with them.

When they began walking up San Benito Avenue toward the playground, Ara George, still sobbing, went home. He was terrified and didn't want to see what happened.

"You're walking into a stupid mess for a bunch of excited kids," Reuben insisted.

"Yes," said Caspar, "and I'm sure to get a bad beating."

When they reached the empty lot, Sommers, his friends, and the woman were taking drinks from a bottle. The woman shouted an obscenity, and the boys cried, "You see, Caspar."

Reuben asked the boys to remain on the edge of the lot, and see that they didn't call anybody names. When he perceived how they obeyed, how hurt they were, he became disgusted with the orderliness of the affair, and lost his head because it was impossible to do anything intelligent about it. He caught Caspar by the arm and insisted that he was going to do the fighting. "You stay out of this," he [Caspar] said. Reuben hadn't had a fight in his life, hadn't found his tongue so inarticulate that it couldn't damage more positively than blows.

"You're excited," said Caspar. "You hate him."

Sommers expressed amazement at his opponent and looked forward to making a splendid impression on his lady friend. "Why, look who they've brought to beat me up," he said entertaining his friends, who snickered and laughed to themselves. Then he boasted that he would use only his right arm, that in view of the inconsequential person he was to face he would have no need for the other, but his opponent quietly rejected the advantage, and with amusement on one side, coats were removed and shirt sleeves rolled.

When the fight began, slowly at first, Reuben felt that he could not just stand there, that it was imperative he do something, act in some manner, but he was helpless, paralyzed with bewilderment, tense with a ferocious rage he knew not how to release. He began to feel a revulsion for all things, and to hate himself for not being an enormous animal like Sommers. There was no civilization in the world. Superiority was based on bulk and brute strength, quantity possessed, not method employed.

Sommers slugged easily, solidly, working into shape, enjoying his advantage of size and strength. His opponent surprised him occasionally with swift, successive jabs, but there wasn't enough force behind them to greatly trouble the big fellow. He laughed and snorted his nostrils clean. "I'm going to give you the nicest beating of your life," he announced.

"Kill him, Roy," the woman suggested. "Massacre him."

Reuben Paul disintegrated in impotent wrath: "Yes, yes, of course. Yes, this was their method of determining the quality of races."

"What did he say?" the boys asked themselves. "Is Caspar losing?" They rubbed their hands together, not knowing how to help him.

When Sommers landed a punch that declared its force with a loud thud, his friends said, "That's it, Roy. That's putting him in his place."

Reuben could not speak, had no words to articulate his objection. For the first time in his life he wanted to do something definite with his entire physical well being, wanted to perform some overt act that would instantly and irrevocably destroy this monstrous irregularity that was for him the negation of civilization, the denial of human history, the repudiation of life itself. And he was indignant with himself because his desire found no outlet other than to savagely swing a club, lowering him to the level of a furious and unreasonable beast.

The small boys shouted into the air, and sometimes, finding it beyond their strength to restrain themselves, replied with a curse at a curse from the woman. Once she ran at the group, scattering them, the smaller ones crying.

"We'll massacre you like the Turks," she said. "You just watch. We'll cut you to pieces the way the Turks did."

These words sunk into Caspar's being, destroying him. The Turks were all right. They were fine. They were his neighbors, his brothers. He did not hate them. He loathed what was ugly in the woman's voice, the hideousness, the deformity she impelled in the earth, and he felt there was no alternative but to smash it out of them, since it was the only method they acknowledged or understood. And he despaired that he was too small, lacked the weight and strength to do it properly.

Sommers fell on him with vicious pleasure. Caspar bled over an eye and at the lips, and to his confused senses it seemed he was falling through space from a great height, the earth infinitely below, waiting. He hammered swiftly with all the strength he possessed, and when blood spurted from his opponent's nose and lips, he became pious with hope; once, only once, God, let him prove to them.

And then he had bumped earth, fallen all the way, hit bottom, and was saying over and over again, an inestimable number of times in an instant: "You damned fool, now look what you've done. You've let him knock you down. Him."

He heard young voices urging him to get up; saw Sommers standing over him, heaving for breath, his shirt bloody and torn, his huge fists tightly clenched, waiting. The young voices were saying, if he weren't mistaken, "He's tired, Caspar. Get up, get up." He felt Reuben bleeding with him, silently, he could not see him, and when he again heard the woman's voice it appeared that he had been on the ground but was now on his feet, slugging and stopping blows that were becoming increasingly painful.

He was tumbling once more, volumes of space circling out of his pain through his ears, so heavy and real that it seemed, if he had time, he might lay hands on space and shape it like clay. His opponent now fought for all he was worth, displeased that what had appeared to be a lark was fast becoming a distressing spectacle, due to the little fellow's incredible stubbornness. Once he was unaccountably knocked down, and lay still, the woman screaming at him at the top of her lungs, the small boys exultant. He lifted himself slowly and swore at the woman, since the entertainment was to have been in her behalf.

It seemed to Caspar that he had begun the fight a long time ago and that it was a thing that would never end. He had never known anything but this fight, and though he endeavored to maintain that he had been at it only ten or fifteen minutes, it was impossible to do so. This was all, all; beginning, end, eternity: downward, thick space whirring from his agony, his head heavy as lead, the solid earth waiting.

He struck earth many times, and each time became more angered with himself, more powerful in purpose and the desire to do, weaker in physical strength. Each time he rose to his feet he felt his blood, his aching bones, his very life thundering, as if it were not himself, "I'll take it again, I will go on lifting myself forever." It would be a joy to be killed, a reasonable and proper climax. They had laughed: laughed with hatred, and Ara George himself, the old country itself, had wept. Reuben was bleeding that finer blood. The boys, fresh green foliage on the ancient vine, were begging him to go on.

He rose once again and sought, desperately, sobbing, to destroy the hatred, but could not move his arms. He had the notion that if only from somewhere he could draw a trifle more strength, if the aching flesh and bone could be healed for but another moment, if only—but he could not, could not, simply could not renew himself. O Armenia, Armenia, he groaned.

Sommers welcomed the opportunity to lower his arms. "I guess you're about done for," he said. He was too weak and tired to place any of his original rancor in his words, and perhaps he was no longer able to feel any. His friends were now inclined to be calm and speechless, the smaller boys did not even whimper, and the woman for some reason shivered.

There was a sudden altercation between Sommers and the woman as they walked from the lot during which his friends were forced to strain against his arms to keep him from striking her.

Reuben wiped the blood from Caspar's face, his fingers trembling over the bruised and cut flesh. The boys gathered around silent with grief but proud somehow of their humiliation.

"You boys go home now," Reuben said. "It's late."

They went off immediately, silently, and it was not until they had gone a half a block that they broke into incoherent speech, not one of them understanding what another said, not one feeling the need to understand.

Caspar's nose seemed broken, two or three ribs were probably fractured, and he was bruised in many parts of his body. He felt most of all a great displeasure with himself because he hadn't quite been able to whip his opponent. On the way home, returning down San Benito Avenue, Reuben began suddenly to cry.

"Jesus," he sobbed, "I don't know what to do about this. God, I can't think of a thing to do. I can't let this go like this." He wept bitterly, ashamed of himself, his grief and his objection ascending the blackness of space, sacred in the stillness of the night.

San Francisco, California

The Broken Wheel

BY "SIRAK GORYAN"

We had a small house on Santa Clara Avenue, in the foreign district where everyone moved about freely and where conversations were carried on across yards and alleys and streets. This house had been the home of a man who had been in the business of roasting and marketing all kinds of nuts. We found small and large pieces of his machinery in the two barns, and in the cracks of the floors we sometimes found nutshells and bits of nutmeats. The house had a clean wholesome smell. There were a number of crickets somewhere near the kitchen sink and quite a few house spiders, the kind that are called daddy-long-legs. There was also a cat. The cat was there when we moved into the house, so we took it for granted. It was a big black tom with a proud demeanor, an aristocratic air of superiority and indifference. At first it lived under the house in the dark, but later on when it got cold it moved into the house. We never bothered to give it a name, but referred to it simply as the *Gadou*, which is "cat" in Armenian.

Our trees were two sycamores at the side of the house, by the alley; an English walnut tree in the backyard that was perhaps twenty years old; a small olive tree; and three lilac trees that were growing close to the front porch. The porch was shaded by a thick honeysuckle plant. There were also geraniums and Bermuda grass and other weeds. After a while we planted two peach trees, a cactus tree, and a castor plant. The peach trees happened accidentally; we hadn't meant to plant them, we had only thrown peach pits in the backyard and the trees had come up by themselves and we hadn't transplanted them. They were growing much too close to one another but they were either very lucky or very stubborn and after three years the leaves that fell from them in the fall were enough to rake into a pile and burn. They were growing just outside our yard but since we had no fence and no close neighbors, except for the family immediately across the alley, we considered the peach trees our trees. It wasn't a question of fruit; we could buy peaches cheaper than they could be grown; it was rather a question of being responsible for the growth of something fine or perhaps a question of blossoms in the spring. Once a year my sister Naomi would bring some of the pink blossoms into the house and place them in a black vase.

We used to see the blossoms in the black vase and suddenly we used to feel that it was all splendid. It seemed to mean that we were alive and we used to laugh about it. In the winter we laughed a great deal. We would be sullen and sorrowful for weeks at a time and then suddenly all of us would begin to laugh. We would laugh fifteen or twenty minutes and then we would be sullen and sorrowful again. It was all splendid and at the same time we felt that it must be pretty sad because it was in us to feel bewildered and futile.

My brother Krikor was responsible for the cactus tree. He came home one afternoon with a piece of thorny cactus in his hand. He said to me, Did you know that all of this country was desert once and that cactus was growing everywhere?

Do you mean, I asked, no one was living here?

Yes, said Krikor. No one but the lizards, I guess, and the snakes and the horny toads and the chicken hawks and things like that. No people.

I thought of our valley without people and streets and houses and I thought it was very strange, very irregular.

Do you mean, I said, all the way to Selma and all the way to Clovis and away over to Kerman, past Skaggs Bridge?

I mean the whole valley, Krikor replied. I mean all this level land between the Coast Ranges and the Sierra Nevadas. All this country where the vineyards are growing now. It was dry here in those days, so they began to bring in the water in canals and irrigation ditches.

Krikor planted the cactus that afternoon and by the time I was ten it was producing splendid red blossoms and a fruit no one knew how to eat; and it was taller than a tall man.

The castor tree happened accidentally too. An old castor tree was growing in the yard of our neighbors across the alley and one summer some of its seeds got into our yard and the following summer we had a small castor tree of our own. It was a spurious sort of a tree, growing much too rapidly and being much too delicate for a tree. A small boy couldn't climb it and the least little storm that came along would tear some of its branches away. But it had a nice leaf and a clean growing odor and it made a lot of shade. We hadn't planted it, but as long as it started to grow we were glad about it. Everyone hated castor oil but we thought the tree itself was innocent enough.

In the summertime it would be very hot and we would have to get up early in the morning to feel a cool breeze. Every summer the city sent out a long tractor to plow into the tar of Santa Clara Avenue and improve the condition of the street. This tractor made a monotonous noise, pounding steadily and hollowly, approaching and going away from our house. In the morning we would begin to hear its faraway *boom-boom-boom* and as it came closer to our house we would hear the noise louder and louder and we used to think that this coming and going was like something in life but we couldn't tell just what. We used to say in Armenian *Yegav noren*, Here it is again. We had no definite basis for our objection, but we sometimes asked what difference it made if the street was a little uneven. No one uses it anyway, we said. Casparian, the man who sold watermelons each summer, passed over the street every afternoon with his old horse and his wobbly wagon, crying watermelon in Armenian, but there wasn't much other traffic. Those who wanted to get around in a hurry rode bicycles.

One year my uncle Vahan, then a young man, drove down from San Francisco in a brand-new Apperson roadster and stopped in front of our house.

How do you like it? he asked. There are only eleven Appersons in America and only one red one. His was the red one. We felt splendid and we all laughed and my uncle Vahan smoked cigarettes. He took his sister, my mother, for a ride to Roeding Park. It was her first ride in an automobile and she felt very proud of her brother. We all thought he was splendid. It wasn't only the Apperson, it was also his nervousness and his energy and the way he laughed and talked. When he came back with my mother he took my sisters, Lucy and Naomi, for a ride to town. My brother Krikor sat on the front porch with a book, waiting nervously for his turn to ride. Krikor said the automobile could go fifty miles per hour. Rouben, our neighbor, was sitting on the porch with us and he said his uncle Levon had a Cadillac which was a more expensive car than an Apperson and could go sixty miles an hour.

Yes, I said, but is it red? He admitted sadly that it was black. There is only one red Apperson in America, I said. It was like saying that one's great-grandfather had seen Lincoln or that one's ancestors had come over on the *Mayflower*; only it was more impressive. You knew that a great big piece of red junk on wheels would come around the corner, thundering, and stop before your house, and you felt that it was a big thing. This is the machine age, and *Over in Europe they are using machine guns in the War*, and, *They are inventing all sorts of things that turn swiftly, saving time*.

My uncle Vahan came home with Lucy and Naomi and went inside for a cup of Turkish coffee. We could hear him telling his sister how splendidly he had been getting along in San Francisco. He had passed his Bar examination and was now an attorney-at-law, but he had made most of his money selling watermelons wholesale. Eventually he hoped to open an office in the Rowell Building right here at home. My mother was very happy about her young brother and we could hear her laughing with him and asking him questions.

Krikor was very ill at ease because his uncle Vahan had not offered to take him for a ride and because he was too proud or too polite to ask for a ride, but I felt, There is a lawyer in our family and he has a red Apperson. We are an enterprising people. I was so happy about this that I couldn't sit still and kept walking on the porch railing and jumping down.

When my uncle Vahan came out of the house, Krikor was standing a few feet from the automobile, admiring it. He was admiring it so humbly, with so much youthful adoration, that my uncle understood what it was that was eating him and said, Come on, you fellows, I'll give you a ride.

Our neighbor Rouben and Krikor got into the car first, and I sat on Krikor's lap. My uncle Vahan started the motor and we went off, making much smoke and a terrific noise. I remember that my mother and Lucy and Naomi stood on the front porch and waved to us. We had an exciting ride through town and felt very elated. When we returned, my mother had cut two cold watermelons and we all sat in the parlor, eating watermelon and talking. It was very hot and we were all perspiring but it was a clear moment in our lives.

My uncle Vahan said, We do not know how fortunate we are to be in such a country as this. Opportunities are unlimited here. Every man is free and he can go as far as he is able. He spoke in Armenian because it was easier for him. He had been thirteen when he came to America and now he was twenty-two. He asked Krikor if he had yet decided on a career for himself and Krikor became embarrassed and began to eat watermelon very rapidly. I hope, my uncle Vahan said, you will decide to study law. And my mother replied, Of course. I thought, Krikor wants to be a musician because he told me, but I didn't say anything. In a day or two my uncle Vahan drove away in his red Apperson and we began to remember all the little details of his visit that we hadn't paid much attention to at first.

Everything was solid and permanent at our house and we didn't notice the time that was passing. One afternoon Krikor came home with a small black satchel. He placed the satchel on the table in our dining room and we all gathered around to see what was in it. We never knew what Krikor was likely to do and we were always prepared for anything. Krikor was very excited and silent. He placed a small key into the keyhole of the satchel and turned it and opened the satchel, and we saw that it contained a cornet. My mother asked in Armenian, What is that, Krikor? and Krikor replied in Armenian that it was called a cornet.

As far back as I could remember we had always had a piano wherever we had lived. There would be times when no one would go near the piano for months and then suddenly all of us would be playing it. My sister Lucy had taken lessons and could play by note. She played serious music like the works of Chopin and Liszt and Mozart. Naomi played by ear and she played the songs that seemed to be without printed music and that seemed to be the songs of the people, "Keep the Home Fires Burning," "I Love You, California," "There's a Long Long Trail," "Smiles," "Dardanella," "Oh, What a Pal Was Mary," and songs like that. I couldn't play by note and I couldn't play by ear but I had managed to invent a few melodies from which it seemed I could never escape and to which I seemed always to be returning, a bit sullenly, as it were. In my despair I used to beat the keys of the piano, employing all the variations of tempo and volume I could devise, and I was always being driven away from the piano by one of my sisters. They said I played as if I were half-crazy. I didn't know why I had to try to play the piano but it seemed to me that I had to. We were all living and it seemed to me that something should happen. I believed this fiercely and when it always turned out that everything remained the same and we kept on doing things over and over again I would be frantic and I wouldn't know what to do with myself. And then once again we would all be laughing.

And now we were to have another musical instrument in our house. Krikor's cornet was a blunt and tangled affair, more a piece of plumbing than a musical instrument. He brought home a music stand and a book on how to play the cornet. By Christmas, he said, I'll be playing "Barcarolle." He blew into the horn and his lips became swollen and sore. Somehow he taught himself to play a very mediocre version of "America" and an even worse version of "My Old Kentucky Home," and he always insisted that I stand up when he tried to play "America."

He practiced a long time and we began to accept the horn as something permanent around the house, like the cat or the crickets or the English walnut tree; but he never learned to play "Barcarolle." Krikor had a very bad time of it from the beginning and gradually his ardor cooled and he began to be suspicious. He would fidget with his music and make a valiant effort to play only the printed notes and then suddenly he would go off and make all sorts of noises, and we knew that he could be heard as far south as the brewery and as far north as the Court House Park because we had been told. After a while he would be too tired to blow any more and he would sit down and look very miserable. He would say, I don't know what's the matter. I have done everything the book says to do and I have practiced regularly. He would look at the horn bitterly and ask, Do you think it's because this horn is so old or is it just that I haven't any talent for cornet playing? I wouldn't know what to think but I would understand how he felt because I felt the same way. There was something to be done, something perfect and precise and graceful, but we hadn't found out what it was.

Everyone for blocks around knew that Krikor had a cornet and when he passed people in the street they would whisper to one another, There he goes. The boy who is making all that noise. He has a cornet and he is trying to learn to play. We thought it was those street cats, but cats don't make that noise in the daytime.

Each summer the long tractor came back and filled the days with its dismal hollow pounding, the nuts from the English walnut tree fell to earth and we gathered them into boxes. Imperceptibly the change was always going on and each spring my sister Naomi placed peach blossoms in the black vase.

One day Krikor said, I have decided to give up the cornet. I can't play it. He spoke deliberately and, I thought, bravely. Less than a week later he came home on a bicycle, riding under the crossbar because he couldn't reach the pedals from the seat. He was almost twelve but he was small for his age. When my mother saw him coming up our street, pumping under the crossbar, his body all out of shape, she ran down the front porch steps to the sidewalk. What is this you've brought home? she said. Get out of that crazy thing. Do you want to cripple yourself for life?

Krikor took the bicycle to the backyard and began trying to lower the seat. He worked hard and after a while he got the seat down as far as it would go, but even at that the bicycle was too big for him and he had to go on riding it from under the bar. My mother carried the bicycle into the house one evening and locked it in a closet. Your father, she told Krikor, was an erect man and your mother is an erect woman and I am sure I am not going to let you make a cripple of yourself. If you must ride a bicycle you had better get one you can ride from the top.

Krikor had been selling the *Evening Herald* after school almost two years and he had been saving money. My mother encouraged him to save his earnings but she did not object to his spending as much as he felt he ought to spend. On his twelfth birthday he came home with a cake which had cost him seven dollars and fifty cents. When we asked why he had gone to such an unreasonable expense and why he had brought home such a large cake when there were only five of us to eat it, he said, This was the first cake the baker showed me and I hadn't ever bought a birthday cake before. I thought it was about the right size. Is it too big?

Lucy said, Why, we couldn't eat this cake in a month.

We had cake at every meal for a whole week and we never stopped laughing about it.

So Krikor took the big bicycle back to the shop and traded it in for a smaller one. He had very little talent for making bargains and the only reason he had bought the big bicycle in the first place was that Kebo, the bicycle man, had insisted on selling it to him. He came home on a smaller bicycle, sitting on the seat where he belonged and my mother said, That's more like it. You look like something now.

It wasn't long before I was riding the bicycle more than Krikor was, and finally we got into a fight over it. We had had fights before, but this was our biggest fight because we had grown bigger. Krikor chased me around the house and then suddenly I turned and chased him around the other way. We were wrestling and doing everything we could to be properly angry and at the same time not really to hurt one another when my mother separated us and said that we could not have the bicycle at all if we could not keep from fighting over it. I knew, and I think Krikor knew, it wasn't the bicycle. We would have fought over something else. The bicycle just happened to be there. It was because we were brothers and because we loved one another and because we had been together through so many different things. One day when Krikor and I were fighting silently in the backyard old man Andreas, who was passing through the empty lot next to our house, ran up to our front door and cried in Armenian. Ester, Ester, your sons are killing one another.

Somehow we began to use the bicycle together, hiking one another. Sometimes I hiked Krikor but most of the time he hiked me. There were lots of brothers in the town who were doing this. We had made a path across the lot and at the end of the lot there was a steep bank of three or four feet. We used to start from our backyard and, after picking up some speed, we used to go down this bank.

One Sunday afternoon in November we decided to ride out to the County Fair Grounds. There was no fair and no baseball game but we wanted to go out there and get on the dirt track with our bicycle. We had done this before and we had enjoyed being in the deserted Fair Grounds because it was different from being out there when all the people were there. It was finer and more private and we had lots more fun being alone. We liked the quiet and the enormity of the place, the strangeness of the empty grandstands. We used to take turns riding the bicycle around the mile track. Krikor had a watch and he would time me and then I would time him and we had a small book in which we kept a written record of our speed.

The castor plant had grown a lot and the peach trees had spread out. Easter and Christmas and Raisin Day had come around, we had thinned the honeysuckle plant to give it new life, we had bought new shoes and new clothes, we had got ill with the flu, but we hadn't noticed and we hadn't remembered. There were a few photographs of us in the family album, but to look at them it didn't seem as if we had changed. We had gone on quietly, sitting through the winter evenings, doing our school lessons, playing the piano, talking with one another, and laughing loudly for no reason. It had all happened and it was all there but we hadn't remembered about it and now we wanted to get on our bicycle and go out to the County Fair Grounds again.

I sat on the crossbar and Krikor got on the seat and we went across the lot. Now for the big dip, Krikor said. We came to the bank and went down it but while we were going down it something happened. The fork of our bicycle cracked and broke and the front wheel sank on its side. It happened almost too slowly to be real and while it was happening, while the fork was cracking and the wheel was sinking, we seemed to be coming out of an endless dream and we seemed to feel that this trivial occurrence was a vast and a vital thing. It ought to have been amusing and we ought to have laughed about it, but it wasn't at all amusing and we didn't laugh. We walked back to the house without saying a word.

My mother had seen what had happened from the window of Naomi's room and when we went into the house, bewildered and frantically awake, she said, Don't you boys realize you've grown? You're much too big for one bicycle now.

We didn't speak of the matter all afternoon. We sat around the house trying to read, trying to feel that everything was the same and that only the fork of our bicycle had broken but we knew that everything was not the same. It seemed to me that we had forgotten our lives and that now because of this little incident we were remembering all the little details that marked the stages of our growth. I remembered the time Krikor and I made a canoe of plaster laths and burlap and tar, because we wanted to go down a stream, and walked with it six miles to Thompson Ditch through a burning sun and saw it sink.

I remembered the time I nearly drowned in Kings River and Krikor swam after me shouting frantically in Armenian. The time Lucy lost her job at Woolworth's and cried for a week. The time Naomi was ill with pneumonia and we all prayed she wouldn't die. The time Krikor came home with a small phonograph and two records: "Barcarolle" and "O Sole Mio."

And I remembered with a sickening sensation the day my uncle Vahan came to our house in a soldier's uniform and played "Johnny Get Your Gun" on his violin; my mother's cheerfulness when he sat at our table and her sobbing when he went away in a train. I remembered all the days she sat in the parlor reading the *Asbarez* and telling us about the misery and the pain and the dying in the old country.

And I remembered the day when we learned that my uncle Vahan had been killed in France and we all sat at the supper table and couldn't eat and went to bed and couldn't sleep because we were all crying and talking about him.

I remembered that I had run down to the *Herald* office each noon for the extra edition about the war and had run through the streets shouting. I remembered the day it ended and the *Herald* printed a front-page etching of our Lord and the words *Peace on Earth, Good Will Toward Men.* How I came home, hoarse from shouting and sick in my soul because it was all over and my uncle Vahan was out there dead. I remembered the times I had walked alone, seeing things and being alive and thinking of my uncle Vahan, and suddenly burst into tears because life was so bright and clean and fierce.

All afternoon and almost all evening there was no talking in our house. My sister Lucy played the piano for a few minutes and my sister Naomi hummed "Smiles" until she remembered that my mother had asked her never to hum that song because her brother Vahan had sung it. We all felt sullen and bewildered. We were getting ready to go to bed when Krikor said, Wasn't it funny the way the bicycle broke under us?

My mother and my sisters said it was the funniest sight they had ever seen and they began to laugh about it. They laughed softly at first. They would stop laughing for a moment and then remember how funny it had been and then they would start laughing again, only louder. Krikor began to laugh with them and it almost seemed as if everything in our world was all right and that we had nothing to feel sad about. I couldn't decide what to do and I didn't think the incident had been funny at all, but after a while I began to laugh, too. All those things had happened and yet we were still living together in our house and we still had our trees and in the summer the city would send out the long tractor again and we would hear it and old Casparian would pass before our house in his wagon, crying watermelon in Armenian. I didn't feel at all happy but I laughed until tears came from my eyes.

Then suddenly something strange happened; it happened inside of me, and at the same time it seemed to be happening all over the world, in the cities, on the surface of the earth everywhere, wherever there were men. I felt that at last I was a part of life, that at last I knew how all things ended. A strange, desolating sadness swept through the earth and for the first time in my life I was feeling it definitely, personally. It seemed as if I had just been born, that I had at that moment become aware of the earth, of man on it, of life, of the beauty and the pain, the joy and the fear and the ugliness. It was all very clear to me and I knew why I had always sat at the piano pounding the keys, why I had fought with my brother Krikor, and why we had laughed together. And because I had been laughing, and because tears had come from my eyes, I sat on my bed and began to cry.

Without saying a word, Krikor began to cry, and after him my sisters began to cry.

My mother said in Armenian, It is no use to cry. We have always had our disappointments and hardships and we have always come out of them and always shall.

When we were all supposed to be asleep, I got up from my bed and went to the door that opened on our parlor and opened it an inch or two. I saw that my mother had taken her brother's photograph from the piano. She had placed it before her on the table and I could hear her weeping softly, and I could see her swaying her head from side to side the way people from the old country do.

The Barber's Apprentice

BY "SIRAK GORYAN"

Across the lake, in Moush, the barber's apprentice, Markar, swinging his arms, bellowing fragments from songs, lumbered through the town, perilously on the verge of falling. He was on his way to the shop of Mustafa, the barber, where he was being tutored in the art of shaving, cutting hair, and extracting teeth. And as usual he was drunk. He greeted all who passed in the street, bowing as low as was safe, and crying, "Effendi," his fat lips slobbering from lack of control. Still, he offended none, and entertained many. All who saw him, whether alien or kin, smiled at him and thought, "It is our Markar, the fool. Jolly as ever."

In a fool the progress of man comes swiftly to nothing, and in his heart the greatest of civilizations crumbles to dust in the twinkling of an eye, but where is the fool who is not loved? He belongs to no village, no city,

no nation, no race; he is peculiar to no epoch, the product of no era.
International, his country is all the earth. Eternal, he is laughter in the
wilderness, born straight from the humor of God. God's orphan, he is
yet loved by all men. The child of every race, he represents none. A
man's a man to him: Hai, Kurd, Turk, Syrian, Circassian, Tartar, Jew,
Greek, Arab, Mongol, or what; it is all the same. All are his brothers; all
are weak, miserable, pathetic. All pursue the same chimeric fantasies of
perfection, heaven on earth, everlasting bliss. All demand more from life
than it has to give. All know the same sickness of spirit. Then why
should not every man laugh and swallow the cup's drink? Why should
not each heart burn with the fire of fluid, the soul sing with its warmth?
Why should a man stay sober? What's a man but a poor, lonely, lost
soul?

The glories of antiquity bore the fool, and his ear is deaf to the
possibilities of the future. Hatred to him is vile, a loathsome, putrid,
stinking thing. How can one man hate another, when each is equally the
victim of life? All that matters to him is the moment, which, in his
impatient soul, drags monotonously, until it is spurred forward by
drink. Then it leaps ecstatically, twirling, somersaulting, dancing, caper-
ing, skipping, tripping, bouncing, and frisking; compressing in one
delirious hour the intensity of ten years. Seeking joy in every moment,
the fool finds despair and desolation the fruit of every hour. Wishing to
sing, he froths at the mouth. Praying, he blasphemes. In being humble,
he is a braggart. Nevertheless, he is loved by all men; and out of his
bountiful pity God himself smiles down on him. He is life's prodigal, the
child who strays from the fold of conventionality, from the solace of
tradition; and the prodigal is the favorite of his father, the most beloved
of his brothers.

After much spinning, stumbling, and bending of the knees, poor
Markar came at length to the little shop of his master, and, wiping his
wet lips on the sleeve of his coat, made a valiant effort to draw himself
erect, to be solid, dignified. In a moment, however, he collapsed to his
normal limpness, and, abandoning the futile plan, entered the shop. His
eyes were wild and bloodshot, his knees infirm, his hands shaky, his
tongue thick and clumsy. Fortunately, Mustafa, a small man with a
kindly heart, was alone. Markar, with misty eyes, could make out only a
blurred figure with a moustache. This swiftly mutiplied and became
three or four moustaches. These were Mustafa, no doubt, Markar
thought.

"Mustafa," he said; "Agha, Effendi, my lord, my master, forgive me. I
am again late. I would have been on time, but I helped a blind man to his
house. He was lost, Agha, and it was my duty. He lived at the end of
town. Blind, Effendi, I have been crying all through the town. Agha, my
eyes are still wet. It is no pleasure being blind. What darkness, Effendi!

What loneliness! Agha, what misery! Could I forsake him? You are my judge, Effendi. Would God ever forgive me?"

Mustafa, pitying his apprentice, took him by the arm and led him to the small room at the end of the shop. Here there was a couch on which, on warm afternoons, the barber took naps, while Markar waited for clients. "Lie down, my boy," said the barber, "You need sleep."

Markar sank into the softness of the couch, his lips laboring with talk of the poor blind man, the creation of his drunken mind, his symbol of humanity's loneliness, the idol before which he bent his soul. "Blind, Effendi," he was saying, "May God protect him from dogs. From cowards. Thieves. May he see in his sleep a thousand suns, each a thousand times brighter than our sun. May his lips kiss the lips of virgins. Agha, how fortunate we are! Effendi, how blessed!"

The barber was not amazed at the young man's eloquence: it was not new to him. "My boy," he said, "your lies are sweeter than the finest truths. Go to sleep." Markar swam to the arms of sleep, and in less than a minute he was snoring loudly. Mustafa returned to the shop, quietly closing the door behind him. He rolled a neat cigarette, lit it, and began to inhale the fragrant smoke. "What foolishness is this?" he thought. "There is not work for me, yet I hire an apprentice, and pay him to tell me lies."

"A blind man," he mused. "How rich is his mind, how warm his imagination. He will never be a barber. Never. From the stench of his drunken breath fall the purest flowers of poetry. And he would be a barber. It is nonsense."

Poor Markar. He slept as if all were well in the world, and his snore was as prosperous as that of the merchant; for in these things men are equal. Let the ragged apprentice sleep beside the neatly garmented dealer in silks; their noses will saw and tear the air in much the same manner. In plain things all men stand together, common, pitiful, and cheap; a dime a dozen in a good market. In the fraternity of nakedness the pauper is the brother of the priest, the poet, and the politician. Take from the grandest of heads its fancy turban; from the pious priest draw away the cloak of black; from the proud heart remove security; from the vain soul take comfort, and what is left? A moan, an itch, a snore, a snivel, a whimper; a leap as of a goat; a bray as of an ass; and a parrot's senseless oratory.

Where is the man? He that out of the material of his coat would stand above his fellows, a superior thing? That from the tinkling of his money would be a small God? Where is he that from the breadth of his back, the strength of his sinews, the height of his head, would be a giant among men? Is he not more grievously brought down by the tiny flea? Is it not sorry stuff that lies beneath the embroiderings of cultures?

Markar slept, snored, dreamed. Only in pain are men one; in pleasure they are divided. The simple man, the good man, is pleased with any roof that does not leak, any bed that is warm. To him bread is bread, and water a blessed thing. Simple, simple things sustain him. If his children are not geniuses, neither are they assassins. Not an angel, neither is his wife an adulteress. The world is good; time does not race him to madness; life is pleasant; God is kind.

But the evil soul, whether of great or humble birth, whether rich or poor, is pleased at no time, and with no circumstance is content. Carry him the tenderest of purple grapes from the hill vineyards; he will growl that they are sour. Place him in a palace; it is a cow shed, he will groan. If the day is warm and the sun bright, he will grumble for rain; if it rains, he will be miserable, saying that he is drenched. Give him one coin; he will say it is not enough. Give him a thousand; he will grumble that he needs twice that many. Tell him that he is king; he will yet fidget and fret. Say he is God; he will cry that it is not enough. This is because the heart in his flesh is bad, the blood in his veins foul, his every part rotten and sore. His vision muddled with poisons, the flower to him is an ugly thing. His sense of smell polluted, the flower's perfume is a stench in his nostrils. His hearing impaired, the song of a bird to him is an annoyance. His touch warty, he thinks the hands of others are diseased. Miserly, he accuses his fellows of stinginess. Deceitful, he labels truths fabrications.

Though ill-clothed, though poor, though drunk and disheveled, Markar slept as soundly as the sultan, and snored as vigorously as the judge on his bench. His dream, however, was purer than that of the prophet: he dreamt of God. Though his breath stank his spirit was sweet. Markar was the lineal descendant of a long line of topers, bibbers, and tipplers; poets, singers, and dancers. The paternal, as much as the maternal, side of his family was well stocked with powerful drunkards and artful storytellers. With the birth of Markar these qualities, never far unrelated, became magnificently merged into a glorious whole, so that drunk the young man was a poet, and sober a drunkard; or the other way round, if you please.

Only a month before, on the seventh day of August, Markar celebrated his nineteenth birthday, drinking himself to eloquence; stalking, pot-valiant, through the hills; stumbling to the doors of peasant farmers, begging them to be happy, in the name of Surp Garabed, the holy saint of the mountains, patron of the poor and humble. On his birthday he sang so beautifully that the birds, who were created to sing, became envious and flew off in humiliation. His roar was so mighty that lions, miles away, were ashamed of themselves. He laughed so heartily that the laughing hyena broke down in despair and wept. He frolicked so nimbly that the hill goats, mistaking him for a superior type of their breed, gamboled and romped after him, bleating happily.

That day, in short, poor Markar was very very tipsy. His spirit soared that day, and his flesh was stronger than the trunks of great trees. But it was the false strength of drink, and when the time came he crumbled to earth swimming with long strides to the deep poise of sleep. Hours later, toward nightfall, his brother Kerop, a boy of thirteen, found him, crumpled limp, smiling pathetically, still asleep. The boy wakened him after much shaking and slapping, and suddenly poor Markar leapt to his feet, shouting, "Who is it slaps me? Who dares slap Markar?"

The boy, sorry for his brother, said, "Markar, I have come to take you home."

"It is Kerop," Markar mumbled to himself; he was ashamed, disgusted. Nevertheless, he took the child's help, and they began to walk. Sleep had sobered him and he was ill with remorse. "Kerop," he said humbly to the boy, "if I drink again, let God pour dirt over my head; let me go down into the ground and never rise. Ach, my head, my head. How lumpish are my limbs, how weak my will, how infirm my faith!"

It was the old theme, and to the boy, familiar with the family taint, perfunctory, words. "Io," he said, "ha, aba, yes, of course, never again. Not another drop, brother Markar. It is a promise, is it not?"

"A promise?" Markar repeated, halting for emphasis. "Yes, Kerop, yes, yes. My head is a stone that beats with pain. I promise; promise." He clutched the small hand of his brother, and they went stumbling down the hill. "I should be dead," Markar thought; "the boy teaches a man to be a man."

Now, again drunk, poor Markar slept, dreaming of sleeping forever, while Mustafa, the barber, sat patiently, waiting for a client, one beard to shave, one head of hair to trim, one rotten tooth to pull.

San Francisco, California

The Moment of Life

BY "SIRAK GORYAN"

Aram, my father, I did not know. There was a framed photograph of him over the piano in our parlor. He was a tall young man with a solemn expression and an old-style moustache with the ends curled up. I knew he was dead and had no remembrance of him but I did not feel that his being dead had ended his life or at least the meaning of it for me.

My brother Krikor said he had known the man and that at one time he had lived in another place and before that in still another place far away. As a family we had done a little moving about from city to city and from house to house and I myself remembered, as if it were part of an early dream, sitting in a wagon moving slowly along a country road on a warm day. I remembered the foliage of trees, the odor of hay and earth and the lonely appearance of the road over which we were passing, but I had no remembrance of my father sitting with us and saying nothing. He was there, however, holding the reins and I cannot understand how it was that I did not have the slightest perception of his presence. I suppose I was awake only a moment or two and then fell asleep.

Afterward, without being told, I knew that he no longer lived and that his picture was the one over the piano. I could not understand how something that had had life could be no longer alive but I could imagine an empty universe, a void without substance and life and light, and this picture of universal death took the place for me of my father's personal death. It seemed awkward that he should be the sort of reality that would never materialize and very often the imminence of his presence in me became so probable that I believed that he would somehow come walking up the street and casually enter our house. I hoped passionately that he would, for I wanted more than anything else to see him and be in his presence. And occasionally, when it rained and I felt an incredible longing for a time and a place which seemed forever lost, I would be impelled to stand on the front porch and look up the street through the rain and have a fearful feeling that he would be there. And whenever I stood on a chair to have a closer view of his face I thought of him as being yet alive in the different places of the earth where he had been, and I felt that there would always be something inadequate about our living in the house on Santa Clara Street because he had never walked through the house.

As a family we lived in the east awhile. The eastern climate was not like the climate of the old country and my father turned westward, seeking the warmer sun and the lighter earth. In this new earth I came to substance and life, and when I was a baby, Krikor said, we had a chicken farm in a town called Camel, but the chickens were always getting sick and dying and my father was always thinking of ways to keep the chickens alive. He borrowed money to purchase an incubator and he borrowed money to purchase special kinds of feed and medicine but the chickens kept on dying and my father was heartbroken. In his spare time he tried to invent small things that would make him rich. He devised a new kind of top that whistled as it spun and he believed the top would fetch him a lot of money. My mother hid the top so that neighbors and relatives would not learn what he had done and laugh at him. He was a tall man with a scholarly appearance and there was something fantastic and frightening about his interest in tops. Once he won first prize for an essay on why every home should have a Victor phonograph, but when he went to the music store to get the cash award he was told the sum would have to apply as down payment on any item in the store costing at least three hundred dollars.

A lot of people around Camel were keeping chickens, so it was natural for the price of eggs to fall very low and before he knew it my father was head over heels in debt. He got our belongings into a wagon and we moved from Camel to the San Joaquin Valley. I remembered the foliage of the trees and the forlorn look of the road but I did not remember my father that day. I had no earlier memory and everything I learned about him I learned from Krikor or from family conversations about him.

He was born in Van in 1876, studied at the American school in the city and became an itinerant teacher. Among other things he taught the peasant to be prepared for the revolution. He was arrested and placed in jail. Through the aid of fellow revolutionists he escaped to Russia. When things quieted down he returned to his native city and married. But there was no security in the old country and besides he had been studying English literature and wanted to weld the language to the land, so he came to America. Several years later his family joined him. In America he found the market for scholars crowded. He did common labor, farmed, taught himself carpentry, kept chickens, invented a top, wrote an essay, and then died. I was a little over two years old and he was in his middle thirties at the time.

Of material things he left very little, two frock coats of very fine cloth and a half-dozen books, four in English and two in Armenian. My mother said he purchased the coats at a secondhand store in New York and wore them to church. The books in English were *Gulliver's Travels; The Beauties of Shakespeare*, selected from each play by Reverend William Dodd; *A Manual of English Literature* by John S. Hart, and the first volume of the works of Edgar Allan Poe containing the "Philosophy of Composition," the "Poetic Principle," and "Poems." The books in Armenian were the poems of Bedros Dourian and a popular satire, whose title translated into English is *The Highly Honored Beggars.* We had also a family Bible in Armenian but it was too old to have been a private possession of my father.

The works in English I began to read at an early age, and while I could not read Armenian, I found enjoyment in merely holding the books because I knew my father had held them and had touched and turned the pages. The strange ornamental print was deeply fascinating to me. At first I was displeased because I knew I could not read the language, but as I grew I was pleased that I could not do so because I came to see gradually that its symbols had become for me symbols of the vast and eloquent silence of my father, and every page of Armenian print seemed a communion with him beyond articulation and beyond language.

He left also a cow. However important milk may be as an item of diet, the by-products of it for Armenians are even more important. When milk is made to sour and congeal it is called *matzoon*, and this pungent substance is used in the making of a very nourishing broth called *tahn-abour*, and as a dressing for other national dishes, such as grape-leaf dolma. By itself it may serve as a satisfying meal provided there is Armenian bread to crumble into it. The cow was pretty important to us. My mother used to walk several miles each day in the countryside for grass to feed the animal. One day when she returned the cow was gone.

Although she knew who had taken it, my mother did not seem upset. She went first to the barn and cleaned out the manure with a spade. She returned to the house and began to prepare supper. I was perhaps four at the time and I was beginning to feel the true implications of situations. Several years later I remembered my mother's silence at the supper table and I understood definitely that it had not been the silence of inward poise but the brooding quiet of shock and disappointment. With the animal gone our meals consisted mostly of onion, cabbage and tomato soups. Nevertheless, there was never a feeling of poverty among us.

Once or twice each year my father's youngest brother Mikel visited us. It would be around Easter or Christmas, and if it was Easter he would bring dozens of colored eggs for me and Krikor and baskets of candy eggs for my sisters, and if it was around Christmas he would bring dresses for my sisters or suits or coats for me and Krikor. He was a tailor and he was studying the piano but he was in the habit of laughing at himself and saying that with his stubby fingers he ought to be out pruning vines and ploughing the earth. He looked something like the photograph of my father. He had a gentle glance as if he felt compassion for all things and a low melancholy voice, something like the voice of the great Armenian tenor Shah-Mouradian. He was actually a little clumsy at the piano but I thought he sang very well. His favorite song was "Kele Kele," a very mournful peasant song, and after singing it he would sit quietly at the piano with his back turned to us and we would all wait to see what he would sing next. He was not at all a cheerful young man or a very aggressive one but we were always glad to see him because there was nothing fake or superficial about him.

Several months after the cow had been taken away, Mikel came to our house. To eat in another's house indicates sincere affection for the members of the household and Mikel asked if he might have a bowl of *matzoon*. I remember my mother's expression of embarrassment. She did not say that there was no *matzoon* in the house because we no longer had a cow, but went to the kitchen to prepare some other dish. My sisters understood the situation and I seemed to understand it but Krikor said, "*Gov dareen* (they took the cow). It is not here anymore." Of course he was not complaining, he was merely imparting information and his object was certainly innocent enough.

Mikel went quietly to the kitchen. I could hear him speaking in Armenian with my mother and whenever they spoke so softly that I could not hear them I could imagine what they were saying from the feelings I knew to be involved.

Mikel asked, "When did they take it?"

"Only a month ago," my mother replied. "We do not really need a cow any longer."

"But of course you need a cow," Mikel said. "Five people, four growing children. How have you managed?"

My mother said it had not been difficult. "They do not look hungry, do they?" she asked.

Mikel said, "Nevertheless, I shall have another cow here tomorrow."

I do not remember another cow, so I suppose my mother would not permit Mikel to buy another cow for us. Instead, shortly afterward, she found employment packing figs at Guggenheim's Packing House on Ventura Avenue, near the Sante Fe Depot, and we began to eat more substantial food.

By the time we had become settled in the house on Santa Clara Street I had acquired a rich store of memories and felt therefore definitely alive. One evening in the fall of the year, while Krikor and I stood about a small crackling fire of dried leaves, I saw through the dusk, crossing the empty lot beside our house, my father's youngest brother Mikel, and there was something so intensely and ineffably real about the moment, the darkening day, the fire and smell of burning leaf, Krikor and myself solidly upon the earth, and the figure of Mikel coming to us, that I believed there could never be death among us, that my father was not dead, and that every moment we chose to live vividly could be made to survive forever. This feeling was so profound in me that I was almost afraid of it. Mikel came to our fire as one child might join others and because there seemed to be something anciently pious about the moment, we could not speak. Standing together about the fire, in an alien land, and yet the same land of our earth, it seemed that all the past and future had met perfectly and became perpetuated in this moment of our consciousness, this instance of our awe and exhilaration at the patience and swiftness of being and our inexpressible gratitude of senses with which to see, to hear, smell, touch, and be. Our religion was life and the awareness of it. We lived and because we were aware, we could not die and this awareness in us made immortal all who lived finally within and through us, my father, and his father, and the family of our whole people.

Noneh

BY "SIRAK GORYAN"

My maternal grandmother was a small sturdy lady in her fifties who believed savagely in a personal God, something she herself had created out of her own life, something almost pagan, a vehement spiritual force born of years of industry and thrift and discipline. She hardly ever went to church and looked upon churchgoers as hypocrites and maudlin weaklings, so that it was difficult to understand her own passionate worship of God. She prayed at the table in a loud and angry voice, and when she uttered the Armenian word for God it would seem that no one could possibly understand the term as profoundly and personally as she understood it. She said, *"Im Ahstvots* (my God)," and never God alone.

We called her Noneh, which means grandmother and is a title of respect for all elderly ladies. She had a bright face with a stern expression and I seldom saw her without a black shawl wrapped around her head. Whenever she entered our house I had a feeling that something definitely of the old world was in our midst. She visited us once or twice every year and stayed as little or as long as she liked, sometimes only a day and sometimes a month or even two months. She came generally when she had quarreled with her other and more well-to-do children and could not bear to stay in their houses.

She liked to quarrel. It refreshed her to become angry and to anger her children and she seemed to feel that such things were proper among people who really loved one another. Whenever she came to our house she would explain her presence by saying, "I cannot tell them a word. They find fault with me and think of me as an enemy. It is an amazing thing. It is an astounding thing." But we could tell from the way she spoke that she was not really upset and that she was even satisfied with the state of affairs she had brought about.

She was very careful about her health and brooded over the health of her children and grandchildren as if they were all helpless and could not survive without the constant protection of her experience and intelligence. She had simple cures for every malady known to man and no faith in doctors. "Lie down and rest," she would say. "You are tired." And if everyone was well she felt that they could not remain well unless she scolded them and worried and fretted about them. "Here, boy," she would say to me, "put on this coat before you go out into the open air. Do you want to catch cold? Haven't I taught you never to go outdoors without proper protection? I cannot understand you American children. You have no sense of what is right and what is wrong. You do things without thinking and then suffer for it. When my son Vahan was your age he was keeping a family of seven people." Then she would turn to my mother and say, "Ester, you had better give this boy more strong food. He has lean face of a horse."

My mother would say, "It is nothing. That is his nature. His father had the same kind of face. He isn't hungry, he is always eating."

Sometimes she pretended to forget our names and she would say impatiently, "This boy is Aram, is he not? He seems to be growing all right."

Before leaving her presence, we bowed and kissed her hand, and if she was feeling well she blessed us and if she was feeling out of sorts she said, "I'll not stand any of your hypocrisy. This is America. We are not in the old country."

She had never gone to school and had not learned to read her own language, but she knew countless folk tales which she related with the accuracy of a poet, never altering so much as a word of a story, no matter how many times she was called upon to tell it. If she happened to misplace a word, a sentence or a progression of the story she would say, "No, it is not so, it was thus," and proceed. She had heard the stories from her grandmothers and from her aunts, but she had not heard the stories she related to us, for these were full of her own personal style, her own philosophy, and expressions she alone could invent. In her way she was an artist. The stories had morals. They were designed to teach young people to have courage, to be honorable, honest and gentle, to help the poor, to have no fear of evil, to be industrious, thrifty, intellectually awake, and above all things, skeptical. The world swarmed with minds scheming to rob from innocent souls their virtue, their peace of mind, and their money. It was not good to have too much faith in man; it was better to have faith in God.

My grandmother was full of song and laughter and anger. Winter or summer, she was in the habit of rising before daybreak and making noise. Through our morning sleep, when we were half-awake, we could hear her going about the dark house, sweeping, bringing in firewood, cooking, shouting at the cat, and singing. She had a large repertory of songs, both religious and secular, and occasionally she sang in a mocking tone of voice the sad love songs of the old country, as if she were criticizing people for believing in such nonsense. But when she sang a religious song she would be passionately serious and she would seem to be very angry at the same time.

In the summer afternoons she sat in our parlor drinking Turkish coffee, rolling and smoking cigarettes, and talking with my mother about what was going on in the world. She had an uncanny talent for getting the latest news and she seemed to perceive the truth of any given state of affairs without being thoroughly familiar with its details.

"Every pumpkin in the country," she would say, "is buying a vineyard. Even Topal Arshag, the cripple, has bought ten acres, and the man cannot walk. All the talk is about raisins; grapes, raisins, figs, apricots, peaches, alfalfa, cows, horses, pumping plants, irrigation, ploughing, pruning, harvesting, marketing. No one talks of anything else. You would think we were a nation of peasants. You would think we had never had our great men, our architects, our musicians, our merchants, and our poets." Then her eye would twinkle with mischief and she would say, "Not to forget our cobblers and barbers and drunkards."

Later she would add, "Well, maybe they are doing the right thing. The important thing is to accumulate money. That is what everyone is after and if raisins are worth money then anyone who feels like it has a right to be a vineyardist. Have you put aside enough grape leaves for the winter?"

My grandmother was fond of going to funerals and weddings. She returned from funerals dry-eyed, sober, and livelier than ever. She would say, "They put old Simon Vartanian into the earth today, and the tears fell in torrents. I remember when he first came to this city and didn't know what to do. He looked hungry and scared as a rabbit. He came to our house one evening and said, 'Noneh, as an old friend of my family, I ask you to advise me. What shall I do?' And it was so amusing, a big man talking that way, that I said, 'Why don't you buy a bicycle?' Of course, I was only making fun of him, but the next day they told me he had bought a bicycle and was trying to learn to ride, and later they told me he was selling paper bags and peanuts (think of it, paper bags and peanuts), and he was carrying his merchandise around on the bicycle. And now after all these years he has left his wife and children a small fortune, all from peanuts and sunflower seeds. His poor wife wept heartily but I think her tears were tears of relief."

And when she returned from a wedding she would feel irritated and unfriendly toward people. "I have never seen such a doltish pair," she would say. "The girl had hands like chunks of meat and she grinned like an idiot, and the groom, he was stupid." She would make a sour face. "He was well dressed," she would say. "Everyone is well dressed in this country. You cannot tell an ox from a scholar here. But he was stupid. I don't know why such people should be getting married. Do they imagine that their children will grow up to be finer than them? It is an astounding thing." But after a moment she would feel that she had spoken hastily and she would add, "No, really, after all they were a charming couple. A little awkward with their limbs and a little graceless but charming enough. The girl was from one of the villages and the boy from Aleppo. They were really charming."

Sometimes my grandmother would be silent for hours and we would know that she was remembering the old country and the quiet life there that had been mangled and slaughtered and violated. She had brothers and sisters in the old country and she knew that many of these had been destroyed and that the others were homeless and hungry and ill. She would spend long hours sitting in a corner, fingering the beads of a rosary and occasionally sighing, "Akh, akh, broken, forgotten, broken, broken." And we know from these spells of hers that her laughter was not trivial but laughter that was born of despair.

She was very fond of the new world, and although she had learned to speak only a few of the simplest and most common phrases of greeting in English, she had no difficulty in going about the town alone and in making purchases. I remember with amusement an anecdote she related to us about an elderly English lady who had been her neighbor for many years. My grandmother and this elderly lady were very good friends and every now and then they stood at the fence between their backyards to chat. My grandmother would say something half Armenian and half broken English and her neighbor would try to understand what was being said and she would try to make some sort of a suitable reply. When she related the anecdote, laughing about herself, my grandmother said, "I cannot understand the lady. I have been speaking Armenian to her for almost ten years and she doesn't understand a word of the language."

She was very fond of walking and sometimes I went with her to unfamiliar parts of the town so that she would not get lost. If we came to a place where trees were in blossom or where there was a smell of earth and heat and leaf and water, she would say, "Breathe deeply, boy. This air gives life. Draw it in deeply. It will make your bones solid and your face round. Let your blood drink this sweet water. Breathe deeply. In the winter these things will be gone."

San Francisco, California

Print

BY "SIRAK GORYAN"

When my brother Krikor was eleven and I was eight I asked my mother if she would give me permission to sell newspapers. She said I was not old enough to go into the streets and Krikor said the same thing, but I could not understand such a thing because I had no feeling of belonging to any special period of life. I was merely alive. I was beginning to be restless and I wanted to get out into things and walk around and make noise. I wanted to be doing something outside of myself and I wanted to see what was going on.

I waited a week and asked again. Krikor said, "You can't sell papers yet. You've got to be at least ten. It's one of the rules." A week later I asked again and Krikor said, "I'll talk to Mr. York about it. If he says all right, all right."

I said I wanted to start making money.

One evening at the supper table Krikor said, "Tomorrow when you get out of school, hurry down to the *Herald* office and I will be waiting there for you. Mr. York wants to see you."

I went to the piano and for a long time I tried to make music. I could hear Krikor and my sisters talking and once I heard Lucy say, "I think we are making a big mistake, letting him go out in the streets at his age." I began to play softly so that I would be able to hear what Krikor had to say and I heard him say, "I know it, but I can't make him understand. He's made up his mind."

I did not sleep well that night. I kept thinking, "Tomorrow after school I am to sell papers." I was glad there was at least something I had to do outside of myself whether I felt like it or not, but all the same I could not sleep. At school the following day I was a good pupil; I did not want to be kept in after classes, and when the last bell rang I hurried from the school building and ran seven blocks to the newspaper office.

Thirty or forty boys were standing on the sidewalk, waiting for their papers, and the presence in one place at one time of so many different fellows frightened me. For a moment I wanted to be home, alone in the yard, but when Krikor stood beside me I felt that I didn't want to be home any longer.

Krikor took me to a small office in the basement of the building, near the press, which was swiftly making clean copies of the evening paper. It was a beautiful sight. I thought I hadn't seen anything more beautiful. Wordlessly I begged life to let me have some relation to the press. It was something man had made, something out of his own mind and restlessness, something apart from nature, and in its way greater than it. The press was black and massive and it made a noise that suggested events, the articulating of history. I was awed and I clutched my brother's hand. There was an odor of ink and paper and warm oil and the odor of the incredibly swift working of thousands of pieces of intricate machinery, all forming a single unit, and I felt elated and a little sick. And the way the papers were assembled and folded and stacked was simply delightful. Through the noise and the odor of machinery was emerging a godly precision and I knew that every copy of the newspaper contained the same words and the same pictures and it all came about through the industry and cunning of man.

Krikor led me into Mr. York's small private office and I saw the man with his feet folded on his desk and an unlighted cigar butt in the corner of his mouth. The walls of the room were covered with photographs of prizefighters, actresses, racehorses, and great men like the President and the governor of the state, and I felt that I was getting myself into a thing that was the heart of living. Mr. York was a small round-faced Irishman with clear blue eyes and an impish expression. He seemed to be in a state midway between wakefulness and sleep, and I could not understand why he was not excited.

Krikor said, "Mr. York, this is my brother Aram."

Mr. York looked at me lazily and frowned, and I thought, "Well, I can see that he doesn't want me." I began to feel miserable because I had seen the press and wanted to have a right to be near it in the future, and it looked as if they were not going to let me be near it. I decided I ought to try to bluff and I made an effort to seem very clever because I thought a newsboy ought to be clever. I stood as erect as possible and began to grin in a way that I hoped would display all wit and daring and energy. I looked idiotic. Mr. York smiled faintly and said, "How old are you, son?" I said I was ten. He smiled again, only in a different way, and I knew he understood I was not telling the truth. "Well," I thought, "it is all over now and I will have to go home."

But I was mistaken, and before I knew it I was in the city streets, holding a half dozen newspapers under my arm, trying my voice on the city people. At first I found it unnatural to shout but after a while it got to be easy, like singing, and I shouted with all my might. It was splendid to be making a noise in the city. It was a privilege and an honor to be allowed to stand beneath the town structures and shout.

I sold only four papers and earned only ten cents, but I felt that my first day had been a success because I had learned how to shout and what to expect from other newsboys. One or two things happened that frightened me a little, but I did not bother about them much. An older newsboy told me to get away from his corner and stay away. He was very unfriendly. And a policeman looked at me.

Nevertheless, walking home with Krikor that evening I felt important.

II

The newspaper press fascinated me and I spent many hours looking at it when it was silent and when it was working, and at the men who kept it in order. These men wore square caps made of old newspapers and they worked in their undershirts because of the heat. Their arms and faces would be smeared with ink, and generally they would be easy-going and amiable, telling stories and singing, but when they wanted to get an extra edition into the streets they would go to work like madmen and the excitement would be terrific. They would rush about the press carrying heavy lead plates, they would climb onto it, loosen screws, remove parts, insert others, and they would pour cans of ink onto a platen and spread the ink out evenly with a brush, and after a while the silent press would begin to stir slowly and a little later it would be roaring at top speed and I would be standing where the folded papers fell into a pile, and I would be reading the headline to see what it was all about.

Once it was double murder and a suicide, and we sold many papers. A man in our town went to his home and found his wife and another man together, and he shot his wife, and he shot the man, and then he opened his mouth and shot himself through the head. When the police reached his house, his wife and the other man were still living, but after an hour they died. It was all in the paper, including early photographs of the three people, and we made a lot of money and the news caused a lot of excitement in the city streets.

That day I got my papers and I ran to the city and I began to shout the headline, but while I was shouting I began to think of the three dead people that were dead from sin and violence and madness, and I began to see them in the room before they were dead, when something slight and sacred and godly kept them erect, when they had eyes and minds and wakefulness and articulation, and then I began to feel that by shouting about this thing we were permitting ourselves to be part of it and that we were transplanting its horror and ugliness to our city, and I felt unclean and after a while I could not shout about it and my jaws seemed locked together and I was clenching my teeth.

I could see other newsboys running through the streets, panting for breath, their faces flushed with excitement. The whole city was full of shouting, people were running out of the stores to buy papers, they were sticking their heads out of windows, and on every hand I could see and I could feel the horror that was coming over our city, and I felt that it was all profanity and cheapness and vulgarity, and that it was wrong. I was standing in the doorway of the Griffith-McKenzie Building, our ten-story skyscraper which we admired so much, which stood at the corner of Fulton and Mariposa Streets, in the heart of our business district, and I was thinking about this ugly thing that had happened and the evil effect it was having on our city, and I saw my brother Krikor running up the street, shouting at the top of his lungs, and I wanted to tell him to stop shouting, that it was wrong, and I felt sorry for him because he was not ashamed and not afraid of what we were doing to our city, but I could not speak. My brother Krikor saw me and he saw that I was not shouting and that I was not running, and he came to me and I saw that he was disappointed in me and I was sorry because I could not help it, and he said, "Aram, why aren't you hustling? What's the matter with you? Are you sick?"

In my heart I had all the words to justify my silence and my inaction but I could not utter them because they were not there in the form of print and they were without grammar and they could not be joined into sentences that would, could articulate a word at a time, and because this was so and I knew I would never be able to make my brother Krikor understand what had happened to me, I felt ashamed of my silence, and all my confusion and resentment were working in me and for some reason I began to feel that I would be crying in a moment, and the futility of this reaction made me ashamed and the more ashamed I felt the more it seemed that I would soon be crying and finally I began to sob, and my brother Krikor began to walk with me through the crowds in the streets, and he said, "I never saw a crybaby like you." And after a while he said, "You're not crying about those people, are you? They're nothing to us. What do we care what they do? We're here to sell papers." And I knew that he had not understood what had happened in me and that as usual I had not been able to reveal the truth I had felt.

By crying I had betrayed myself, so I was ready and willing to make a compromise. I was displeased because I had not been able to be precise about my feelings as the press was precise about everything that came to it. The press could take any situation, any event, no matter how complex, and in no time it could get print in line, making words and sentences, that approximated the event, and finally the whole thing would be precise and definite, and it would be in words on paper, and the words would never be destroyed and they could not be dissolved and modified like feelings.

It was no use trying to say more than I had the language to say, so I dried my eyes and blew my nose and in order to end the matter as quickly as possible I told my brother Krikor that I had been shouting at first but that suddenly I got sick and had wanted to vomit, but that now I was all right again, and I saw that my brother Krikor was smiling with relief, and then we were running up the street together, shouting the headline, and I felt that I would never again lie down on the job and that I would always shout my headlines, no matter what the news happened to be.

We ran together to the corner of Fulton and Mariposa streets, and there I turned down Mariposa and my brother Krikor went on up Fulton, and I crossed our Court House Park and entered the residential district of our wealthiest people, and I made a lot of noise by myself in our quietest streets, and the people came out of their fine houses to find out what it was all about, and I kept on shouting and the more I shouted the more I understood that it would have to be this way because the language of the heart was too subtle to be caught in print, and I caused my share of confusion in our city, and at the end of the day all my papers were sold, and I had a lot of nickles and dimes in my pocket, and I had forgotten all about the profanity of what we were doing, and the cheapness and the vulgarity.

San Francisco, California

Hate

BY "SIRAK GORYAN"

I

The War got into us. It was the big thing everywhere. We were told not to eat too much, not to waste anything; everything was precious. We were told to buy War Stamps. We were sending thousands of soldiers across the Atlantic to the War, and it was taking money. We were encouraged to earn money and buy War Stamps, twenty-five cents each. All of us were in it; Miss Gamma said that we, the children, were soldiers just as much as the men in uniforms. It didn't sound a lot like the truth, but we were feeling the War. There were parades. We saw soldiers marching. We saw them piling into trains at the South Pacific Depot; we heard their mothers and sisters crying at the depot.

Everything was Germany. Germany was a criminal. It was a criminal nation. We learned this indirectly, but we learned it. Germany was committing a monstrous crime, Belgium. The Germans were wiping it off the map. Men, women, and children. The forests, the fields, the towns, they were all being destroyed by big shells. Even in the Atlantic, in that big sea, Germany was committing its sins; down went the *Lusitania*, our own ship, a great ship, and down went all those people, many of them great people, and that rich cargo. Down into the Atlantic. A submarine sent it to the bottom of the sea, a German submarine. But why? Because of Germany. The War. Nothing sacred. Down with all those people on the ship. Nearer My God to Thee. Sad. Ugly. They were not soldiers, but they went down.

It was a thing a boy dreamed about; startling, a thousand living people sliding into the cold water of the Atlantic, at night. Horror. And the Germans slipping away under the sea in their submarines. The Germans doing such things. What in thunder. Why? A great big ship, so many millions of dollars, in the sea, down. I used to be sick thinking of the *Lusitania*. I used to see the people in the sea, sinking.

I began to hate. Yes, they were criminals. The Germans were something else, different, something unlike us. And we saw them in *Shoulder Arms* with Charlie Chaplin. At the Kinema Theatre we sat on the edges of our seats and cheered Charlie, the hero of the War. Charlie made mistakes, but in the end he won the War for us. We saw the Kaiser in the picture, and we booed him, all of us, all the kids of our town, and all of us stayed to see the picture a second time, and the second time we saw the Kaiser we jeered him louder than before. He was Germany, that moustache, the way he turned the ends upward, a man who had been responsible for so many deaths, for so much destruction, the sinking of the *Lusitania*. We saw him in the Kinema Theatre. He was the man who brought about the discovery of the poison gases, of tanks, of big berthas, of everything destructive. And Chaplin, our funny little idiot, he made a monkey of the Kaiser. It was too good. We laughed and laughed, and it was sad all the time, because we knew, they could never fool us, even if it was a comedy, we knew men were dying out there, but we laughed until we had to stop laughing. And not only us, the people too, everybody. Right at the height of the War, when men of all nations were dying like flies, we were in that little theatre laughing. There is really no period in history when men do not laugh. It will always be recorded that during the War people everywhere were laughing. In spite of the grief.

The world's villain, that was the Kaiser.

It was everywhere, this hate. I had a cousin, a small boy, three years old who had just learned to talk. His name was Simon, and as soon as he learned to talk he said, "I will chop off the Kaiser's head." And there you are, even the infants. What did Simon know about the Kaiser? What could he know at his age about anything? Still, he was in it too. No one had taught him to hate the Kaiser. It was just there, and it was the biggest thing of the time. He had got it out of the atmosphere. All the three-year-olds wanted to chop off the Kaiser's head.

We used to talk about the War. We used to climb the walnut tree in our backyard, a half dozen of us, and sitting in the tree, we used to think up various ways to destroy the Kaiser. There was a boy who was very good at inventing tortures. His name was Albert Savin, and he himself was really a crybaby, but he was the best inventor of tortures in our neighborhood. The major object of each of his tortures was to get the Kaiser as close to death as possible and then to leave off for a while and then to begin again with another torture, only a little worse. In this way the Kaiser would die a thousand ghastly deaths and always he would stay alive to be tortured again. The worse torture we invented was simply to have him shot. That was too simple, although too inadequate. No one wanted him only to die. All the little boys wanted him to suffer enough to make up for all the suffering he had caused. We used to sit in the tree and talk for hours about torturing the Kaiser. Some of the tortures would be funny. We would be thinking of Charlie Chaplin and we would think up funny tortures, surprises and so on. We would invite the Kaiser to some important banquet, for example, and we would have a big chair for him to sit in. It would be an electric chair. The Kaiser would be sitting in the chair, eating food, and then suddenly we would turn on the current. We wouldn't turn it on enough to burn him to death right away, we would drag it out slowly, and everybody in the room would be standing around him, laughing, making faces at him, jeering him, reminding him of the *Lusitania*, of Belgium. I do not know who invented this torture, but I remember the day it was invented. It was a clear summer day and all of us boys had felt very lively in the tree, thinking of these tortures. For hours we had dwelt upon good ways of hurting a man without hurting him to death. In the evening when we started talking about the War, it would still be in our minds, my brother Krikor's and mine. It would be there as an ugliness. We would be ashamed of ourselves, all those monstrous things we had talked about, laughing. It was not right to think of such things. It was not decent, not honest. We were talking ourselves into being savages. When we were alone we felt the ugliness of our talk. We felt sorry for what we had wanted to do. We knew that we were letting a rotten thing grow in us.

II

But it was everywhere. Not in us alone. It was in the newspapers, in the dreams of everyone in our city. That was the worst part of it. That and the fact that so many wasteful things had been done to drive us all insane, the sinking of our ship the *Lusitania,* the killing of all those men and women and children, the destruction of all those cities, all those homes, the destruction of all that peace. The quietness of Europe, smashed, the calmness turned to running, running, human legs, human hearts, fleeing, the fear, the horror, the disruption in the mind of man. Nothing whole, everything breaking, and the roar of guns. It was all a part of our lives. We came to believe that we hated somebody and something; our minister, a quiet and a godly man, he too shook his fist at it all, trembling. He too hated. God, he said, Oh God, grant, grant that we may crush this thing, grant that we may destroy once and for all, destroy, destroy! He prayed to God in such language. So it was everywhere. And it came to this:

There was a family of Germans, good people, who had a house in our neighborhood, on San Pablo Street. They were fine people, clean, simple, and, well, they were splendid people. There was a son and his name was Herman, and he was about the same age as my brother Krikor. Herman had two sisters, fine girls, but this is about Herman himself. He was a quiet boy, a bit sullen, who spoke with a slight accent in spite of the fact that he was a native of our valley. We got to talking about torturing the Kaiser. I am ashamed, but I want to keep myself in this account. I did a little talking myself. I invented a few tortures of my own. But I thought it was only a game and they would never do anything cruel to anyone. I thought we were getting rid of steam, that's all. But there were others, bigger boys, and after a while these boys became angry. They worked themselves up and they got nervous and wanted to do something themselves. Somebody mentioned Herman. Somebody said he was a German, and since Herman was a German, and since Germany was a criminal nation, well, there are boys who are boys who are no better than grown men, there are a lot of boys who are just like their fathers, and this crybaby Albert Savin and another boy named Edgar Rife, these two boys began to stir up trouble. They began to stir up hatred for Herman, who was a fine boy and a fellow who hadn't ever done anyone any harm.

It all started in our walnut tree, but it spread out and it left our tree and it was in the whole neighborhood, among all the bigger boys in our neighborhood, boys over twelve and thirteen. All this hate came together in a mob of these boys, nine or ten of them, and the boys decided to get Herman. My brother Krikor went along with them, and I went along too. I knew we were doing a crazy thing, but I couldn't keep myself from going along. I wanted to see. I didn't want Herman to get hurt, I didn't want his feelings to be outraged, but I couldn't get myself to stay home. I felt it would kill me if I stayed home and didn't see what really happened. My brother Krikor walked with me, and we stayed behind the bigger boys. We were not really part of the mob, but we felt that it had all started in our tree, therefore we were responsible, and we wanted to see how much ugliness we had created by talking.

The mob of small boys went to San Pablo Street, moving along like any mob, talking loudly, thinking rotten thoughts. Edgar Rife went up to the front door of Herman's house and knocked. The rest of the mob stood across the street, waiting. Herman's mother opened the door, Edgar Rife talked with her a moment, and then returned to the mob.

"He's not home," Edgar said. "His mother said she thought he went to town. He'll be along pretty soon."

There was a lot of talk. Everybody was feeling ugly. The whole thing was disgusting. My brother Krikor looked very pale and he seemed nervous. He said in Armenian, "I hope he doesn't come home. I hope he is visiting somebody."

But Herman came home. Somebody saw him walking up San Pablo Street, and the mob began to run toward him, feeling great hatred for Germany. Everything began to happen rapidly, stupidly. Somebody said, "Are you a German?"

Herman said, "Yes." Somebody said, "Do you hate the Kaiser?" Stupid, ridiculous. Herman said, "No, I do not hate anyone." Then somebody slapped Herman in the face. I saw the red mark on his cheek and the amazement of his eyes. He tried to run. Somebody tripped him and he fell. Somebody jumped upon him, and he was being struck and kicked. I did not think boys could be so beastly. I did not believe it was in them to be so cowardly. I began to cry when Herman began to cry. It was because of these things that were in us, these rotten things, slapping a boy and tripping him, knocking him down and striking him, sinking a ship and destroying a village, shooting men. I cried like a fool baby, and my brother Krikor's lips trembled and he bit his lips, and the boys brought blood from Herman's face, and it was the ugliest, the most cowardly scene I had ever seen.

It didn't take two minutes. It was all over in no time, but it was a vile thing. We were supposed to be little soldiers, little heroes, all that rot; we were supposed to be defenders of decency, and look at what we had done. And they said to Herman, when he was bleeding at the nose and at the lips, "Now, do you hate the Kaiser?" And he shouted, "No, no, I hate you," and he swore and he shouted, "Go ahead, kill me." And they saw that he would not hate the Kaiser, and they let him up. They laughed at him, and mimicked the way he was crying, and they walked behind him, shoving him, striking him from behind, kicking him. All the way to his house they did these things, and when he reached his house, he did not run. He was walking up the steps of the front porch when his mother came out of the house and saw him. She began to tremble, and the boys began to shout at her. She ran to her son and helped him into the house. She did not say anything to the boys; she was too amazed. The boys stood in front of the house a little while, shouting names and laughing, then they went away.

I thought of those two people inside their house, that mother and her son. It was a terrible thing. And that night when we were in bed I said to my brother Krikor, "Krikor, do you hate the Germans?" And my brother Krikor said, "What?" He had heard me, but it was a difficult decision. We were supposed to hate them; everybody hated them. It was proper to hate them; it was part of the time. I said again, "Do you hate the Germans, Krikor?" And I waited for my brother to reply. He did not say anything for a little while. I knew that he was thinking. He hated all those wasteful things that had been done, he hated the murder and the destruction, but people, living people, no, in his heart he could not hate living people. Krikor said, "No, I do not hate them. They are the same as all of us." And I said, "Do you hate the Kaiser, Krikor?" And he said, "No, I do not hate the Kaiser." And in the dark we talked about these things, and I said, "Krikor, do you hate the Turks, those people who have done so many things to us?" And my brother Krikor said, "I do not know, Aram. I never thought of them as people. They have families like us. I have always thought of them as something—well, I don't know what."

But I could tell that he did not hate them. I could tell that he hated only that which was rotten in man, in Turks as well as in all of us, that Goddamned rottenness. And then he said, "But think of all those things they did, all that pain they made. I don't know what I hate, but I know I hate something. Those boys out there. What they did today. That was nothing fine. I hate that. That is the thing I hate. Any of those boys alone are all right. But what they did. That was a rotten thing."

Summer Laughter

BY "SIRAK GORYAN"

There was a dark man from the city of Moush who was the father of my cousins Goorken and Dikran and Peter, and Mary and Ruth. His name was Aslan and he was a tailor until the price of raisins and dried peaches began to go up and then he sold his shop and bought twenty acres of vineyard and orchard seven miles from town in a northwesterly direction. His friends told him he was making a mistake, but he was not in good health, and he believed farming would bring him around. He was a tailor and all his life he had worked with cloth, with needles and thread and scissors and it had taken his health. His wife was my mother's elder sister and he was a member of our family. He was a man of quiet disposition, slender and slight, with melancholy eyes and a thick black moustache. He was not fitted to be a farmer, but he wanted good health and he had a family to bring up.

One afternoon in August he came to our house in a one-horse surrey and in the evening Krikor and I rode with him in the surrey to his vineyard and orchard. The surrey moved slowly over the country road and it was very quiet in the world. There was a sound of wind in tall grass and the strange sound of unseen birds hurrying through the air. Frogs were croaking and we could hear crickets from nearby and from far away. The crickets sounded like ticking clocks and the racket they made was like a mockery of time. We could hear the horse plodding along slowly and the creak of the surrey wheels. There was some sound but it was very quiet in the world because we were not talking and because we could feel Aslan dreaming or thinking to himself. And there was something about the evening smell of grass and tree and dust that made us feel the silence.

Far ahead in the landscape we could see the sun curving through the evening to another place of the earth and we could see the Coast Range Mountains. To the east of us and to the west of us were these high places of our earth and in the great valley between them we had our small lives and we had them close to the ground. We heard the whistle-scream of a northbound train that always tightened something inside of us and hurt, and a little later we could hear the low steel-grinding of the train but could not see it.

There were alien places in the earth, far from our valley, places we knew by name through print, Chicago, Philadelphia, New York, London, Paris, Berlin, Vienna, and there was also our small city with its familiar streets and structures, with its country roads and vineyards and trees and our sky and the faces of our people. It was good to be on the great earth and to have a specific place in which to be known and loved and to have meaning. I thought, while [the] surrey moved, of the alien places, the vast cities, the unseen mobs of life, the multitude of strange faces all living, and a sickening loneliness came over me. We were on the earth, but we could never be in all of its places to feel the magnitude of our living, to know the enormity and wonder of our simultaneous being, and in order to reach one place we would always have to forsake another place so that always we would be in one place, within ourselves.

Aslan sat quietly and we could feel him thinking. He was sitting alone in the front seat so that we could not see his face but we could feel that he was silent because he was thinking. We knew that he was a kindly man and we loved him. We were not afraid of his silence but after I had heard the train and had wondered about the great earth I began to feel fear and I sat closer to my brother Krikor. I did not know what he was thinking but I sensed that he too had heard the train and had been moved by it as I had been moved.

The silence began to be very strange and we began to be too awed to speak. At first we hadn't wanted to speak but now we were afraid to speak. We began to look upon the back of Aslan and suddenly we saw that it was trembling gently as with laughter. This trembling increased and after a while we could hear Aslan laughing softly to himself. We did not know what to think. Then suddenly he turned around and we saw his face and we saw that there were tears in his eyes, although he was still laughing.

"My dear boys," he said, still laughing in a strange way, "please, please forgive me. I have been sitting here and not talking and you are my guests. I did not mean to be rude but I began to think about things and I forgot about you. This road is like a road I knew as a boy in the old country and I began to remember that life. I did not mean to forget about you."

Tears were dripping down his face into his moustache. He stopped the surrey and said, "Come, please come and sit by me." Krikor sat beside him and I sat beside Krikor and the surrey began to move again. I did not know what to say. Krikor said, "How was it there? How was it in the old country?"

"It was just like it is here," Aslan said. "Everything was like this, the earth, the sky, the sun; only I was a boy."

Later he stopped laughing and when we turned into the dirt path that went up to his farmhouse his eyes were dry and he looked calm and he was telling us about his boyhood in the old country and how large the melons were over there. He said, "I have been rude. I began to think; everything is so beautiful and fine as it has always been, in this country, and in our own country, and I forgot that you were with me, and I ask you to forgive me."

That winter he died, but all summer he made a marvelous effort to be a farmer.

The Death of Children

BY "SIRAK GORYAN"

Emerson School was haunted. Its twin boxlike structures of gray stone, with their high bare walls and small dark windows, were joined by a bridge of wood, and at night its appearance was dismal and cold and depressing. Even in the light of day it had a desolate aspect and almost all of its pupils secretly hoped that it would burn and be destroyed. It was a comparatively recent structure, and there was an Assyrian carpenter in our neighborhood who told us he had helped to construct the school, but he thought of it always as being very old in a way that something decayed and rotten is old. Around sundown every night bats swooped out of its cracks, and flew, in spasmodic jerks, about the schoolyard. And we could think of no living thing uglier than a bat, which is a rodent that flies, but cannot sing and has no feathers and none of the graces of feathered things.

The western building contained the intermediate grades, and the eastern building contained the fourth, fifth and sixth grades. Both buildings were haunted. It was said that if you were to pass between the two structures at night, you would hear dead teachers scolding pupils of many years ago. You would hear old lady Timanus saying, "Now listen, class. Listen carefully. Two times eight is sixteen, is it not? Very well then, how much is two times sixteen?" Then you would hear giggling and mischief, the ghosts of former boys and girls scurrying about the classroom.

Frank Sousa said that he himself had heard these awful things with his own ears. We took it for granted that he had and we stayed away from the school at night.

One winter evening on my way home from selling papers I came to the dark school and when I remembered that it was haunted I began to feel afraid. I had planned to take a shortcut by walking through the two buildings and cutting across the school grounds to Santa Clara Street, but when I remembered the unwholesomeness of the place at night, I decided to walk around it. From across the street I looked up to the small window of the room in which I was a pupil, the fourth-grade room, and just as I did so I heard much noise of a fearful sort, and the lights of the room went on, which was ghastly.

Then I knew that I was running.

Years later I decided that it must have been the night janitor sweeping the room. But I could never account for the noise. One man could never have made so much noise, so it must have been my imagination. At any rate, no one believed the school was not haunted, and certainly we haunted it during the day.

We had all the dimensions of real beings, we had weight and form and movement, and yet there was something unreal about all of us, the small boys, the small girls, the old and the young teachers, the program, the sitting with books and print and numbers, the smell of school and chalk, the asking and answering of all those childish questions. There was something startling about our sleeping and waking and being alive all over again day after day, and at moments we could feel that it was all fantastic, but these moments would be few.

There were all kinds of us.

There was Maria Tapia, the little Mexican girl who had more grace than anyone else in the school but no ability to learn, no understanding of grammar, no talent for arithmetic. She did not seem real. She walked as if she were not on earth, and as if she were on earth by mistake or by miracle, and she spoke softly, piously, enunciating her words with the rhythm of song.

When America entered the World War, Miss Gamma's two brothers left the university at Berkeley to enlist in the army, and our teacher came to class with bloodshot eyes and a dazed expression on her face. She made an admirable effort to teach us geography, and then announced that owing to the momentousness of the occasion our class would spend the remainder of the day at games, recitations and singing. She asked if someone would volunteer to stand before the class and sing some patriotic songs. No one offered to do this. Then Maria Tapia stood in the aisle beside her desk and said, "Meess Gamma, do you wish I should sing 'Juanita'?"

Everyone in our class was astounded but most astounded was Miss Gamma, our teacher. Her sad face was caught tightly with amazement, and she said, "Why of course, Maria. Come to the front of the class." The little Mexican girl moved to the front of our room without embarrassment. She said, "Juanita," and began to sing in her native tongue. She sang, not with her lungs and lips, but with the shape of herself that was invisible and could only be sensed, and sensed only by us who were living with her, midway between the reality of sleep and the reality of wakefulness, and all of us felt that she, certainly, was not real, not merely one more little girl. And we understood that it was all right and even proper for her not to know about grammar and arithmetic and all the other pointless things that we were being taught.

There was Carson Wampler, a sullen-faced boy, the son of no-account Southerners who had come west in a wagon, penniless, hungry, and mean, and who lived in a tent somewhere south, by the Santa Fe

Railroad tracks. Carson came to school, even in the winter, without shoes. In the summer it was traditional for all of us to go barefooted and only a few children of the rich wore shoes to maintain their superiority. A number of boys made fun of Carson and called him names, and in the end it turned out that everyone disliked him and looked down upon him and he was always alone, silent and sullen and without shoes. For a long time I saw his pinched face and for a long time I was on the verge of going up to him and speaking to him and showing him I loved him, but there was something about his loneliness and his defiance that was too noble to be touched, and I was afraid to speak to him. His feet were very large and the skin was thick and cracked, and when it was very cold he stood alone in the schoolyard and shivered, and it seemed that all the world was like that, that life itself, the hard life and the life that was noble and secret, was cold and forsaken.

He stopped coming to school suddenly and I began to wonder where he was and if he ever got a pair of shoes. He became in time the vague sort of identity I sometimes met in dreams and in remembering him it would seem that he had never really lived and that I had actually known him only in the secrecy of my pity for man and life. But I could never forget the defiance of his pinched face and the loneliness that stood with him, shivering.

II

When, after a number of years, I had almost completely forgotten him and had given his identity to the face of man, I saw him again. I was riding in a Ford with a relative through the vineyard country near Malaga. It was winter and the vines were without leaves and the landscape was brittle and bare but somehow precise, with the quiet precision of death, and therefore beautiful, and Carson, grown taller but with the same pinched face, was standing over a vine near the edge of the road, and he was holding a hoe. I was so pleased to see him again, to know that he had always been a reality and that I had not invented him, and so pleased that he was still living that I called his name and greeted him.

While the automobile was moving we saw one another and after I had called his name, Carson thumbed his nose at me and made a face. He did these things in a way that was saddening. The gestures were maudlin and I felt sorry for him and angry with myself. I felt that I had brought about the destruction of a noble thing by wishing to touch it and share it. Of course the whole mess was partly the fault of the automobile. There was so little time for friendliness that Carson, doubtlessly confused and suspicious, automatically performed the swiftest and safest gesture he knew, and it is only to be regretted that there is no gesture among boys so simple and direct as thumbing the nose to indicate understanding and goodwill. I am confident that shortly afterward he felt very much ashamed at what he had done, and that, had there been time, he would have been pleased to rectify the error.

I did not see him again.

There was Alice Schwab, a large-limbed, rose-cheeked, German-Jewish child, the daughter of a watch repairer. She was the neatest and best-behaved child in school and every morning she came to class with an apple, an orange, or some flowers for her teacher. Once she brought a large shiny eggplant to class. It was as big as her head and it glowed like a small moon. It was from her father's garden and Miss Gamma spent ten minutes praising the eggplant as a vegetable and Mr. Schwab as the father of the pupil who had brought the vegetable to class. There was something about the eggplant that I did not definitely understand, something it had to do with what ultimately happened. We tried to paint the eggplant during our drawing period but none of us seemed to be able to do it. The color of the eggplant was the most delightful thing about it and we found that none of us could make such a color. It had a delicious look and everyone thought that it must have a sweet flavor, but Miss Gamma frowned and said it was not for eating, it was for admiration. The vegetable rested on our teacher's desk until it began to decompose, and then it vanished without the slightest reference to the evanescence of all earthly and material things.

Alice was not a pretty girl; hardly any girls are pretty at nine, except to their parents; on the contrary, she was ugly. Her features seemed unrelated and she herself seemed to be an exaggeration of the idea of good girl. In spite of all this, there was something important about her. It was style perhaps, and even though there was a touch of the pompous and fraudulent about everything she did, she had the most impressive manners of anyone at the school.

She wore her thick brown hair in braids hanging down her back, her face glowed with cleanliness, her eyes leapt with intelligence and alertness, she stepped primly, turned pertly, and spoke sharply and emphatically and with finality. There was nothing negative about her and she seemed to be the most wholly alive person in our class. She was hardly ever incorrect in her answers to questions, and if occasionally she seemed to be a shade misinformed everyone, including Miss Gamma, felt that, no, the book must be wrong, Alice could not be. If we were to have taken a vote, she would have been unanimously elected the girl in the fourth grade most likely to succeed in life. She was teacher's pet and everyone knew that she herself planned to become a teacher, and no one liked her, and everyone thought that she was a nuisance with her high-toned ways.

One morning, her lips trembling, Miss Gamma said:

"Everyone will please rise and bow his head. Alice Schwab is dead."

Then all of us loved Alice and were shocked and felt sorrowful and wondered how it was that she of all people had not lived.

And there was another who came quietly like a shadow, and he became my secret brother, whom I loved even more than my brother Krikor, and he was of my life, the life that had been left suspended in the dark earth of our people, that had been cut off from my form and face and the form and face of my brother Krikor, and he came from the pain and grief of our torn land, an orphan and an unlaughing thing, from Van, our ancient and beloved, the city of my father and my own city and the home of my heart, and I saw that horror had silenced him and that I could never know the truth of his life, which was my life, that I could never feel as he felt the abysmal gloom that had fallen over our land, and when he died and I lived, I lived only partly and one of the forms of my life turned inward with him to death and memory, and I stood without a brother, and I was alive, yet there was living death in me.

One winter morning the door of our classroom opened and our principal, Mr. Dickey, brought into our midst a boy in strange clothes who was small and frightened, and I saw that this boy was an Armenian and there was something about his shy presence that made me ill with joy, for I knew that he had come from our country and that he had seen all that had happened there and that somehow, in spite of it all, he was still living, and through him everything was saved, our cities, our hills and plains, our streams and trees, our churches, our laughter and song, and that through him we were still a people and a nation, whole and imperishable, and I wanted to get up from my seat and speak to him in our tongue, and I wanted to protect him from the strangeness of our room, from the eyes that were staring at him, and I wanted him to lift his head and know that here in this new country he was not alone and that he had brothers here.

I went to this boy during recess when we were in the schoolyard and we talked in our language and became brothers, and he told me of the things that had happened and he said that all of a sudden they were driving his father and mother and his brothers and sisters along a road at night, and their house was burning, and he could see men being struck by soldiers with whips and with blades, and he could hear screaming and praying, and it was ghastly but he could not cry because it was not a small thing that a boy could cry about, and then they killed his father before his eyes, and his mother became insane with grief and could not keep on walking, and his brothers became separated from him, and he could not find his sisters, and he was cut off from everyone he knew and loved, and for a long time he walked with all the people who had been driven from their homes, and along the roads he saw the bodies of dead men and dead women and the bodies of many dead children, and all over the country it was the same and everywhere were the bodies of children who had died.

And afterward he could not talk about it anymore and he said, "I cannot tell you everything. There are many things I cannot tell you, but everything is smashed, and I cannot believe that I am alive."

He came to school a year or two, and suddenly my mother called me to her and she said, "Do you know that little boy, Goorken, who came from the old country? He is dead." And she showed me a photograph of him that had been printed in the *Asbarez* and she read the account of his life, and it was then that, standing in our house, I could feel a form of my life turning inward with this boy to return to memory, and it was then that I stood without a brother and felt the living death in me.

Raisins

BY "SIRAK GORYAN"

A man could walk four or five miles in any direction from the heart of our city and see our streets dwindle to land and weeds. In many places the land would be vineyard and orchard land, but in most places it would be desert land and the weeds would be the strong dry weeds of deserts, and in this land there would be the living things that had had their being in the quietness of deserts for centuries. There would be snakes and horned toads, prairie dogs and jackrabbits, and in the sky above this land would be buzzards and hawks, and the hot sun. And everywhere in our desert would be the marks of wagons that had made lonely roads, so that we knew men were living in this dry country.

Two miles from the heart of our city a man could come to the desert and feel the loneliness of a desolate area, of a place lost in the earth, far from the solace of human thought, and it was a tremendous thing to know that we had men in our valley who were slowly filling this desert with the moments of their lives, their minds, their quiet talk, and their energy. Standing at the edge of our city, a man could feel that we had made this place of streets and dwellings in the stillness and loneliness of the desert, and that we had done a brave thing. We had come to this dry area that was without history, and we had paused in it and built our houses and we were slowly creating the legend of our labor. We were digging for water and we were leading streams through the dry land. We were planting and plowing and standing in the midst of the garden we were making.

Our trees were not yet tall enough to make much shade, and we had planted a number of kinds of trees we ought not to have planted because they were of weak stuff and would never live a century, but we had made a pretty good beginning. Our cemeteries were few and the graves in them were few. We had buried no great men because we hadn't had time to produce any great men, we had been too busy trying to get water into the desert, and the shadow of no great mind was over our city. But we had a playground called Cosmos Playground. We had public schools named after Emerson and Hawthorne and Lowell and Longfellow and Edison. Two great railways had their lines running through our city and trains were always coming to us from the great cities of America and somehow we could not feel that we were wholly lost. We had two newspapers and a Civic Auditorium and a public library one-third full of books. We had the Parlor Lecture Club. We had every sort of church except a Christian Science church. Every house in our city had a Bible in it, and a lot of houses had as many as four Bibles in them.

Or a man could feel that we had made this city in the desert and that it was a fake thing and that our lives were empty lives, and that we were the contemporaries of jackrabbits. Or a man could have one viewpoint in the morning and another in the evening. At any rate, the dome of our courthouse was high and it was shaped as a dome should be shaped, but it was ugly and it looked spurious because a dome had nothing to do with our desert and our vineyards and it had very little to do with what we were trying to do in the desert, and it was largely a cheap imitation of something out of Rome or out of Greece. We had a mayor but he wasn't a great man and he didn't look like a mayor. He looked like a farmer and he *was* a farmer, but he was elected mayor. We had no really great men in our city, but the whole bunch of us put together amounted to something that was very nearly great, and our mayor was not above carrying on a conversation with a Slavonian farmer from Fowler who could speak very little English, and our mayor was not a proud man and he sometimes got drunk with his friends, and he liked to tell folks how to dig for water or how to prune muscat vines in order to get a good crop, and on the whole he was an admirable man. And of course we had to have a mayor, and of course *somebody* had to be mayor.

Nevertheless, there was something small and almost pathetic about our enterprise. It wasn't on a vast scale and it wasn't even on a medium-sized scale. There was nothing slick about anything we were doing. Our enterprise was neither scientific nor inhuman, as the enterprise of a growing city ought to be. Nobody knew the meaning of the word efficiency, and the most insipid word ever used by our mayor in public orations was *progress*, but by *progress* he meant, and our people understood him to mean, the paving of the walk in front of the City Hall, and the purchase by our city of a Ford automobile for the mayor. Our biggest merchant was a small man named Kimball, who liked to loaf around in his immense department store, with a sharpened pencil on his left ear, and he liked to wait on his customers personally, even though he had over two dozen alert clerks working for him. I am sure they were alert during the winter, and if they sometimes dozed during the long summer afternoons, it was because our whole city slept during those afternoons and there was nothing else to do. And this sort of thing was the rule all over our city, and it gave our city an amateur appearance, as if we were only experimenting and weren't quite sure if we had more of a right to be in the desert than the jackrabbits and the horned toads, and as if we didn't really believe we had started something that was going to be very big and that would eventually make a tremendous change in the history of the world.

But in time a genius appeared among us and he said that we would change the history of the world, and he said that we would do it with raisins. He said that we would change the eating habits of man, at any rate.

Nobody thought he was crazy because he wore spectacles and looked important. He appeared to be what our people liked to call an *educated man*, and any man who had had an education, any man who had gone through a university and read books, must be an important man. He had statistics and the statistical method of proving a point. He proved mathematically that he would be able to do everything he said he was going to do. What our valley needed, he said, was a system whereby the raisin would be established as a necessary part of the national diet, and he said that he had evolved this system and that it was available for our valley. He made eloquent speeches in our Civic Auditorium and in the public halls of the small towns around our city, and he said after we got America accustomed to eating raisins day in and day out, we would begin to teach Europe and Asia and maybe Australia to eat raisins. He said that if we could get the Chinese, for example, to eat our raisins, our valley would become the richest valley in the whole world. China, he said, was swarming with Chinese. He shouted the exact number of Chinese in China, and it was a stupendous figure, and all the farmers in the Civic Auditorium didn't know whether to applaud or object. He said that if we could get every living Chinaman to place only one raisin, only one, mind you, in every pot of rice he cooked, why, then, we could dispose of all our raisins at a good price and everybody in our valley would have money in the bank, and would be able to purchase all the indispensable conveniences of modern life, bathtubs, carpet sweepers, house electricity, and automobiles.

Rice, he said. That's all they eat. But we can teach them to drop one raisin in every pot of rice they cook.

Raisins had a good taste, he said. People liked to eat raisins. People were so fond of eating raisins they would be glad to pay money for them. The trouble was that people had gotten out of the habit of eating raisins.

It was because grocers all over the country hadn't been carrying raisins for years, or if they had been carrying them, the raisins hadn't been packed in attractive packages.

All we needed, he said, was a raisin association with an executive department and a central packing and distributing plant. He would do the rest. He would have an attractive package designed, and he would create a patented trade name for our raisins, and he would place full-page advertisements in the *Saturday Evening Post* and other national periodicals, and he would organize a great sales force, and, in short, he would do everything. If our farmers would join this raisin association of his, he would do everything, and our city would grow to be one of the liveliest cities in California, and our valley would grow to be one of the richest agricultural centers of the world. He used big words like *cooperation, mass production, modern efficiency, modern psychology, modern advertising,* and *modern distribution,* and all the farmers who couldn't understand what he was talking about felt that he was very wise and that they must join the raisin association and help make raisins famous.

He was an orator, this man, and he was a statistician, and he was a genius. I forget his name, and our whole valley has forgotten his name, but in his day he made something of a stir, and for a while it looked as if he had had the right idea.

The editor of the *Morning Republican* studied this man's proposal and found it sound, and the editor of the *Evening Herald* said that it was a good thing, and our mayor was in favor of it, and there was excitement all over our valley. Farmers from all over our valley came to town in surreys and buggies, and they gathered in small and large groups in front of our public buildings, and they talked about this idea of making the raisin famous.

It *sounded* all right.

The basic purpose of the raisin association was to gather together all the raisins of our valley, and after creating a demand for them through national advertising, to offer them for sale at a price that would pay for all the operating expenses of the association and leave a small margin for the farmers themselves. Well, the association was established and it was called the Sun-Maid Raisin Association, and a six-story Sun-Maid Raisin Building was erected in our city, and an enormous packing and distributing plant was erected, and it contained the finest of modern machinery, and these machines cleaned the raisins and took the stems from them, and the whole plant was a picture of order and efficiency.

Every Thursday in those days I went down to Knapp's on Broadway and got a dozen copies of the *Saturday Evening Post,* and in those days the magazine was very thick and a dozen of them weighed sometimes as much as twenty-five pounds, and I used to carry them in a sack slung over my shoulder, and by the time I had walked a block my shoulder

would be sore. I do not know why I ever wanted to bother about selling
the *Saturday Evening Post*, but I suppose it was partly because I knew
Benjamin Franklin had founded it years ago in Philadelphia, and partly
because I liked to take a copy of the magazine home and look at the
advertisements of automobiles and Fisk tires and flashlights and Jell-O
and Cream of Wheat. I think for a while I even got in the habit of reading
the stories of George Agnew Chamberlain. One Thursday evening I had
a copy of the *Saturday Evening Post* spread before me on our living-room
table, and I was turning the pages and looking at the things that were
being made and advertised in our country, and on one page I read the
words, *Have you had your iron today?* And it was a full-page advertisement
of our Raisin Association. And the advertisement explained in impecca-
ble English that raisins contained iron and that wise people were eating a
five-cent package of our raisins every afternoon. It banished fatigue, the
advertisement said. And at the bottom of the page was the name of our
Association, its street address, and the name of our city, and it was true,
we were not lost in the wilderness, because the name of our city was
printed in the *Saturday Evening Post*.

And these advertisements began to appear regularly in the *Saturday
Evening Post*, and it was marvelous that our little city was coming to be a
place with a name and that it was coming to mean a place for people who
were actually living. People were hearing about us. It was very expensive to have a full-page advertisement in the *Post*, but people were being
taught to eat raisins, and that was the important thing.

And for a while they actually did eat raisins. Instead of spending a
nickel for a bottle of Coca-Cola or for a bar of candy, people were buying
small packages of raisins. And the price of raisins began to move
upward, and after several years, when all of America was enjoying great
prosperity, the price of raisins became so high that a man with only ten
acres of vineyard was considered a man of considerable means, and as a
matter of fact he was. Some farmers who had only ten acres were buying
brand-new automobiles and driving them around in our city.

And everybody in our city was proud of our Raisin Association, and
everything looked pretty fine, and values were way up, and a man had
to pay a lot of money for a little bit of desert. Then something happened.
It wasn't the fault of our Raisin Association. It just happened. People
stopped eating raisins. Maybe it was because there was no longer as
much prosperity as there had been, or maybe it was because people had
simply become tired of eating raisins. There are other things that people
can buy for a nickel and eat, bread and milk and meat and other things.
At any rate, people stopped eating raisins. Our advertisements kept
appearing in the *Saturday Evening Post* and we kept asking the people of
America if they had had their iron, but it wasn't doing any good. We had
more raisins in our Sun-Maid warehouse than we could ever sell, even to

the Chinese, even if they were to drop *three* raisins in every pot of rice they cooked. And the price of raisins began to drop, and the great executives of the Association began to worry, and they began to try to think up new ways to use raisins. They hired chemists and they invented a raisin syrup. It was supposed to be at least as good as maple syrup, but it wasn't. Not by a long shot. It didn't taste like syrup at all. It simply had a syrupy texture, that's all. But the executives of our Association were desperate men and they wanted to dispose of our surplus raisins and they were ready to fool themselves, if necessary, into believing that our valley would grow prosperous through the manufacture and distribution of raisin syrup, and for a while they did believe this. But people who were buying the syrup didn't believe it. And the price of raisins kept on going down, and it got so low that it looked as if we had made a mistake in the first place by pausing in this desolate place and building our city, and it looked as if we *were* the contemporaries of jackrabbits.

Then we found out that it was the same all over the country. That prices were low everywhere, and that no matter how efficient we were, or how cleverly we wrote our advertisements, or how attractive we made our packages of raisins, we couldn't hope for anything higher than the price we were getting, and our great six-story building looked very sad, and all the old excitement died away, and our great packing house became a useless ornament in the landscape, and all its mighty machinery became junk, and we knew that a great American idea had gone down to death. We hadn't changed the taste of man. Bread was still preferable to raisins. And we hadn't taught the Chinese to drop a raisin in their pots of cooking rice. They were satisfied to have the rice without the raisin. And so we began to eat our raisins ourselves. It was really amazing how we learned to eat raisins. We had talked so much about them that we had forgotten that they could actually be eaten. And we learned to cook raisins. And they were good stewed and they had a fine taste with bread, and all over our valley we were eating raisins for food because we couldn't sell them. People couldn't buy raisins because they were a luxury, and we had to eat raisins because they were a luxury.

Explosion

BY "SIRAK GORYAN"

This tailor Aslan who sold his shop and bought a farm was not a strong man, not a farmer, but he wanted to be on the earth the last days of his life. He wanted to be near things that were growing, to be reminded of things he had seen in the old country as a boy and as a young man, trees, and the land, and sunlight on the land. These are big things to a dying man, and we do not know how really important these things can be.

He had no business trying to be a farmer, but he had made up his mind to get something out of his last days. He was ready to do anything to get something out of his last days. He began doing these things when he bought this farm.

The farm was like a garden, especially around the house. In the yard were seven tall eucalyptus trees, and along the banks of the irrigation ditch that ran close by the house were a number of other kinds of trees, an old apple, which was loaded with fruit when my brother Krikor and I visited the farm, two nectarine, three plum, a pomegranate, a mulberry, two fig and four olive, a real garden. The trees of the orchard were peach and apricot. Half the farm was orchard and half vineyard. The vines were muscat and malaga vines. By the ditch there was also a weeping willow. The whole place was splendid and there was always the clean smell of water running through the ditch. It was all marvelous, even the smell of cow dung that came from the barn, even the smell of pig and mud that came from the pigpen, and no matter how foul a smell might be by itself it would be splendid in the strong sunlight of summer, and the bad smells would mingle with the fine smells and become a part of the whole thing, the whole smell of water and grass and sunlight on the earth.

The house was a large house and it had great big rooms and many windows, and it was the sort of house a man could move around in, and feel alive in. It was big and it didn't make a man feel as if he was caught in narrowness, the way small houses make a man feel. When the sun came up in the morning, the house would hold the strong warm light, and he used to stand in the center of a room and stretch himself and yawn, and take deep breaths, and say in Armenian, *okh, okh*, splendid, splendid.

It was pretty sad about him, about the way he was getting all he could into his last days, and it was no secret that he was in pain, and that at times this pain was severe. Now and then, in the evenings mostly, when we sat in the yard talking, when his face could not be seen, he would say casually, "Do you know? I can feel them tugging at me, tearing me away. It is remarkable how they do it. It is like a lot of little fingers pulling small pieces away from my lungs." Consumption. We knew that he had had it mildly for years, and that it was no longer mild, and that he was on this beautiful farm, waiting to die. He was waiting for his last thing to happen to him, and it was not a pleasant thing to be waiting for, and at times he would become irritable, not with others but with himself, and he would do impulsive things. He would walk alone, for instance, through his orchard at night, and come home coughing.

At first he was quiet about himself and he wanted to live all he could but after a while he disliked waiting, and he said that he would not go to bed, never, that he would not lie down and let it destroy him. He said, "I would like to be walking." And we understood what he meant.

One day he came from the field and out of a clear sky he said, "I am going to kill the cow." And a few days later a lot of his relatives and friends came to the ranch with their families, and the men helped him tie the cow, and he killed it with an axe. In the evening there was a picnic under the trees by the ditch, but the picnic is not important. He was a man who wanted to do a number of things before he died.

And not long afterward he came home and said there was hard-pan in his orchard, and he said he was going to dynamite the hard-pan. The proper time to do this was in the winter when the trees were without fruit, but he was not a farmer and he had made up his mind to do what he liked. There were more important things to do in the summer, if he wanted to work, but he seemed to like the idea of making explosions in the hard earth, and it was more than evident that he knew that he was not doing the practical thing. It was plain that he was tired of doing practical things.

My cousins, his sons, and my brother Krikor and I, all of us boys asked if we might go out into the orchard with him and watch how it happened, but he said, "My dear boys, I am very sorry, believe me I regret it very much, I would not think of not pleasing you, but this is dangerous work, and if one of us happens to forget, if one of us becomes careless, it may mean a serious accident. So please be satisfied to play in the yard. Swim in the ditch if you like, but do not come into the orchard today." And then he did a very remarkable thing. He lifted his younger son Peter and embraced the child passionately. He put his tools and the box of dynamite on a field wagon with flat metal wheels, and he drove the wagon away, walking beside it.

I didn't know what to think, but it was all very remarkable, and for some reason this little boy Peter was crying, and it was a moment of great sadness, even though the day was very bright and warm. Every half hour or so, all morning, we heard the loud faraway boom of an explosion, and had long talks about how it must be happening, and we tried to visualize how the earth would smell and leap into the air. Then for almost an hour we did not hear an explosion and we wondered what had happened, and after a while we saw him coming across the yard, and his face was scratched and it was black and bloody, and his overalls and shirt were torn, and his elbows and knees were skinned and red, and he looked disgusted. We ran up to him, and he said, "Goorken, go into the orchard and bring back the wagon. Do not touch anything on it. I have had a little accident."

We walked behind him to the house, and when his wife saw him she was holding a pan of water in her hands, and she dropped the pan, and the water splashed on her shoes and dress and she began to tremble. He said, "Please do not be alarmed. It is nothing. Nothing. I put the dynamite into the ground and lighted it and forgot to walk away, that is all. I was standing there and it carried me off my feet, but it was nothing."

He went into the house and began to smoke a cigarette, just as he was. He wasn't at all interested in washing himself and changing his clothes, he just wanted to sit down and smoke a cigarette. He just wanted to think about how funny it was. All of us boys began to ask him questions and at first he tried to make replies, but after a while he said, "Not now. In the evening I will tell you all about it."

His daughter Ruth came to him and said in Armenian, "*Hairig*, Mama is crying. What shall I do?" And he got up and said, "Heat some water for me. Let your mother cry. There is nothing you can do. I must bathe and put on some new clothes."

In the evening after supper when everything had quieted down, we sat in the yard with him, and he told us how it had happened. Only he exaggerated to make us laugh. He said that the explosion had lifted him a half mile into the air, and that while he had been in the air he had seen the dome of our courthouse, and he said that he had come down very gently, like a feather falling.

He said also, but more to himself than to us, "I cannot understand it. Another man would have been killed instantly. Anyone but me would have fallen on his neck."

San Francisco, California

Jazz

BY "SIRAK GORYAN"

There was a symphony in our city, but it was without form, and it lacked grace. It began with silence and darkness and sleep, and as our city awoke to the moment of day the music and tempo of this symphony became louder and swifter, and every day the music would be composed of different sounds and different rhythms, but after a year and after two years, and after we had had time to remember about all of the days combined, we could understand that all of the days made a whole symphony, and it was the symphony of our life. It was of our movement on the earth and it was of the sounds we made as living things.

Through our sleep we would hear train bells or we would hear the hoofbeats of horses and it would be day, and we would be awake and we would begin to hear the earth, and this hearing of it would be within us even when there was silence. We would leave our beds and we would hear the splashing of water as we washed, and we would hear the burning of wood in our stove and the boiling of water in our kettle, and the tinkle of spoons and knives and forks and dishes, and these small sounds had beauty and meaning.

And in the schoolyard we would hear the voices of hundreds of ourselves, each with a name and a form and a past that extended through centuries of life to the heat of the earth and to the solidity of stone, and suddenly the school bell would ring sharply, by electricity, and all of us would become silent by the order of our elders, and we would march to our rooms and our desks, and we would become a part of the shapes of these things that man had made out of nothing, and we would hear the voice of our teacher, Miss Gamma, preparing us for understanding.

And in our city we would hear the movement over cement walks of our people and their talk, and the coming and going of wagons and automobiles and streetcars. We would hear the sawing of wood and the hammering of nails and the turning of cement mixers and the riveting of bolts in new buildings that we were placing on the sand of our desert, and we would hear the midday whistle of our packing houses, half a dozen at one time with the sun directly overhead. And in the stillness of summer days we would hear the pounding of the long tractor that ploughed into the soft tar of our streets, and in the country we would hear the drumming of pumping plants that brought water from the bowels of our desert. And it was all music and it had beauty and rhythm, but we could feel that it was not whole, and we felt that in our time all of these sounds would come to be integrated in one great work of music and that through this work our life would have the meaning of something exceptional and splendid, and that it would be preserved.

And when there was silence we sometimes heard this music again, in patterns and rhythms of our breathing and our own consciousness. Sometimes in our silence we would hear again the sleepy drone of the pipe organ in the Liberty Theatre, and the singing and praying of the Salvation Army people on street corners, and the fall of rain, and the frantic scrambling of the pianola in the Bijou Theatre, and the shouting of traveling evangelists in circus tents, and the hysterical screaming of women who had come to Jesus.

We could hear again the cry of Casparian, the melon peddler, the thin whistle of popcorn wagons passing along Santa Clara Street, the coming and going of freight and passenger trains, at night and during the day, the sudden spring melodies of birds, the ferocious howling of cats at love, the ringing of church bells, the piercing scream of fire alarm sirens and the rush of fire engines and wagons. And we would hear the music of steam calliopes that came to our city with circuses from all the cities of America, and the eloquent oratory of sideshow barkers at the country fair, church singing and Sunday sermons, Liberty Loan speeches, the garrulous chatter of strangers who placed portable stands in our gutters and tried to sell our people new kinds of suspenders and garters that came direct from Cincinnati, Ohio, and had patented features, and we would hear the applause of hundreds of people at the public band concerts in the Court House Park on Sunday nights during the summer months, and we would hear these things in our silence as music, and the speeches, when we remembered them, would be without words, and all of these sounds and rhythms would become related in remembrance and from them we expected a great work of music to issue, and in waiting for this great work we were restless and impatient, and finally my brother Krikor bought himself a piece of junk that was supposed to be a cornet, and I sat at our piano and made all sorts of stupid and pointless and futile noises.

And always in the midst of the remembrance of all the sounds we had ever heard we would hear fragments of words and melodies from songs that had come down to us out of the great moments of lives and years gone by, and we would hear, "Drink to me only with thine eyes," and "Come back, come back to Erin," and "Maryland, my Maryland," which was to me the tenderest expression of a mortal of his longing for a specific place on earth, and we would hear "Kathleen Mavourneen, the gray dawn is breaking," and "In the gloaming, oh my darling," and "Where my heart is I am going," and "Fare thee well, fare thee well," and "Silent night, holy night," and we would feel through the fragments of these old songs the everlasting tenderness of the human heart, and we would not be able to remember where we had heard the songs or how they had got into us and become a part of us, but they were always there, going on by themselves, and it was impossible to forget them.

And we did not know that hundreds of years before our city began to be built this very music of man on earth that we so badly wanted to hear, this song of the mind and the soul and body of man, had become a reality and we did not know that what was imperishable in us and most admirable had already been preserved in the measures of symphonies of great men, and we had the feeling that what was going on in us and about us was something new because we had not been long on earth, and we believed that the sum of all our moments of life would somehow come to be preserved in great movement of harmonious sound.

And in the end we found that it all came to a kind of nervous noise that was being heard all over our country, and it was called jazz, which was a new word, and everybody was twitching on dance floors to this new music.

We did not have a phonograph in those days, but we didn't need to have one because we could hear the music everywhere, and we could almost feel it in the new way people had of doing things, of getting up and being awake, of talking, walking, of eating and working, and at first we felt great disappointment because all the magnificence of our hope had come to this fidgetiness, but after a while, after one year and two years and three years, after all the moments of our swiftest growth, after my brother Krikor had come home with a phonograph and we began to buy records, after the War and the parades and the excitement of the War, we came to feel the real significance of this music that had come out of our continent, and out of our national grief and despair and loneliness, and we came to feel the real depth of this music, and we came to know that beneath its pathetic garishness and smartness was the same old tenderness of the human heart, and the same old longing for precision and love and beauty.

Yea and Amen

BY "SIRAK GORYAN"

I

We had God, above all things, blessedness, belief, and the longing for precision, and we had the presence of vast and unseen things, oceanic, the swelling of unseen seas, the furor of dream storms, rock hail, wind and sleet, and the roar of deep rivers of soul, canyons of mind, tall ageless trees, the universe of remembrance. God within us, and the wailing of babes, and the oratory of mighty men, the stride of mobs within us, the surge of history, turning in us, squirming to unworded language, the first of all things mortal and the last, and the stampede of Arab horses, the glamour of wars, the ache of bleeding men, and God, our face in the light of sun, and the face of man everywhere, and the swift life in us, our godliness.

We had our being in God, and the word was the word of all men, of all life, of every shape and sound and substance, the ever-heaving sea, the silent sky, the movement of all living things, seen and unseen, and we had vision and stance and touch, and the earth was beneath our feet and we stood upon it, and over us was the firmament, and beneath the touch of our hands was the texture of living things and things that stood without life, of leaf and fruit, rock and earth, fire and water, and within us, our God.

God, silence and sound, motion and immobility, good, evil, wholeness, the secret and solace of our house, the author of our fable, the fact and the truth in us, precise and interminable, the fact of my father who was no more of our earth and of my brother Krikor, and of my mother and my sisters, the meaning of us, the cause, the beginning and the end, our shape and the rhythm of our living, the witness and fountain of our laughter, laughing in us, our grief and gravity, the joy of things seen, the mystery of pain and pleasure.

We used to pray. To be related to all things, to have relationship with things living and things dead. From the beginning, God. That circle, backward deeply to the time before the coming of the face of man, that quiet, and the darkness of the long night. And we were an end and a beginning and we used to pray to be related to the coming and going of men, to the appearance and disappearance of the faces and forms in all the regions of the earth, to be a part of every act of man, the good and the evil, all things performed, all thoughts and hopes and griefs, all joys and pains, and through prayer we were joined to remembrance and through sleep we came from the dark void to the slow, silent beginning of history and through physical growth, beginning as small living things, unthinking yet with the grace of God, beginning as fish and bird and beast, we came to the form of man, the first, and through prayer and sleep and remembrance and belief we came slowly to the form of God in us, to unity, and the earth came to the moment of our beings, to the last thought and to the latest hope: to be precise yet universal, to be immediate yet eternal, to have meaning but no small meaning, to be one thing precisely and at the same time to be the embodiment of all things, and therefore there was evil in us along with the good, and it was the evil of man and of godliness.

There was a wish in us to destroy, to bring things to an end, and it would make us frantic, because alongside of this wish there was an even stronger wish in us to build, to bring things to a beginning, to create new things, to make new shapes, new meanings. The earth was full of the things man had made, but we had made nothing, and we wanted to make many things, and we could not, so we destroyed. We broke things, smashed them, and we swore at them, and it was the same as praying. We used to take an electric lamp and look at it and think about it, about the nice shape, how incredible and clever it was, what it did, the fragile glass, the fine wires inside, and what it was for, the making of light at night, so marvelous, so admirable. Then we used to break the lamp. We had made nothing. We wanted to know about these things. God was in all the good things man had made, and we wanted to see God in all things. We asked one another if there wasn't something wonderful we could make. And the answer was always yes. Certainly there were splendid things to come, and we would think a long time about these splendid unknown things, these material things whose shapes were still unknown to man, but we would never be able to devise a new shape, and we knew that we had to do *something*, so we destroyed. Sometimes even the godliest of men will blaspheme. We wanted to draw God from possibility but God would not come out to us, so we smashed whole things, broke them to pieces, cursed them. And it made us frantic, because we loved God and we knew that the fault was in us and that we were not whole.

We had an alarm clock and one day it stopped working, and my brother Krikor sat at our dining-room table and took it to pieces. "I will make it work," he said. He held the metal parts in his hand and showed them to me. "See the little cogs on this wheel," he said. "See this little spring." And he could say nothing more. He put the small pieces of the clock together again, and he wound the clock, and he said, "Now it will work." But it would not work. God and precision were hidden inside, but the clock was dead and my brother Krikor wanted to restore it to life, to do at least that much, but it would not work, and it was a terrible thing to want to do a good thing and not be able to do it. But he had patience, and he was pious, and he took the clock to pieces again, working with it tenderly, and he spread all of its parts before him on the table, and he admired the parts again, and he had so much admiration for all the little screws and wheels and springs, for the whole idea of the clock, that I began to be afraid. I began to feel that it would certainly not work again, because it was a dead thing, and he could not know how to restore it to life, and I could see that he was loitering with it, that he was praying to it. After a long time he assembled all the pieces of the clock and it was whole again, and he wound it, and it would not tick.

My brother Krikor held the clock in his hand, and he looked at it with anger and bitterness, and I could see that he no longer wanted to build and that he wanted to destroy, and he went out of our house and I saw him hurl the clock against the wall of our barn. And the glass broke, and the clock fell to the ground, smashed and dead, and my brother Krikor sat on the steps of our back porch, and he said, "Everything I do is like this." And it was a tragic moment for us, because we knew that this was merely a prefatory incident, and that there would be other and greater things to make and mend. And we wanted God to be a part of these things, and we believed, and we knew that if God would not come to us, we would blaspheme, we would smash and destroy, even though we wanted most to build and to mend.

II

The shapes of things were holy to us, the mere shapes, for they were the outlines man had given to reality and to God, the designs with which man had graced the void. In all things, as in all time, God. In ugly things as well as in beautiful things, in precise as well as in imperfect. Levi's Junk Yard, the cemetery of objects, broken-down wagons, old automobiles, Dorts, Saxons, Moons, Jordans, beds, bed springs, piles of pipe, bottles, implements, we used to visit the place as mourners visit a grave, and we used to stand and look at the ruins of our time, our own Babylon, rubbish, and a rotten oily smell, the curve of a fender, we used to feel sadness for these dead things, and we used to wonder if there was not something we could rescue and restore to life, if some old wheel could not be turned again. Death, and time passing, even among the things of the mind of man? All things toward decay?

We had an enormous stove in our kitchen, an old-style stove, with the name Excelsior, Troy, and we adored this thing. Those shapes, those swift straight lines, the sudden curves, the round lids, the oven doors on hinges, and the whole mass of it, the whole idea, and the space it filled, the reality it was. And the old chairs, which we studied as tourists study the architecture of a great cathedral, and the tables, the small things, the plain objects, visions of God. A stove, a chair, a kettle, a frying pan, a doorknob and a door, and a window, and the idea of rooms, walls, floors, ceilings, the shape of reality, things solid, things square, and round, something turning with grace but quiet and steady, something immense and patient, the whole house, the street, the city, and all streets and all cities.

We not only looked at things, we saw in them the unity and the eternality of God. And the piano, well, it was a thing apart, a magnificent thing, a gigantic triumph, a thing in itself beautiful, yet of still a greater beauty, the beginning of poetry and mathematical precision, one, two, three, the notes with names and meaning, the music, known and possible, Beethoven and Bach, and three, four, five, the heart of man pounding down to our time, the silent shape and the fingers of Chopin, our God.

We made pilgrimages to Levi's to study death, the passing of shapes, the disgrace of age and inutility, to see the God that was perishing in ugliness and imperfection, the substance that was without life and grace, to know the yea and the nay, the whole idea of man and reality, the brightness as well as the horror, the beauty as well as the sin, the ultimate sin, death. And we used to be sad, the junk would sicken us with sadness: all that hope, all that energy, all the dreams of man to end thus: junk, decay, and that rotten oily smell.

We knew these things were of our earth and their decay was saddening, and we looked about for the everlasting thing, the object with shape that could never be destroyed. We lost faith in clocks. We lost faith in electric lamps. We smashed these things.

In the spring, the fresh blade of grass, the new leaf, the new flower, these were surely a part of the everlasting thing, but there was still another object, a brighter thing, a lovelier shape, and it came to us, as so many things did, by accident.

One evening on my way home from selling papers I saw a bird in the street, running beneath parked automobiles. A bird in the city, on the streets, a thing of feathers. It was a lost and frightened hen, and I caught it and placed it under my arm and took it home.

I felt sorry for the bird. It was frightened and nervous under my arm, and whenever we came into the light of a street lamp I looked into its eyes and they seemed to be full of sadness, of longing for home and friends, of almost mortal loneliness. And I talked to the hen in Armenian, all the way home I tried to comfort it, and I said, "Do not cry, do not be afraid," for I felt that it must be crying to itself. A domestic bird lost in the city, trying to find a place to roost under automobiles. And I took the hen into our house and showed it to my brother Krikor and my mother and my sisters.

"I found this chicken," I said. "It was lost in the street, and I crawled under an automobile and got it. At first it ran away from me, but I talked to it and got it."

I was very happy. I put the hen on the floor and it began to walk around in our dining room. It would stop walking and bend its head on one side and listen to us laughing. We laughed for a long time, because it was so funny to find a bird and bring it home and see it walking in the house. It was very amusing, and all of us had the feeling that we had a very distinguished guest at our house that night.

In the morning the hen was no longer unhappy. It walked about in our backyard, and in the sunlight it was a very handsome bird. My brother Krikor brought out a hammer and a saw and he made a small house for the hen, and a small coop, and we put the hen into this coop, and we began to wait.

We wanted an egg. Not just any egg, but *the egg*, our egg. I had found this hen. I had saved it from the city. It might have been run over by an automobile. It might have frozen to death. Now, therefore, an egg.

We made a nest for our hen, and began to wait for our egg, thinking of the miracle of *the egg*. We talked and I wanted to know about the shell, how it could be so firm and clear, and how the shape of the egg could be so fine and precise. How? My brother Krikor said that he did not know. It happened. It was impossible to explain how. It was like everything, like leaves and flowers and man, miraculous but simple and effortless.

One day passed, and there was no egg. We began to feel uneasy. We began to worry. There was only one accurate and proper ending for this incident: an egg, *the egg*. Out of the void it would have to appear in the world, something detached and perfect and yet something related to all the varieties of things, to all the shapes, the mother of them. An egg? The universe, God, the simplicity of the universe, the grace of God. Another day passed, and still no egg. We went to the hen and looked at it, talking. We were beginning to be afraid that it was without the germ of life. We were beginning to be angry. We wanted to see a precise thing, abstract and pure and perfect. We had already studied clocks and electric lamps. We were afraid that we would begin to blaspheme. There were all kinds of eggs. We could go to the store and get a dozen in no time, but we wanted this egg, we wanted it to come out of the void to us, and we were beginning to be afraid.

Then one day while we were sitting at our table eating lunch, we heard our hen exulting. We went to the small coop, all of us, my brother Krikor and my mother and my sisters, and there in the nest we saw a beautiful white egg, and it was a marvelous thing, and our hen was walking up and down, exulting. There in the nest was God, the beginning, and everything seemed splendid and precise in the world, and everything was definite and graceful like the egg, and it was a thing to admire and to worship. And my brother Krikor held the egg in his hand, and he smiled upon it, as if all the errors of man were here corrected, or as if the most remarkable of miracles had just taken place, and looking up into my brother's face I felt all his joy and his delight, and I was happy. And the egg was a statue of grace, sealed and solid and whole, the germ of life and of all things, the idea of seed and incipience, the first shape, the earliest grace. And it was God, and it was artlessness that was greater than the greatest art of man, and it was beauty and the universe, wholeness and the symbol of everlasting life on earth, everlasting renewal.

The things men made could end, they could decay and break and fall to pieces, but this, this oval of whiteness could never end, and out of its shape and out of its meaning all the shapes of man could be abundantly increased, and here it was, our egg, in the palm of my brother's hand, and there he was smiling upon it, because the egg had made him whole, because it had sealed him inwardly, because it had repudiated the ugliness of all broken and decayed things, restored him to piety and faith, returned him to God, yea and amen.

The Barber Whose Uncle Had His Head Bitten Off by a Circus Tiger

Miss Gamma said I needed a haircut, my mother said I needed a haircut, my brother Krikor said I needed a haircut: the whole world wanted me to get a haircut. My head was too big for the world, seven and seven-eighths, maybe eight and seven-eighths. Too much black hair, the world said. Who do you think you are?

Me? I said. I'm nobody. I'm too busy to get a haircut, that's all. What do I want with a haircut? What's wrong with a lot of hair?

Everybody said, "When are you going to get a haircut?"

There was a big businessman named Huntington who used to buy an *Evening Herald* from me every day. He was a man who weighed two hundred and forty pounds, owned two Cadillacs, six hundred acres of alicante vines, and had over a million dollars in The Valley Bank, as well as a small head, all bald, right on top of him where everybody could see it. He used to make railroad men from out of town walk six blocks to see my head. "There's California for you," he used to shout in the street. "There's climate and health. Lord God," he used to roar, "there's hair on a head."

Miss Gamma was pretty bitter about the size of my head.

"I'm not mentioning any names," she said one day, "but unless a certain young man in this class visits a barber one of these days and has his hair cut, he will be sent to The Reform School."

She didn't mention any names. All she did was look at me.

"What's the big idea?" my brother Krikor said.

"Remember Samson," I said. "Remember the wrath of Samson when they took away his hair."

"That was different," said my brother Krikor. "You're not Samson."

"Oh no?" I said. "How do you know I'm not? What makes you think I'm not?"

I was glad the world was sore at me, but one day a sparrow tried to build a nest in my hair, so I hurried uptown to a barber. I was sleeping on the grass under the walnut tree in our yard when a sparrow flew down from the tree and started working its way into my hair. It was a warm winter day and the world was sleeping, and I was sleeping. It was very still everywhere in the world. Nobody was rushing around in an automobile and the only thing you could hear was the warm and cool, joyous and melancholy hush of reality. The world. Ah God, it was good to be alive somewhere. It was magnificent to have a small house in the world: a big front porch for the long summer afternoons and evenings. Rooms with tables and chairs and beds. A piano. A stove. Pictures out of the *Saturday Evening Post* on the walls. It was strange and miraculous to be somewhere in the world. Alive, able to move through the pneumatics of time and space, morning, noon, and night: to breathe and eat and laugh and talk and sleep and grow. To see and hear and touch. To walk through the places of the world under the sun. To be in *the place*. The world.

I was glad the world was there, so I could be there too. I was alone, so I was sad about everything, but I was glad too. It is the same anyway. I was so glad about everything I was sad. I was so glad and sad about everything I wanted to dream about it: the places I had never seen. The magic cities of the world: New York, London, Paris, Berlin, Vienna, Constantinople, Rome, Cairo. The streets, the houses, the people alive. The doors and windows everywhere. And the trains at night, and at night the ships at sea. The dark melancholy sea. And the bright moments of all the dead years, the cities buried under time, the places rotted and ended: the once-living forever dead and forever alive because the living of the earth lived everlastingly. Ah Jesus, in 1919 I dreamed a dream one day: I dreamed the end of flux and decay and death. I dreamed the eternal moment of sun in sky and warmth in the world.

Then the sparrow flew down from the tree to my head and tried to build a nest in my hair, and I woke up.

I opened my eyes, but didn't move.

I had no idea a bird was in my hair until the sparrow began to sing. Never before in my life had I heard the cry of a bird so clearly, and what I heard sounded very startling and new, and at the same time very natural and old. The bird simply sang, but what I seemed to hear was, "Weep, weep, weep, Oh weep, there is nothing to do but weep." And yet the bird articulated this melancholy message in the most joyous spirit. There had been no sound in the world and then suddenly I had heard the music and oratory of the sparrow. For a moment, while I was still half-asleep, the whole business seemed altogether natural: the bird in my hair, talking to me, and the remarkable contradiction in the meaning of the message and its spirit. On the one hand grief, on the other joy.

Then I realized such a thing was not proper. It was not proper for a small bird to flutter around in anybody's hair.

So I jumped up and hurried to town, and the sparrow, properly frightened, flew as far away as it could go in one breath.

The world was right. Miss Gamma was right. My brother Krikor was right. The thing to do was to get a haircut, so sparrows wouldn't try in anybody's hair.

There was an Armenian barber on Mariposa Street named Aram who was a farmer by rights, or maybe a blacksmith, or maybe a philosopher. I didn't know. I only knew he had a little shop on Mariposa Street and spent most of his time reading the *Asbarez* and other Armenian papers, rolling cigarettes, smoking them, and watching the people go by. I never did see him giving anybody a haircut or a shave, although I suppose one or two people went into his shop by mistake, in all innocence.

I went to Aram's shop on Mariposa Street and woke him up. He was sitting at the little table with an Armenian book open before him, sleeping.

In Armenian I said. "Will you cut my hair? I have twenty-five cents."

"Ah," he said, "I am glad to see you. What is your name? Sit down. I will make coffee first. Ah, that is a fine head of hair you have."

"Everybody wants me to get a haircut," I said.

"That is the way with the world," he said. "Always telling you what to do. What's wrong with a little hair? Why do they do it? Earn money, they say. Buy a farm. This. That. Ah, they are against letting a man live a quiet life."

"Can you do it?" I said. "Can you cut it all away, so they will not talk about it again for a long time?"

"Coffee," said the barber. "Let us sip a little coffee first."

There was a small gas range at the back of the store, a sink and faucet, a shelf with small cups and saucers, spoons, a can opener, and other things.

He brought me a cup of coffee, and I wondered how it was I had never before visited him, perhaps the most interesting man in the whole city. I knew he was a remarkable man from the way he wakened when I entered the store, from the way he talked, and walked, and gestured. I knew he was a very remarkable man in the world, a barber on Mariposa Street. He was about fifty and I was eleven. He was no taller than I was and no heavier, but his face was the face of a man who has found out, who knows, who is wise, and yet loves and is not unkind.

When he opened his eyes, his glance seemed to say, "The world? I know all about the world. Evil and miserliness, hatred and fear, uncleanliness and rot. Even so, I love it all."

I lifted the small cup to my lips and sipped the hot black fluid. It tasted finer than anything I had ever before tasted.

"Sit down," he said in Armenian. "Sit down, sit down. We have nowhere to go. We have nothing to do. Your hair will not grow in an hour."

I sat down and laughed in Armenian, and he began to tell me about the world.

He told me about his uncle Misak who was born in Moush.

We drank the coffee and then I got into the chair and he began to cut my hair. He gave me the worst haircut I had ever gotten, much worse than the ones I got at the barber college across the tracks, free, but he told me about his poor uncle Misak, and none of the student barbers across the tracks could make up a story like that. The whole bunch of them put together couldn't do it. I wouldn't be surprised if all the student barbers in the world couldn't make up a story half as good as the sad story of his poor uncle Misak and the circus tiger. I went out of his shop with a very bad haircut, but I didn't care about that. He wasn't a barber anyway. He was just pretending to be a barber, so his wife wouldn't bother him too much. He was just doing that to satisfy the world. All he wanted to do was read and talk to decent people. He had five children, three boys and two girls, but they were all like his wife, and he couldn't talk to them. All they wanted to know was how much was he making.

"My poor uncle Misak," he said to me, "was born a long time ago in Moush and he was a very wild boy, although he was not a thief. He was wild with people who thought they were strong and he could wrestle any two boys in the whole city, and if necessary their fathers and mothers at the same time. Their grandfathers and grandmothers too," he said.

"So everybody said to my poor uncle Misak, 'Misak, you are strong; why don't you be a wrestler and earn money?' So Misak became a wrestler. He broke the bones of eighteen strong men before he was twenty. And all he did with his money was eat and drink and give the rest to children. He didn't want money.

"Ah," he said, "that was long ago. Now everybody wants money. They told him he would be sorry someday, and of course they were right. They told him to take care of his money because some day he would no longer be strong and he would not be able to wrestle, and he would have no money. And the day came. My poor uncle Misak was forty years old and no longer strong, and he had no money. They laughed at him, and he went away. He went to Constantinople. Then he went to Vienna."

"Vienna?" I said. "Your uncle Misak went to Vienna?"

"Yes, of course," said the barber. "My poor uncle Misak went to many places. In Vienna," he said, "my poor uncle could not find work, and he nearly starved to death, but did he steal so much as a loaf of bread? No, he stole nothing. Then he went to Berlin. Ah, there is a place in the world, Berlin. There, too, my poor uncle Misak nearly starved to death."

He was cutting my hair, left and right. I could see the black hair on the floor and feel my head becoming colder and colder with exposure. And smaller and smaller. "Ah, Berlin," he said. "Cruel city of the world, streets and streets and houses and houses and people and people, but not one door for my poor uncle Misak, not one room, not one table, not one friend."

"Ah God," I said, "this loneliness of man in the world. This tragic loneliness of the living."

"And," said the barber, "it was the same in Paris, the same in London, the same in New York, the same in South America, it was the same everywhere, streets and streets, houses and houses, doors and doors, but no place in the world for my poor uncle Misak."

"Ah God," I prayed. "Protect him, Father in heaven, protect him."

"In China," said the barber, "my poor uncle Misak met an Arab who was a clown in a French circus. The Arab clown and my uncle Misak talked together in Turkish. The clown said, 'Brother, are you a lover of man and animals?' And my uncle Misak said, 'Brother, I love everything in God's holy firmament. Men and animals and fish and fowl and rock and fire and water and everything seen and unseen.' And the Arab clown said, 'Brother, can you love even a tiger, a ferocious jungle tiger?' And my uncle Misak said, 'Brother, my love for the ferocious jungle beast is unbounded.' Ah, my uncle Misak was an unhappy man."

"Ah God," I said.

"The Arab clown was very glad to hear about my uncle's love for the wild beasts of the jungle, for he too was a very grave man. 'Brother,' he said to my uncle, 'could you love a tiger enough to place your head into its yawning mouth?' "

"Protect him, God," I prayed.

"And," said Aram the barber, "my uncle Misak said, 'Brother, I could.' And the Arab clown said, 'Will you join the circus? Yesterday the tiger carelessly closed its mouth around the head of poor Simon Perigord, and there is no longer anyone in the circus with such great love for the creations of infinite God.' My poor uncle Misak was weary of the world, and he said, 'Brother, I will join the circus and place my head into the yawning mouth of God's holy tiger a dozen times a day.' 'That is not necessary,' said the Arab clown. 'Twice a day will be enough.' So my poor uncle Misak joined the French circus in China and began placing his head into the yawning mouth of the tiger.

"The circus," said the barber, "traveled from China to India, from India to Afghanistan, from Afghanistan to Persia, and there, in Persia, it happened. The tiger and my poor uncle Misak became very good friends. In Teheran, in that old decaying city, the tiger grew savage again. It was a very hot day, and everyone felt ugly. The tiger felt very angry and ran about all day. My poor uncle Misak placed his head into the yawning mouth of the tiger, in Teheran, that ugly rotting city of Persia, and he was about to take his head out of the tiger's mouth when the tiger, full of the ugliness of things living on the earth, clapped its jaws together."

I got out of the chair and saw a strange person in the mirror, myself. I was scared and all my hair was gone. I paid Aram the barber twenty-five cents and went home. Everybody laughed at me. My brother Krikor said he had never seen such a crazy haircut before.

It was all right, though.

All I could think about for weeks was the barber's poor uncle Misak whose head was bitten off by the circus tiger, and I looked forward to the day when I would need a haircut again, so I could go to Aram's shop and listen to his story of man on earth, lost and lonely and always in danger, the sad story of his poor uncle Misak. The sad story of every man alive.

Home

My cousin drove the broken-down Ford to the front of the house and pulled the emergency brake because the regular brakes were no good, and the car skidded and choked and stopped. He got out and came around the house to the backyard and stood a little while looking up at the sky. Then he came up the steps and on into the kitchen.

I was almost through shaving.

It's going to be a swell day, he said.

That's fine, I said.

He poured himself a cup of coffee and sat down and began to have breakfast. Bread and butter and coffee and Armenian cheese and black olives.

I dried my face and poured coffee into the other cup on the table and began to eat.

It was a big percolator and he drank four cups and I drank three; I would have had four cups myself, only there wasn't any more coffee in the percolator.

It was still dark when we left the house.

We've got a swell lunch, he said. I fixed it myself.

Anything to drink? I said.

Beer, he said. Six bottles. I've got them in a box with wet burlap on the bottom and top, so they won't get too hot.

Can't we get some ice? I said.

Well, sure, he said. But it'll melt.

That's all right, I said. We can drink the beer before we have lunch. It won't melt before ten in the morning, will it?

It gets pretty hot after daybreak, he said.

I don't like warm beer, I said.

I know where we can get some ice at this hour, he said.

Is it very far out of the way? I said.

No, he said.

I'll crank, I said.

No, he said. Let me crank. I know how to get this motor going.

He cranked and the motor started and we got in and drove away.

I don't suppose there are any streams up that way, I said.

There used to be a brook somewhere up there, he said. It might be dry this time of year, though.

Did you bring the guns? I said.

Hell yes, he said. If you hit anything with that twenty-two, it'll be luck.

Why? I said.

Something's the matter with the damn sight, he said.

Maybe it's your eye, I said.

I got a good eye, he said. It ain't my eye. I aimed at a cottontail not more than twenty yards away and missed.

It's probably your eye, I said.

No, my eye's all right, he said. According to the sight I should have hit the rabbit at the ear.

I'll hit a cottontail at the ear at thirty yards, I said.

Not with this twenty-two, he said.

Anything you say, I said. How about the shotgun?

It's O. K., he said.

Anything the matter with the sight? I said.

No, but you don't need the sight, he said.

Oh, I said.

The old Ford rattled down Ventura Avenue and then slowed down and my cousin pulled the emergency brake and the car skidded and choked and stopped in front of a Coal & Ice place that had an office up front and a light on in the office. My cousin went up and tried the door, but it was locked. He looked through the window and saw a man sleeping in a chair, so he knocked at the door. After a while the man opened the door and said, What do you want?

Pennsylvania coal, my cousin said.

Ain't got no coal this time of year, the man said.

O. K., my cousin said, we'll take ice, then.

How much ice do you want? the man said.

How much is your ice this morning? my cousin said.

Same as ever, the man said. Say, he said, what's going on here?

He yawned and woke up.

Give me a dime's worth, my cousin said.

The man disappeared and came back half a minute later with a cube of ice in a canvas bag.

Got a pick? my cousin said.

Sure, the man said.

The man brought the ice to the car and my cousin took the ice out of the canvas bag and put it on the running board. Then he took the ice pick from the man and began chipping the cube and putting the pieces between the wet burlap around the bottles of beer.

My cousin gave the man a dime, and the man went back to his office and chair.

My cousin chipped the cube into small pieces and put the pieces in the wet burlap; then he cranked the car and got in.

We turned north near the County Hospital, and then it began to be day. The sky was very fine and the hospital looked very sad.

Were you ever in a hospital? my cousin said.

Yes, I said.

What did you have? he said.

Nothing, I said. I was visiting.

Visiting who? he said.

Do you remember Kerop who died? I said. You weren't very old when he was around.

I remember, he said.

Well, I was visiting him, I said.

What did he have? my cousin said.

T.B., I said.

What sort of a guy was he, anyway? my cousin said.

He was O. K., I said. I used to take him grapes and figs and peaches. He wasn't very old when he died. He wasn't forty. I was ten or eleven.

When we reached Clovis the sun was up and the town was very pleasant-looking. My cousin drove around town four or five times, looking at the place.

What made you do it? he said.

What the hell, I said, he was sick. He used to come to our house on San Benito Avenue when he was well. He was a good guy. He used to drink and gamble a lot, but he was O. K. His own brother wouldn't visit him at the hospital, so I used to visit him. He knew he was dying and he knew I knew he was dying, and he always smiled when I took him grapes. I don't suppose you remember him very well.

I know he was alive, my cousin said, and that he died. I don't remember just exactly how he looked.

He was as much your third uncle as he was mine, I said.

Nobody seemed to like him, my cousin said.

He tried pretty hard to get along, I said. He just didn't have any talent for farming. Or anything else either. He used to come to our house on Sundays as a rule.

My cousin pulled the emergency brake and the car stopped in front of a general merchandise store. There were no people in the town.

Do you want to walk around in this town? he said.

How about some more breakfast? I said.

Got any money? my cousin said.

About a dollar and twenty cents, I said.

All right, if we can find a place, he said.

Ham and eggs, I said.

Eggs scrambled, my cousin said.

Mine straight up, I said.

We got out of the car and walked along the main street of the little town. There wasn't much to the town. It was just a lot of sad-looking wooden buildings facing a couple of sad-looking streets, a lot of sad-looking store windows, a lot of sad-looking doors and signs and second-story windows. And just beyond the town you could see the vineyards. It was just a little place in the country surrounded by vines. The town itself was sad-looking, but it was very pleasant being there early in the morning.

My cousin went behind a shack that was empty and for rent.

Did I ever tell you about the nigger who went up to the doctor? my cousin said.

No, I said.

I like the one about if the wife was along they would have been able to save the horse and wagon too, I said.

That's a funny one too, my cousin said. I like the jokes of this country more than the serious things. The serious things are funny too, but they're funny because they ain't supposed to be funny. Do you remember that guy who came to town and pitched a big tent and preached?

You mean that revivalist? I said. Sure I remember him.

He was all right, my cousin said. I didn't like the sawdust on the floor and the wooden benches and the canvas roof. That didn't seem like a church. He was an earnest man, though. It was very funny when he prayed. I could hardly keep from busting out laughing. The people were a lot funnier than the preacher. They were scared to death.

We went back to the main street of the town and found a restaurant, only it was closed.

There wasn't a soul in town, even though the sun was up and it was beginning to be hot.

Shall we wait for this place to open up, my cousin said, or shall we go on and eat some of the lunch and drink a bottle of beer each in the country?

This place may not open up for hours yet, I said.

I don't know why they ever started this place in the first place, my cousin said. I'd like to meet the guy who did it.

What sort of a guy do you think he'd be? he said.

I figure he'd be a sort of an amiable sort of a guy, I said.

I don't mean amiable, my cousin said. I mean what the hell do you figure made him go and open up a restaurant in a town like this?

Maybe he's got a big appetite, I said. Maybe he takes care of that.

I'll bet ten to one that's the answer, my cousin said. He's a little guy with a big appetite. He doesn't want to go hungry, *any time*. He wants to have stuff near by all the time. So he has the restaurant. If the worst comes to the worst, he can eat all the hash himself.

I think we've solved the whole thing, I said, so we don't need to wait.

We went back to the hack and my cousin cranked it and we drove out of the town.

The hills were brown and dry. The grass was all dead and dry. We traveled about ten miles and then it was the place my cousin said was fine. It was a good place. It was cool and very pleasant, although the weather was very hot. There were trees that had grown up by themselves, on the slopes of the hills, and shade, and beneath the trees was grass that wasn't dry. We ate three beef sandwiches each and drank a bottle of beer each, and then we took the guns and the rest of the lunch, except the beer, and began to walk.

The beer was nice and cold. The sandwiches tasted very good.

We walked about an hour and didn't see anything to shoot, so my cousin shot at a white butterfly with the twenty-two and missed.

See, he said, something's the matter with the sight.

Give me that God damn gun, I said.

I shot at a butterfly and missed too.

Sounds all right, I said.

Sounds just like a twenty-two, my cousin said.

Where the hell's that brook? I said.

What brook? my cousin said.

What do you mean, what brook? I said. *The brook.* Didn't you speak of a brook this morning?

I don't think there's any water in it, my cousin said.

It ain't a brook unless there's water in it, I said.

All of a sudden my cousin fired the shotgun and I saw a jackrabbit jump and run.

Something's the matter with the sight on that shotgun, I said.

No, my cousin said, on second thought I decided not to kill an innocent animal. After all, what good would it do me?

We walked two hours before we found the brook. There was a little water in it, but the water was stagnant and stank. Nevertheless, we sat down on the cool grass and talked.

My cousin wanted to know some more about the man who died in the County Hospital. Kerop, our third uncle. I told him, and then he told me about a boy who drowned in Thompson Ditch. A friend of his named Harlan Beach.

He was a pretty good guy, my cousin said.

It was very quiet and pleasant. I lay flat on my back and looked up at the sky. A lot of crazy years had gone by all right. A lot of crazy things had happened all right. It was September again and it was very pleasant. It was very hot, but it was very pleasant too. This was my valley, where I had been born. This earth and sky was home. This temperature was. My cousin was. The way he talked was. The memories he knew were part of it. The people he remembered. I looked up at the sky and remembered New York. I had lived there less than a year ago, when I was twenty years old but it seemed as if it were ten years ago, or twenty, or a hundred. And it seemed as if I had never lived there, or had only dreamed of having lived there, a long summer and winter dream of sultriness and stickiness and crazy buildings and crazy crowds and crazy subways, and then bitter cold, snow and wind, and the black sunless sky. Homelessness and chaos and sultriness and no air to breathe and then the black sky and then the white snow and then cold, and all the time the crazy city.

My cousin talked in English, and I talked partly in English and partly in Armenian. Then he began to talk partly in English and partly in Armenian, and after a while we talked in Armenian only.

Poor Kerop, my cousin said. Poor, poor, poor. He used to walk; now he does not walk.

My cousin moved the palms of his hands together which is the Armenian symbol of the ending of a thing.

It ended, he said.

Let us eat bread, I said.

Let us eat bread and remember, my cousin said.

We ate all the sandwiches.

Then we started walking back to the car so we could drink the beer.

There were no animals or birds to shoot along the way. There were a number of kinds of small singing birds, but we did not shoot at them.

Let us salute the absent inhabitants of the world, my cousin said.

That's a noble thought, I said.

We lifted the guns to our shoulders and pointed them at nothing in the sky.

To the dead, my cousin said.

We fired the guns.

The sound was half-crazy and half-tragic.

To Kerop, I said.

We fired again.

To Harlan Beach, my cousin said, and again we fired.

To everybody who once lived on this earth and died, my cousin said.

We fired the guns.

The shotgun made ten times as much noise as the twenty-two.

Give me the shotgun for this next one, I said.

My cousin gave me the shotgun and I gave him the twenty-two.

Who will it be? he said.

To my father, I said, and I squeezed the trigger of the shotgun and it had a powerful kick.

To *my* father, my cousin said.

We fired again.

To my grandfather, I said.

To *my* grandfather, my cousin said.

To Gregory the Illuminator, I said.

To Bedros Tourian, my cousin said.

To Raffi, I said.

We would walk a little way and stop and name someone who was dead and fire the guns.

To Antranik, my cousin said.

To Khetcho, I said.

Poor Khetcho, my cousin said in Armenian.

To Mourad, I said.

We saluted many Armenian soldiers and scholars and writers and priests. We saluted many great men who were dead.

We made a lot of noise in the hills, but it was all right because there was nobody around.

When we got back to the car the beer was not quite as cold as it had been in the morning, but it was cool and very good to drink.

We drank the beer and my cousin cranked the car and we got in and drove out of the hills into the warm, quiet, lovely valley that was our home in the world, in time, in the time of living.

The Insurance Salesman, the Peasant, the Rug Merchant and the Potted Plant

Arshag Gorobakian was a small man who earned his living as a salesman for the New York Life Insurance Company. He worked exclusively among his own people, the Armenians. In twenty years, he often told a new client, I have sold three hundred policies, and so far two hundred of my clients have died. He did not utter this remark with sorrow and it was not intended to be a commentary on the sadness of life. On the contrary, Gorobakian's smile indicated that what he meant by two hundred of them dying was simply that these were men who had cheated death of its awful victory, and at the same time made a monkey out of the New York Life Insurance Company. All shrewd men, he often told a new client. Men like yourself, in all things practical and brilliant. They said to themselves, Yes, we shall die, there is no way out of that, let us face the facts.

Here the insurance salesman would bring the printed charts and statistics out of his inside coat pocket and say Here are the facts. You are forty-seven years of age and, by the grace of God, in good health. According to the facts you will be dead in five years.

He would smile gently, sharing with the new client the thrill of dying in five years and earning thereby an enormous sum of money. In five years, he would say, you will have paid my company three hundred and eighty-seven dollars, and on dying you will have earned twenty thousand dollars, or a net profit of nineteen thousand six hundred and thirteen dollars.

That, he would say, is a fair profit on any investment.

Once, however, he talked to a peasant in Kingsburg who didn't believe he would be dead in five years.

Come back in seventeen or eighteen years, the peasant said.

But you are sixty-seven years old now, the insurance salesman said.

I know, the peasant said. But I shall not be swindled in an affair like this. I shall be alive twenty years from now. I have planted three hundred new olive trees and I know I shall not be dead until they are full grown. Not to mention the mulberry trees and the pomegranate trees, and the walnut and almond trees.

No, the peasant said, the time is not ripe for a bargain of this sort. I know I shall be alive twenty years from now. I can feel it in my bones. Shall I say something?

Yes, the insurance salesman said.

I shall live *thirty* years longer, not twenty. You will admit I should be cheated in a deal of this sort.

The insurance salesman was small, courteous, quiet-spoken, and never aggressive.

I can see, he said, that you are a man of giant strength—

Giant strength? the peasant roared. Shall I say something?

The insurance salesman nodded.

What you say is the truth, he said. I am a man of giant strength. What death? Why should I die? For what reason, countryman? I am in no hurry. Money? Yes. It is good. But I am not going to die.

The insurance salesman smoked his cigar calmly, although inwardly he was in a state of great agitation, like a routed cavalry officer trying desperately to round up his men and organize another offensive.

Death to you? he said to the peasant. God forbid. In all my life I have never wished another man's death. Life is what we enjoy. The taste of the watermelon in the summer is the thing we cherish.

May I say something? the peasant interrupted.

Again the insurance salesman nodded.

What you say is true, he said. The thing we cherish is the taste of the watermelon in the summertime. And bread and cheese and grapes in the cool of evening, under the trees. Please go on.

I do not wish any man's departure from this warm scene of life, the insurance salesman said. We must face the facts, however.

He shook the documents in his hand.

Our world is a crazy world, he said. You are a strong man. You enjoy the taste of the watermelon. You are walking in the city. An automobile strikes you and where are you? You are dead.

The peasant frowned.

Ah, yes, he said. The automobile.

In the event that you are killed accidentally, which God forbid, the insurance salesman said, you will be rewarded doubly.

The confounded automobiles, the peasant said. I shall be very careful in the streets.

We are all careful, the insurance salesman said, but what good does it do us? More people are killed every year in automobile accidents than in one year of a great war.

May I say something? the peasant said.

Say it, the insurance salesman said.

I have half a mind to be protected, the peasant said. I have half a mind to take out an insurance policy.

That is a wise plan, the insurance salesman said.

The peasant purchased a policy and began making payments. Two years later he called the insurance salesman to his house and reprimanded him severely, although politely. He complained that although he had spent several hundred dollars, he had not so much as come anywhere near being killed, which he considered very odd.

I do not want the policy any longer, he said.

The insurance salesman told the ironic story of another man who gave up his policy after two years, and three weeks later was gored to death by an angry bull. But the peasant was not impressed with the story.

May I say something? he said. There is no bull in the world strong enough to gore me. I would break his neck. No thank you, I do not want to be insured. I have made up my mind not to die, even for a profit. I have had a hundred chances of walking in front of an automobile, but always I have stepped back cautiously and allowed it to go by.

That was fourteen years ago, and the peasant, a man named Hakimian, is still alive.

The insurance salesman, however, preferred people more enlightened than peasants. He himself was a graduate of college. His preference was for men with whom he could talk for hours about other things, and then little by little move in with the insurance speech. He would often drive two hundred miles to San Francisco to talk with a dentist who had graduated from college.

Once he decided to drive his Buick across the country to Boston. It was a journey of ten days. Along the way there would be much to see, and in Boston he would visit his sister and her husband and their eleven children. He drove to Boston, visited his sister and her family, and met a rug merchant who was a college graduate. Three times in ten days he called at this man's home and carried on pleasant conversations. The man's name was Haroutunian and he was extremely fond of conversation. The insurance salesman found him brilliant on all subjects. But when the subject of life insurance was introduced he discovered that his friend was, bluntly, in no mood for it. At least, not for the present.

The time came for the insurance salesman to return to California. Before departing, he was paid a visit by the rug merchant, Haroutunian, who was carrying a small potted plant.

My friend, the rug merchant said, I have a brother in Bakersfield, which is near where you live. I have not seen him in twenty years. Will you do me a favor?

Of course, the insurance salesman said.

Carry this plant to my brother with my greetings, the rug merchant said.

Gladly, the insurance salesman said. What plant is this?

I do not know, the rug merchant said, but the leaf has a wonderful odor. Smell it.

The insurance salesman smelled the plant and was disappointed in the smell of the leaf.

It is truly a heavenly smell, he said.

The rug merchant gave the insurance salesman the name and address of his brother, and then said:

One more thing. The agricultural department in each state demands that a plant being transported be examined for plant insects. There are none on this plant, but the law is the law. You will have to stop a minute at the agricultural department of each state. A formality.

Oh, the insurance salesman said.

His word had been given, however, so he put the plant into his car and made his departure from Boston.

He was a very law-abiding man and the plant caused him quite a little trouble. Very often even after he had found the agricultural department of each state, the inspector was out of town and wouldn't be back for several days.

The result of the whole thing was that the insurance salesman got home in twenty-one days instead of ten. He drove a hundred miles to Bakersfield and found the rug merchant's brother.

The plant was safe and was now growing small red blossoms that gave off an odor which to the insurance salesman was extremely unpleasant.

Three thousand six hundred and seventy-eight miles I have carried this wonderful plant, the insurance salesman said, from the home of your brother in Boston to your home in Bakersfield. Your brother sends greetings.

The rug merchant's brother liked the plant even less than the insurance salesman did.

I do not want the plant, he said.

The insurance salesman was a man who was hardly ever amazed by anything. He accepted the brother's indifference and took the plant home with him.

He planted it in the finest soil in his backyard, bought fertilizer for it, watered it, and took very good care of it.

It is not the plant, he told a neighbor. It nauseates me. But some day I shall perhaps be going back to Boston to visit my sister and, when I see the rug merchant again, I know he shall ask about the plant and I shall be pleased to tell him that it is flourishing. I feel that I have as good a chance as any man to sell him an insurance policy some day.

The Russian Writer

In Russia I ran into a small, undernourished, high-strung, mournful-looking young writer who spoke better English than I do, only with an accent, and he said, Comrade, I have read everything. I have read many of your American writers. I know the works of John Dos Passos, Ernest Hemingway, Jack London, and many others. Still, I know nothing. I know nothing about anything. I am twenty-seven years old. I am a writer too. You are a writer too. Still, if I may say so, Comrade, do you know anything?

If memory serves, he was only an inch taller than a midget. He smoked one Russian cigarette after another, inhaled deeply while he talked, and even more deeply while he remained silent. The other Russian writers in that city were taller men, or fatter, or quieter, or dumber. One of them was a giant. This small writer told me this big one was the worst of the lot, although they were all bad.

Forgive me, he said, if what I say seems counter-revolutionary, but we are the worst writers in the world. We are the very worst. We are the ultimate of worseness.

Here, he said. Here are six of my books. You cannot read Russian, thank God. Look at the print. All of it is the worst writing in the world. Where is Chekov? Where is young Gorky? Where is Tolstoy? Where is Andreyev? Have they all died in us? I have read your stories, he said. You are a very bad writer. My God, you write badly, but everybody is not dead in you. You are not bad as we are. We are the way we are because they are all dead in us. In you two or three of the Americans are alive. That is why you are so bad. You are always jumping around because they are all so alive in you. My God, everything you write is awful, but it is much less awful than everything we write. Comrade, he said, do you know anything at all?

Well, I said, I know when it's raining.

So, he said. Again. Again you can laugh. It is not funny, though. *I* do not even know when it is raining. Yesterday the sun was shining and I sat in this room writing a story and I did not know the sun was shining. I thought it was raining. I tell you I thought it was raining all the time. It is because we are so sad. You have heard them laughing. It is false. Listen to them next time they laugh and you will know it is false. It isn't false when *you* laugh. It is crazy, but it isn't false. How can you laugh, Comrade?

I'll tell you an American joke, I said. It will make you laugh. I told him the one about the father and the beautiful daughter on the train to Cleveland that was held up by train robbers. You know the one. Where the father says, If only your mother had been here, Alice, we would have been able to save the luggage. Every time I tell this story it makes me roar with laughter. Every time somebody else tells it I've got to laugh too. It's a great, goofy, American joke. I laughed all over the room, and the young writer went into hysterics, slapping his knee, bending over, running around the room, and bumping his head against the walls.

When he stopped laughing, there were tears in his eyes.

Did you hear me laughing? he said. Did you feel the grief of that laughter? Do you know another?

I told him the one about the two Forty-Second Street fleas that went out adventuring one summer night. Remember?

The little writer went crazy over this one. His face got red from too much laughing and then suddenly he sat down on the floor and began to cry.

My God, he said, we can't even laugh. Please forgive me, Tovarich. Please tell another.

I knew a hundred more, but I didn't want to upset him like this. If I had known these jokes were going to upset him this way I wouldn't have told them. It was sad, the way he laughed like a young American who'd spent all his life in the slums of some big city; he sounded like a kid who'd been brought up in the slums of New York or Pittsburgh or Chicago or Frisco.

You must tell me a Russian joke, I said.

He looked at me with an amazed expression on his face.

A Russian joke? he said. We have no jokes. The people do not make up such stories as these. We have some comedy. There are many comical peasants, and many pompous executives who are very funny to observe, but no jokes. We do not tell jokes. We won't admit it, he said, but everybody is dead in us. We are the very worst writers in the world.

I told him I didn't believe it. Late that night I asked the other writers about him. They spoke of him with the humbleness of inferiors. He is a great writer, they said. He is one of the very greatest. We believe that he will be greater than Chekov. He is only a baby now. He writes like a crazy man.

That's what I thought, I told them.

That same night I left that city and continued my journey.

The Two Thieves

Bakrot Moushegian, the sign painter, sat in the poker game across the table from Telesco, the boy from Clovis. Bakrot was a young Armenian with hair like wire, a hard-working fellow who had been studying oil painting from public-library books on the subject. Telesco was one of the Italians who had grown up during the war, during the excitement of those days. He was a farm boy with strong, clumsy arms.

Bakrot was getting very poor hands. He was thinking of leaving the game after another deal. He looked across the room at the boys playing pool, then down the wall at a gang of fellows telling stories.

It was Sunday night again and the weather was hot. Generally in March the weather would be cool, even cold, but this night it was hot.

Telesco was thinking of winning fifteen or twenty dollars and going up to Frisco for a week or so to see about work. He was tired of the farm and wanted to get up to the big city. One of his brothers, Patrick, had got into trouble in Frisco, but Telesco wasn't thinking of that. Ever since Patrick went up to San Quentin for trying to hold up a gasoline station Michael Telesco had forgotten him. It was as if Patrick had died. Michael Telesco believed it would be the same for him, the same for all of them, Patrick, Michael, Joseph, Nicholas, and Antonio, all of them. Antonio was only a boy, only thirteen, but already Michael could see that it would be the same for him too. Michael had come home one morning at six from a bad night of gambling and had seen Antonio walking by the dry ditch, talking quietly. In the early morning this noise had sounded strange to Michael, and he had wondered if Antonio was crazy. "Is Antonio going crazy?" he had asked himself in Italian. "Is my little brother Tony going nuts?" He could see Antonio plainly and he could recognize his voice, and yet, although he loved Antonio more than any of his other brothers, he felt that already Tony was getting to be like all of them. He was afraid to go out to his little brother and ask what the matter was. He went inside and got into bed. When he got up at noon Antonio was home from school for lunch and seemed to be all right. Michael did not mention what he had seen. He said, "What are you learning at school these days?"

Antonio laughed and said he was learning nothing. He was getting into a lot of trouble with the teachers and the principal because he couldn't behave anymore and the principal said he was going to come out to the house and talk things over with the old man.

Michael asked Antonio why he couldn't behave anymore, and Antonio said, "I don't know. Mr. Higgins says I am the worst Italian he has ever met. So you can see what the trouble is."

Michael told Antonio to be good. "Antonio," he said, "for Papa's sake, don't be different from the rest of them and don't be the worst Italian in the world." In Italian he said, "Where will it get you?"

Antonio told Michael he didn't know where it would get him, and from this Michael knew that it would be the same with Antonio too; he was like the rest of them. One dead, one in prison, one in card games all the time.

Bakrot Moushegian and Michael Telesco had never been very good friends, but they had met in card games many times and they had quietly taken a liking to one another. Bakrot played the same sort of quiet game that Michael played and neither of them belly-ached when they lost, which was unusual. Fellows like Pete Brown and Johnny Wells were always belly-aching, even when they won. Outside of card games fellows like Pete and Johnny were all right. They were like the rest of the boys who came to The Mecca to play pool or poker. Once in a while, during a game, Bakrot Moushegian would toss his package of cigarettes across the table to Michael Telesco and Michael would quietly take a cigarette and toss back the package. Bakrot never did this for anyone else, so after a while it came to mean that Bakrot and Michael were friends.

Bakrot Moushegian was supporting his grandmother, but lately he hadn't been making much money and he was beginning to be worried. Sign painting had never got him much money but it had always kept him going. He had furnished a small house on Santa Clara Street and he had kept groceries in the house. A year ago he had bought a radio for the old lady so she would have music all day and most of the night and she had been very happy. But lately everything seemed to be falling to pieces. He was behind in his payments on the radio and he had a letter in his pocket from the music house people telling him they would be forced to take the radio away if he didn't make a payment in a few days. He had been trying his hand at oil painting in his spare time. He liked it very much because it was different from sign painting. A few old Armenians had seen his paintings and they had encouraged him to go on with his work, but when he had explained that he was not making any money, no one offered to buy one of his paintings. Bakrot didn't care much for radio music but he knew that the old lady did, and he hated to think that she would be deprived of the music if he didn't get hold of some money somehow. He was thinking also that maybe, if things kept up, he might even find it impossible to take groceries home.

The hands were always very poor and Bakrot was losing steadily. He had entered the game with only four dollars and after an hour he had only sixty cents worth of chips. Michael Telesco's luck had been even worse than Bakrot's, and it looked as if they would both leave the game at the same time. They were never known to quit unless they were broke or far ahead of the game, but tonight it looked as if they would get up because they would *have* to get up. Bakrot and Telesco left the game together, and although they had never known one another very well, they walked together up Mariposa Street toward the State Theatre. They began to talk quietly, not about the card game, but about other things.

Telesco said, "I got a letter from a company in Chicago that teaches aviation by mail. I don't know where they got my name. I never did think anybody knew I liked flying."

Bakrot said, "You can get books on aviation at the library. I didn't think they had so many different books there until I looked up oil painting. I am studying how to paint from the books. My paintings are very bad right now, but I hope to learn from the books."

The street was almost deserted, and there was no traffic, but it was only a little past ten. It looked like everybody was home listening to the radio. The State Theatre looked forlorn and fake, blinking its lights for no one to see. They walked before the box office and Michael took a long look at the girl in the coop. All the boys on the street took looks at the girl in the coop, Loretta Stone, and Bakrot thought Michael's interest was of that kind. In fact Michael said, "I like that girl very much," but it seemed to Bakrot that behind Michael's words there was another meaning, because nobody talked that way if he liked a girl.

They seemed to move forward with this new idea, as they stood on the corner of Mariposa and Fulton, looking up both streets, and suddenly Michael said, "My idea is to get north to Frisco in a hurry."

Bakrot was thinking that if they could do it, quickly, and get back to the poker game—no one would have any idea. They could say they had gone to the lavatory in the Traveler's Hotel around the corner. He hadn't yet come fully face to face with the intention, but it was in the back of his mind, and when Michael Telesco intentionally bumped up against him, indicating the metal weight in his pocket, Bakrot knew they meant to get all the money from the box office and go away in a hurry.

"I'll do the hard work," Telesco said. "You go to the girl and ask what is on, when it ends, what the comedy is, and anything else you can think of. When I open the door of the coop and hold the gun to her back you tell her to give you all the money she has, and keep her quiet too. She is only a girl and the money isn't hers. If she's nice, she won't even mind. It depends on how you talk to her."

Bakrot was already anxious to get the job done and he no longer troubled to think about the possibility of something going wrong. "All right," he said, and they turned swiftly toward the theatre. On the way Telesco said, "No waiting. Everything swift. One, two, three. My father got a half cent a pound for his raisins. You can't stay alive and stay honest at the same time." But this was just talk and Bakrot was not interested in it. He was working on a nice facial expression. He walked a few steps ahead of Telesco.

He went up to the coop and looked into the girl's eyes, smiling with his lips but looking at her very sternly with his eyes. "What is on now?" he said.

The girl said, *"Me and My Gal."*

Bakrot saw Telesco walk to the back of the coop, his right hand in his coat pocket. Telesco seemed very steady. Bakrot, holding his head steady, moved his eyes from one door to another. It would be bad if someone came out of the theatre while they were at work, or if someone peeked through the door and saw them and then got out the manager and some of the ushers.

"Who's playing in this picture?" Bakrot said.

"Spencer Tracy and Constance Bennett," the girl said.

Telesco was at the back door of the coop now and he was working the handle of the door, but apparently it was locked. Then suddenly it opened and Bakrot saw that Telesco had brought out the gun and was working very calmly. He spoke to the girl.

"Will you please let me have all the money?" he said.

The girl was horribly frightened, so he smiled and said, "Everything's all right. You won't get hurt. Just don't make any noise and do what I tell you. Give me everything you've got."

Michael was holding the gun to the girl's back and telling her to work swiftly. She began silently to place currency before Bakrot. There was quite a bundle of currency and quite a lot of silver. Bakrot placed the money casually into the pockets of his coat, feeling that he might be the manager on the way to the bank. Telesco slipped swiftly from the coop, closed the door, and walked hurriedly up Mariposa toward Fulton. Bakrot turned and ran across the street, after asking the girl to be still at least a minute or two. She seemed, he thought, a nice sort of girl: steady and unhysterical.

A half block from The Mecca, where they had been playing poker, Telesco and Bakrot met. They were very solemn and dignified. Telesco was thinking that something was wrong somewhere. He seemed to feel that what they had done couldn't be quite so simple as it seemed to be, and he began to hope everything proper would take place in a hurry, so he could smoke a cigarette in peace. He felt that everything had worked too perfectly. Bakrot asked what he should do with the money and where they should go first, to The Mecca, or his house.

Telesco said, "We'd better get back into that game." They entered The Mecca again, Telesco going in ahead of Bakrot, who stood in front of the establishment waiting for something to happen. Then he turned and entered the building. He sat in his same chair and was dealt a hand. Telesco began looking toward the door, waiting for someone to come in, but Bakrot tried harder to seem at ease.

They played one hand and Telesco won the pot. Everything seemed too easy to be right, and they felt that it wouldn't be long before they would find out what they had done.

When they were looking at their second hands, two men entered the place and began to talk to Joey, at the bar. They looked like men who would make things right, so Telesco threw in his hand and walked to the lavatory. Bakrot followed him, but went out the back way and down the alley. Telesco followed him swiftly and at the corner they saw the two men again getting out of a roadster. The men walked up to them and said, "You boys better come with us."

Bakrot and Telesco felt relieved and got into the car.

One of the men said, "You boys just held up The State Theatre."

Bakrot smiled and Telesco said, "You must be mistaken," but at the station they didn't try to deny it anymore.

Later when they knew everything was correct, Telesco said in Italian, "Have you a cigarette, brother?" Bakrot said. "I don't understand Italian, Mike. What you talking about?"

"Nothing," Telesco said. "Let me have a cigarette, will you? I feel better now."

After a while a sad-looking old cop with a book and a pencil came and stood looking at them for a while, as if he couldn't believe his eyes. Then he began to ask questions and to write the answers down in the book.

"How old are you?" he asked Bakrot.

"Seventeen," Bakrot said.

"How old are *you?*" he asked Mike.

"I'll be seventeen in September," Mike said.

The old cop stood looking at them a while longer and then without a word he turned and went away.

The Poet

My room is small and full of things, consequently there is barely room for two people in it. Nevertheless, I have a pupil. The table, which I use for study and for drawing and painting, is really much too large, and everything else in the room is out of proportion. The bookcases rise to my height on every side of the room, except where there are windows. I have a small phonograph and about fifty records. These must be in their places. On the floor I keep those daily accumulations which I feel may someday come in handy, newspapers, magazines, shells, pebbles, fresh and dry leaves, and the instruments related to my work, that is to say, pencils, pens, paints, and brushes.

From the newspapers I hope eventually to draw material for a novel of modern times, but this is not my real work. I am primarily interested in form and motion and color, without regard for people. I do not mean that I am not interested in people: I mean simply that writing is not my profession, and while painting is also not my profession, it is at least the one activity in my life which enables me to give meaning to the material world. The novel which I have in mind will doubtless never be published, for it is not my desire to gain recognition and I wish only to satisfy myself in regard to the world we are living in. I shall begin writing the novel sometime this fall, when the atmosphere in this city is gray and cheerless, making it difficult for me to paint. My novel will not be a brilliant one. I intend only to do this: repeat briefly the names of those who, during July and August of this year, were born, those who were

married, and those who died. These two months are months of warmth
and richness.

In the evenings, when my work is done, I sit in my room and read
Blake or the Bible, or I look at the advertisements in old copies of the
Saturday Evening Post. Blake I like and find companionable, and the Bible,
of course, is simply the book of my boyhood and the book of man's
boyhood. I read it to revive humility, to restore myself to that piety
without which man is a fool. But the magazine—that is where I have my
fun. Four years ago it was fat, the advertisements were many, and they
were extravagant with color and rhetoric. They were about fountain
pens, flashlights, candy, automobiles, toothpaste, about everything for
sale. It is rather good to know that these things have lost some of their
glamour for the people, that sales campaigns do not go so well anymore.
It is very pleasant to sit and realize that hardly anyone is rich these days
and that only millionaires can afford to buy flashlights.

The pupil who sometimes visits this room is Peter, a tall Norwegian
whose trade is house-painting. He is interested in poetry. He visits me
whenever he pleases and we talk. He brings cigarettes and sits across the
table from me and we speak of poetry. I met him one evening at the Book
Harbor, an old bookshop on Sutter Street, and he began to talk. He said
that all his life he had searched for something in the world he could not
define, something nevertheless real, and that at last he believed he had
found it.

Poetry, he said. It is poetry that I have been seeking.

That was three years ago. Since then I have spoken many times with
Peter and he has shown me all the poems he has written. At first he had
no intention of writing poems. I suppose it was *my* idea. I am unable
somehow to believe in audiences, in appreciation, and I doubtless asked
Peter why he himself didn't write a poem now and then if he loved
poetry. He was amazed, almost terrified. It was very strange seeing a
huge man blush, but I believe I did not do wrong. I do not know how to
write, he said. I am not very good at English. It takes me hours to read
one poem. I could never write one.

I do not remember how I got around this sensible objection or if I even
tried to get around it, but I believe I suggested that he buy a tablet and a
pencil and just keep the matter in mind.

See what happens, I said. You can never tell, perhaps before you know
it you will have written a poem.

But, he said, I *have* paper. I *have* pencils.

They won't do, I said. You must buy a tablet *for* poetry, and a pencil for
the *writing* of poetry. It is necessary. Do this and remember about it. The
other paper and the other pencils—they are different.

In those days I was reading another man, Amiel. Amiel is no giant, not
a great man, a coward in some things, but there is something honest

about him, something so steadily honest that one must admire him. I remember that I was sitting in my room, reading Amiel, when I heard footsteps coming down the hall.

It was Peter. He was a changed man, and I thought, Yes, he has written a poem. It is on his face. I do not know why I felt glad. I felt as if I had scored a great triumph, one of those private successes never recorded by historians, but one nevertheless worthy of perpetuation.

He came in and sat down.

At last he said, I am very nervous tonight. You see, I bought the tablet and the pencil. It felt very silly, you know, but I wanted to do what you said. I took the tablet and the pencil home and I left them on the table in my room and went to bed. In the night I woke up and smoked a cigarette because sometimes I wake up and smoke a cigarette. Then I went back to bed, but I couldn't sleep. So I got up and smoked another cigarette. I had forgotten about the tablet and the pencil. I was afraid. I am not a writer, you know, but I like poetry.

He looked sorrowful.

Well, anyway, he said, I sharpened the pencil with my knife and I opened the tablet. At first I couldn't write one word. I mean I was afraid, you know. I didn't want to write anything wrong. I thought somebody was watching me and I felt maybe if I wrote something wrong somebody would take the pencil away. I sat at the table a long time and then I forgot all about everything and I began to write.

He inhaled deeply and then crushed the cigarette. I did not say anything.

The poem, he said timidly. I have brought it with me.

He removed the tablet from his coat pocket and placed it before me. I read the poem carefully three times and then I said, It is good. You must go on writing.

Of course it was a very bad poem, but that wasn't the point at all and even great poets have written bad poems.

After that he wrote many poems and every new poem contained some definite improvement. At first his poems were technically weak, no continuity of thought. It is the same with all beginners, I suppose, but afterward the poems improved. The man himself improved. He became more calm, more dignified, more pious, and he began to speak very deliberately, watching his words, making them do what he wanted them to do.

He began to be a poet. He began to be alive, and such a change is the greatest poetry, even if it is never written.

The Monumental Arena

At the waterfront they told me about the trouble.

They put the blame on one head and then on another. The men were sullen.

There was one who had been clubbed. He was a sad-faced Scandinavian. What this boy said I could understand.

He said it was a thing he could not speak about to the others because they had one idea in mind, and he had several. They were good men, he said, but he was a man who could read a book and stand up and go to work and, working, remember what he had read. Every word, he said.

They had clubbed him and he was without hate. He even laughed, saying it was funny. The man who clubbed him, doing it with hate. He said he saw the man, a police. The man was frightened. He felt sorry for the man. And then the club came down on his head and he laughed out loud and became unconscious.

When he awoke, he was in the smell of the emergency hospital. Six others were there, one a woman. He felt all the ugliness and lost his temper because the woman, who was really hurt, was swearing and crying and saying she could kill every cop on the waterfront.

He got up, he said, feeling angry, and was about to lift the table from the floor and smash it against the wall, because it was too much to hear the woman swearing and crying, and then he remembered how funny it was, and sat down.

The young doctor asked if he was all right. He told the young doctor he was all right all right, only if he didn't have a little drink he might get sore, and he didn't want to. The doctor told him sure. He swallowed the drink and began to smile, the woman still crying. Now it was as bad as before and he knew it, only he was accepting it differently, because of the drink. It was a lie, but he said what of it? Since it was *all* a lie? It was better to smile. He felt sorry for the young doctor. For the man who had clubbed him he felt *bitterly* sorry, because he knew the man was a coward when he might not be.

He talked quietly, saying it was not easy for him to listen to the woman crying. He told the young doctor he was going away. He wrote his name in the book and told the doctor he had no address because he had no money and would not stay in a free place. He said the doctor did not like it, and began to swear. The doctor gave the Scandinavian a dollar and the Scandinavian accepted the dollar, because it was different. It was the way the doctor swore that made it different. It wasn't a shame. The doctor was a young man who had gone through college and learned about curing the body of pains, and the way he swore made the acceptance possible.

It was a thing to remember, to place against the lifted club of the police and the insanity of the weeping woman.

He walked down the steps of the emergency hospital, smiling, because it was true. There was and could be one of one kind as much as one of another. The swearing of the doctor proved it: angry kindliness or angry hate, decency in man or the other thing.

At the waterfront I listened to the young Scandinavian. At the same time the others talked, I could understand the significance of the talk without understanding the words, because the words were only the outward form of the thing, which is not important, and the talking was the thing itself. But I could understand the significance *and* the words when the Scandinavian talked because they were one and the same.

The strong body has a wisdom beyond language, but if you are clubbed and your equilibrium is destroyed and you fall, laughing, and waken in the smell of a hospital, and hear weeping, and feel sudden insanity, and learn of decency in man, the body is apt, if you have read two or three books by good men, to find articulation and to utter timeless belief and faith, its humility and its pious anger, and this boy spoke without effort, speaking for himself.

He said he was sorry for everybody because when he was clubbed and while he was laughing and while he was falling and his balance was being taken from his body and mind and he could not determine who or what to hate or love there occurred in him only one thing, white, like snow, quiet, like weeping music, and this thing was *pity*. It was pity for the man who had struck him and pity for all the others on strike, for the rich who were using the police and the clubs of the police, and for all rich and all poor in all cities and in all countries, for man everywhere, caught in the monumental arena, helplessly the victim of a vicious and stupid game, wanting something, wanting a breath of free and pure air, escape, to go beyond the walls of the arena, to stand alive and whole. He said he saw life caught in the small arena as he fell. The air there, he said, was stifling. He could feel life suffocating, and he did not know what happened finally, except that he remembered nations of them running against the wall of the monumental arena, and that was all.

When he awoke in the hospital he could almost remember what happened after, but he could not quite do it, and all that he remembered was *their* running and *his* pity. Then he heard the woman weeping and swearing, and he wanted to destroy the whole place.

He said he could not understand.

We want something, he said, but we do not know what. It is all in the books, our wanting, but we do not know what.

He looked at the others who were talking, and smiled.

They think they want more money, he said, but that isn't all. Better working hours, he said, but that isn't all either. It is something beyond these. More, he said. More and beyond. It is in all the books, not in the writing, but it is there. And many died, he said, wanting. Something we have lost perhaps, he said. We cannot remember what it is but sometimes, sometimes in sleep, we remember that it is lost, and when we get up in the morning we think it is money we want, but that isn't all. The rich are sometimes more miserable than the poor, and they have enough money to buy everything that can be bought. There is a mistake in some place of our life.

He took the dollar from his pocket and smiled at it. It was the gift of the young doctor.

I have had it two days and I am never going to spend it, he said. When I left the hospital, he said, I needed a drink badly and I went to The Palace Bar. Then something happened and I would not spend the money. It was the way the doctor swore, wanting to help me and help everybody, and if I used the money it would destroy the feeling I had of gratitude. I am keeping it, he said. Either, he said, for giving to another when the time comes, or for giving back to the doctor. It is money, he said, if I spend it. If I do not spend it, he said, it is many things, maybe what we have lost and are trying to get back.

Seven Fragments

1. I'M NOT BREAKING YOUR HEART
DON'T START BREAKING MY HEART

It was the worst winter I could remember. There was heavy fog, or drizzle, or rain all the time, and one morning I read in the paper that a hurricane or something had come in from somewhere in the Pacific and wreaked havoc. I guess that's how it is with something like that. You don't know about it till you see the papers. Trees had been broken down or lifted up by the roots, roofs had been blown off, telephone poles had fallen, and about six people had been killed.

I read the names of the dead in the paper, but they were people I didn't know. I was afraid one of them would be Bess. That scared me at first, but afterward it gave me a laugh.

Maybe I got that kind of a feeling because I had been up all night and it was still raining. I can't remember exactly how I happened to get on that trapeze, unless it was nothing more than the bad weather all the time, the people I was seeing all the time I didn't want to see, and all the other little things you never pay any attention to until they put you on board and start carrying you away. In any case, I had been on that trapeze about ten days and nights when I read in the paper about the hurricane. I hadn't known about it when it happened because I had been living in another world. I had been in small barrooms until two in the morning and after that I had moved over to Joe's on Broadway where there was a little game of stud. I had been sitting in the game every night till daybreak.

After that I bought papers and magazines, as they came out, and got in a cab and went home.

It wasn't anything. It wasn't tragic. I guess I just wanted to go along that way for a while. I wanted her to be happy and that was the best way for me to keep from phoning her and starting everything all over again. The number was always in my mind, but I hardly ever went near a phone booth. I'd see her a lot too and feel glad about everything, and every once in a while I'd hear her and want her so badly I'd feel awfully proud of myself for being somebody who could behave intelligently, instead of romantically. We were through. We'd said so. We liked each other more than ever and we'd agreed to let it stay good and not let it get bad.

After that, she was the first to phone. She wanted me to know she was in love again.

You must fall in love again, she said.

I'll do my best, I said.

Etc. A story.

2. THE STILLNESS OF NIGHT

February is gone, March is almost gone, spring is here, and the swallows of a certain monastery have returned and driven away another variety of birds from the eaves. So stillness finds a man at a new moment of nothing: February, March, spring, swallows, and so on. All it is, all of it, is sex and fury. Loneliness, art, religion, all of it, that's all. The hash of all things. The incurably alive, that's who we are: we long for the great glowing magic loveliness and power and delight that a woman is; we have it; then we long to function, to be artists, for instance, or something else; then once again we long for a new half-dozen things a woman is; then we long for the poise of labor; then for woman; then labor; then again; and again. I think tonight that I am the worst great writer that ever lived. I know everything; I have visions of everything not yet revealed, but I won't work; I won't report what I know, and I won't reveal to others what I have seen. I don't like to work. I walked along the ocean and it made me very hungry. There was nothing filling to eat, so I went to the grocer's and bought a can of Armour's hash and prepared it and sat down and ate it! I was very thirsty so I drank a quart of wine, and afterward six or seven glasses of water; and I'm still thirsty; perhaps I'm dying. I daresay I live too tensely, inwardly, although I am often very much at ease; as a matter of fact ease is my average. There is a tenseness within me, however, that has nothing to do with ease; I am at ease and yet tense, eager, curious; whether I ought to be or not; whether, I mean, there is anything around to be eager or curious about. Also planning is constant and endless within myself; I am continuously in the midst of plans; I instinctively insist that I shall create a future, a present, and a past; and I do so. I raise hell all the time doing things which will be sweet to me a year from when they are done; or two; or twenty. Of course I am too wise and honest to be other than tense and eager and full of plans: living at its best to a realist, to one who is wise, is a boring event; my job is to keep it from boring me; and I do so; I am not dreaming my time away; that's the difference; I could and won't. Anyhow, I really don't know: this is merely one of my moments of quiet, stillness, and disquiet and confusion.

3. PUBLIC SPEECH

Since I saw you last I have grown a moustache, as you see. I am going to make a one-hour speech in five minutes, I hope. Or else a five-minute speech in an hour. That depends on how lucky I am. My father was a preacher; if there's anything to this theory they're talking about, speech-making ought to be a cinch for me. The theory I'm referring to, I think, is Einstein's. At the outset let me say that as far as I know everything is worth saving. This leaves nothing to be said, so in order to go on speaking, I'll have to elaborate or modify or make reservations. What, for instance, do I mean by *everything*? That is a good question for a heckler. Everything, as far as I know, is nine times out of ten and sometimes ten times out of ten, *you*; that is, me. Everybody. One at a time. I think each of you is worth saving. I know I'm worth saving. Money is another thing, but I won't go into economics and all like that. Is Capitalism worth saving? Yes and no. Is Communism? Same. Is a man worth saving? Yes. And no maybe. Who shall save the man? Any man? His brother, or who? Well, I think I know the answer: his brother can't save him, nobody and nothing can save him. The question is, Who can save the man? The answer is, The man himself and nobody else. That seems very simple. But how's the man going to do it? I don't know. He's got to find out for himself. God's given him what it takes to find out; the rest is up to him. A rabid Communist, I believe, would not hesitate two seconds to say I'm talking nonsense. I, in turn, would not hesitate two seconds to say he's talking nonsense. I have no quarrel with the race of man; it is a good race; it's the best there is to have anyway. My quarrel is with one man at a time. That is said to be the Christian approach; it is in a way; and then again it isn't because you don't have to be a Christian to believe that every man should be answerable to himself; myself, I'm a Presbyterian. The thing to save is not, in short, civilization, and I'll tell you why; civilization never belonged to the millions anyway; it was made by and perpetuated by a handful of men; one at a time; the mob merely wallowed in it as it were; civilization is mostly the manners of an age, the mode of living, the pattern of feeling, believing, and so on, which the mob has gradually picked up from these few things, which are the work of men here and there: from music, from literature, from painting, from sculpture, and if I may, from the vigorous manner of living of somebody special—that is an art too; that is truly the main art of man; the one all the other arts hope to elevate. Since civilization is the work of only a handful of men, we don't need to save civilization; we need to save ourselves, that's all.

4. THERE'S NOTHING IN THIS WORLD I WOULDN'T DO FOR YOU

Before he had met her he had been dead, going along easily, not minding particularly, pleased about small things, music over the radio, work, the ocean, people at bars, poets, gamblers, a little travel now and then; but after he had met her he had come to life and once again grown furious about all things, either with adoration or hatred. She was a girl who thought of him as a hero.

Your picture in the magazine, she said. I just had to come and find you. You were so proud.

What magazine? he said.

Time, she said.

That's an old picture, he said. I've changed a lot since that one was taken. I'm almost twenty-seven.

You're the only person I've ever seen who looks like his picture, she said.

Are you pleased that I seemed proud? he said.

Yes, she said. I am very proud, but you are prouder. That's why I said I would come out and see you.

I'm glad you came, he said.

I write poetry, she said.

I never could, he said.

Everything you write is poetry, she said.

How old are you? he said.

A story.

5. SAROYAN

What I've always wanted to do is create greatness immediately. That came from my *being* great, as against *wishing* to be, someday. The thing created wasn't going to make me great. It was going to happen as a consequence of my *being* great. No thing created by me could of course be anywhere near as great as myself because the thing created would be created immediately, out of one variation of the greatness, not out of all variations of it. That was why I wished to create each variation of greatness, so that in the end every variation of it would be caught, placed on record, for my personal reference, as well as for any man's.

I am amused, confused, displeased and amazed when I am told that my work suggests that I must be half-mad. If this is so, then the most sane man in the world, who does not write, is all-mad, not half. There is no disease in me other than the disease of mortality which I make no effort to conceal. I disbelieve in hiding of any sort. Out into the open is my policy. From birth dishonesty has been an impossibility for me. When I am false, out of politeness, or in order not to hurt anyone's feelings, this is immediately known, much to my regret. There are times when I would rather be untruthful than cruel, but even at these times I am truthful. I can never be one of the parlor people. They lie to one another all the time, know each of them is lying, and yet somehow are able to get along. That kind of behavior is all right somewhere, but not where I am. Where I am it is absurd behavior. They could get along telling the truth too.

6. REUNION IN VIENNA

One thing you can always say about Hollywood is that whatever happens in the rest of the world while you're there is more dramatic to you than a tense moment in a movie. In spite of the fact that you regard the events as cinematic, which should let you off easy, you get all worked up about them.

I was there for a week and have just returned to San Francisco. While I was there the newspapers kept me in touch with affairs outside the realm of moving pictures and yet somehow very much like everything in pictures.

At the bar at Musso & Frank's I ran into a young scenario writer I shall call Harry Gimpf, which is something like his name anyway. Harry was a vigorous, funny, sort of unimportantly ruthless Jew. I'd seen him at parties, drunk and eager to lay hands on extras and other beauties. Now, at the bar, his face was pale, almost sickly, he was frowning tragically, and tears were coming out of his eyes. The morning paper was folded open on the bar.

What's the matter? I said.

He named a friend who had died of a heart attack. I'd heard about the man who had died. I thought it was kind of touching for Harry to be so deeply grieved about the passing of his friend, but he said it wasn't that.

He pointed to the map of Spain in the paper.

The Loyalists are through, he said, only he used the vulgar word which has so many meanings and usages. It's all over, he said.

What are you crying for? I said. I figured there was something
personal in it somewhere.

We're losing on every front, he said.

Who? I said.

All of us, he said. Hitler taking Austria. Franco taking Spain. Japan
taking China. And now Poland and Lithuania.

Russia taking Communists, I added.

That too, Harry said.

Etc.

7. SAROYAN

I am he, but not really, and yet very really, except for moments such as
now when he is outside, or inside out, I watching and he too. I, the
Armenian, of the tribe Saroyan, and he Saroyan, of the tribe and not of
it, neither Armenian nor American nor anything but himself, clean-
shaven at his best, fresh, very much alive, delighted, eager to eat and
drink and have, and full of contradictions, believing everything, disbelieving everything, loving everything and hating everything.

He, the writer. The writer who can't write, who is published only
because he can't, whose confidence is so great it is ridiculous, whose
faith in himself is greater than a Mohammedan's in Allah. I am he. How
is that?

Now Is the Time:
A Sideshow of the World Today

THE BARKER: Hi-ya, hi-ya, hi-ya, step right up little ones, dear ones,
beloved ones, step right up and enter the world, precious ones, come
forward, see the show from beginning to end, hi-ya, hi-ya, hurry, hurry,
the show begins every minute, hurry, hurry, hurry.

*A troop of fourteen or fifteen small boys and girls arrives from left and right
and enters the world. The door leading to it is marked: The World, Admission
Free, If Not Accidental.*

*The children from the right are well dressed, neat, snobbish, wear spectacles,
are anemic, and all like that; the ones from the left are in rags, mean, tough, sore,
or somewhat scared, although a few from the right are just as scared; the ones
from the left hold themselves back to let the upper-class ones in first, with the
exception of one boy who pushes up among the ones from the right and is given a
dirty look by a boy of his age, whom he threatens savagely with a cocked right; the
upper-class boy says,* Well, *with that superior amazement, and stands back to let
the lower-class boy go in first, which he does with swagger.*

Curtain, upward: Children gone.

Scene: Saloon, or barroom, empty but for a young man, the eternally young young man of the world; to the left is The Barker and his elevated box office. The young man is at a table with a glass of beer. No beer left. He acts the young man in the world: talks to himself, gestures, looks through his pockets, finds a dime, looks at the nickel-in-the-slot phonograph, finds a number, goes around looking for change.

THE BARKER: Hi-ya, hi-ya, there he goes, watch him; wants music now; wants to drown his sorrow in song; got a dime in his hand and wants two nickels; anybody around here got two nickels?
THE YOUNG MAN: Hey, Mac, got two nickels? (As if in reply to a question) Yeah. I want to hear that song. "You Can't Stop Me From Dreaming."
THE BARKER: Can't stop him from dreaming. Stayed awake all night humming they couldn't stop him from dreaming; now he's back again and wants to hear it orchestrated. Hi-ya, hi-ya, watch him, he's young, he's handsome, he's educated, he's unemployed, he's in love, watch him, he's a dope.
THE YOUNG MAN gets two nickels for his dime.
THE BARKER: Transaction, hi-ya, watch him, watch him.

The Young Man goes over to the nickel-in-the-slot phonograph, drops his nickel, pushes in the lever, and instead of "You Can't Stop Me From Dreaming" orchestrated is heard "The Blue Danube": music-box style.

THE BARKER: Hurry, hurry, here's the river, slow Vienna three-quarter-time river.

The Young Man exits.

THE BARKER: Hurry, watch him go, watch the others come. Watch them come and go.

The music ends.

THE BARKER: It is now Wednesday. The scene changes. What you have here now is no longer a barroom, it's a parlor in a moving picture, I guess. Hurry, hurry, here they come. The girl, I believe, and the boy. Together, forever.

The Handsome Movie Boy and the Lovely Movie Girl come in and embrace passionately.

THE BARKER: Here they are again, the lovers, the fathers and mothers, the sons and daughters, watch them.

THE GIRL: Oh Tony.

THE BOY: Sandra.

THE BARKER: Hear em? Tony. Sandra. Desdemona. Othello. Romeo. Juliet.

THE GIRL: I love you.

THE BARKER: And I love you.

THE BOY: I love you.

THE BARKER: And you too.

THE GIRL: We are alone.

THE BARKER: Watch them, folks, it's all free.

THE BOY: I love you.

THE BARKER: All right, all right. You said that; don't you believe it, or what? So you love her, so what?

THE GIRL: We're alone, darling.

THE BARKER: There's a girl that's subtle.

THE BOY: Are we alone?

THE BARKER: He's subtle too.

THE GIRL: Unless somebody's hiding.

THE BOY: Who could it be?

THE BARKER: It might be the entire population of the world, out front. Bank night.

THE GIRL: Do you love me?

THE BARKER: Of course I love you, you lovely thing, you. Look at you. I adore you.

THE BOY: I'll love you, always.

THE BARKER: Hurry, hurry, they're in love. Watch them stand around and enquire.

THE GIRL: When you're gone I shall miss you.

THE BARKER: He's a soldier, folks. Always has been, always will be. It's the World War. He goes to the front. She gets a telegram saying he's killed. She walks the streets and goes lower and lower every minute. The report is exaggerated. He isn't killed. After the Armistice he comes back and bumps into her in the streets of London. Like this. Hurry, watch them. It's romance, it's love, it's beauty, it's sweet, it's sad.

THE BOY: Hello, sister.

THE GIRL: Hello, handsome.

THE BOY: I've seen you somewhere.

THE GIRL: Have you?

THE BOY: What's your name, Baby?

THE GIRL: Toy. What's yours?

THE BOY: Well, let's say it's Joe.

THE BARKER: Hurry, hurry, there they go.

THE GIRL: I like you.

THE BOY: I kind of like you.

THE GIRL: We're alone.
THE BARKER: Still alone; and always will be.
THE BOY: Yes. What did you say? Let me look at you.
THE BARKER: Watch him look at her. He remembers.
THE GIRL: You're not . . . Tony?
THE BOY: Sandra.
THE BARKER: Hi-ya, hi-ya.

The Boy and the Girl embrace passionately, the girl sobbing.

THE BOY: You poor kid, you poor lovely kid.
THE GIRL: I. I. They said. Are you all right? They said. I. Oh, my darling, it's too late.
THE BARKER: Why?
THE BOY: I'm all right.
THE GIRL: My darling.
THE BOY: I knew I'd find you.
THE GIRL: It's too late.
THE BARKER: It's the movie, folks. Come closer. Watch them. It's sad, it's beautiful, it's the greatest story of all time. She thought he was dead, so she died. Now he's back again and she still loves him. It's too late. It's too early. Time for another reel yet.
THE BOY: We'll begin all over again. We'll go back to the beginning, darling.
THE BARKER: Listen to her cry. It's lovely. It's hooey, it's false, but it's the truest story ever told. It's phony, but it's beautiful.
THE GIRL: It's too late.
THE BOY: Sandra.
THE BARKER: Hi-ya, hi-ya, step up, precious ones, and watch him, listen to him. There he goes.
THE BOY: SANDRA. SANDRA.

The Boy shakes the Girl who is sobbing and kisses her neck, her forehead, her eyes, her hair, and her mouth.

THE BOY: We'll begin all over again.

The Girl sobs.
The Boy takes her hand and they go.

THE BARKER: Back to the beginning. Hi-ya, hi-ya, you're just in time for the great silent opera of the dead, music by every composer that ever lived. Hurry, hurry.

The lights go down. The conductor raises his baton. The prelude begins. Ends. The singers come out and sing.

In costumes, three men, three women: one at a time, stepping forward, each of them sings without making a sound; then two at a time; then three; four, five, and six; then the opera really gets going; there are duels, while the duellers sing, and one or two women, practically pass out lyrically soprano; there are arguments; a man is bound with a rope; a woman is stabbed, singing; a man is wounded, puts his hand over his heart and sings till he dies; a woman falls on his prostrate body, singing; and so forth and so on, until everybody is dead.

THE BARKER: O.K., my friends, get up and go away. That was fine.

The opera people get up and go away.

THE BARKER: And now, war. Hi-ya, hi-ya, WAR. Come closer, folks. It's all in fun.

A troop of four soldiers in the uniforms of theatre-ushers walk out, following a General.
They stop near the center of the stage.
From the other side of the stage comes another General and another troop of four soldiers. The Generals shake hands.

FIRST GENERAL: Hi-ya, Sam.
SECOND GENERAL: Hi-ya, Joe.
FIRST: How are tings?
SECOND: Okey-doke, pal. How wit you?
FIRST: Can't kick, comrade. What do you hear from the mob?
SECOND: Revolution of course. What's new wit you?
FIRST: Same old ting.
SECOND: Shall we start?
FIRST: What's the hurry. Let the men rest for a while.
SECOND GENERAL *(stands before his men and shouts)*: At ease.
FIRST GENERAL: At ease.

The soldiers mingle, form two groups, two from one side with two from the other. One group starts a crap game, the other a poker game.
The Generals sit at a table and a waiter starts bringing them boars' heads and wine and other things to eat. The soldiers quarrel about cheating.

FIRST GENERAL: Heah, heah. None of that.
THE BARKER: Hi-ya, hi-ya, WAR.

Two women join the soldiers. They are very luscious and all. The Generals stop eating.

FIRST GENERAL: I take the blonde.
SECOND GENERAL: I take the redhead.
THE BARKER: Hi-ya, hi-ya, WAR.

The women take the arms of the Generals and music arrives. They kind of cake-walk around two or three times, then away. The soldiers are all disgusted, if not deeply hurt. They go back to their games.

THE BARKER: Hi-ya, hi-ya, this is war.

The two Generals come back exhausted and lie down to rest and sleep. The women flirt with the other soldiers, go off with one from each group, dancing as before.

THE BARKER: Hi-ya, hi-ya, this is war: who will win? The women or the men? Step closer and see for yourself.

The two soldiers come staggering back, followed by the women, dancing more vigorously than ever.

THE BARKER: War. War. War.

The two soldiers lie down beside the two Generals and go to sleep.
The two women go off dancing with two more soldiers who return staggering after a moment and lie down beside the others while the women flirt with the remaining soldiers and go off dancing again with two more who in turn come back after a moment exhausted, with the women more frisky than ever.
There is one soldier left in each group. The redhead works on one, the blonde on the other, but with no luck. They show their knees, but the soldiers won't be tempted. They show their left bosoms, but no, the last two soldiers won't get into the spirit of the thing.

THE BARKER: You're wasting your time there, sister.

The two soldiers start flirting with each other, go off dancing, while the women look disgusted.

THE BARKER: This is war. Who will win, the women, the men, or the others. Hi-ya, hi-ya.

The last two soldiers come back, weakly flittering, and lie down beside the others. The women try to flirt with the sleepers, but can't get anywhere, so they go off, laughing spitefully.
A messenger from the left, another from the right, arrive simultaneously. First one, then the other, blows a horn not unlike the kind revelers blow on New Year's

Eve. The Generals jump up, accept envelopes from the messengers, open them, read, and say simultaneously:

THE GENERALS: Impossible. My men are exhausted.
THE BARKER: Hi-ya, hi-ya, this is war.

Each General scribbles something on the note and hands it back to the messenger who blows the horn again, turns and goes, and the Generals lie down again; after a moment the messengers reappear, blow their horns, hand new messages to the Generals who again are disgusted.

THE BARKER: *(for both Generals, and with more style than either of them are capable of, under the circumstances)* Com-pan-y, at-ten-tion. This is war. Hi-ya, hi-ya.

The soldiers leap wearily to their feet, get their guns, fall in. The Generals walk around behind their troops.

THE BARKER: Read-y. A-im. Fi—re.

The guns are popguns. The army at the left retreats, pursued by the right army, and off stage.

THE BARKER: Hi-ya, little ones, see the whole show from beginning to end, step right up.

The Russian Singer

There is a Russian in this town, Hollywood, who is a singer. He has read my books and claims I do not know what I have written. He claims *he* knows. He claims he is my best reader and he says I myself, Saroyan, Wheelyam Sar-o-yan, as he says, do not understand my stuff, which I wrote.

He is a serious man, an excellent singer of Russian songs, expert on the guitar, deeply sorrowful, extremely courteous, extraordinarily unhappy. He claims he is dead, not alive. He asks how I, writing as I do, saying what I say, am able to be so much alive. I tell him I don't know how.

He then declares that I do not know what I write.

He plays the guitar like a crazy man, and I swear he knows less about the way he plays the guitar than I know, and I swear I write my stuff exactly the way he plays the guitar. In short, we are brothers. This is exact.

He is, strictly, at heart, one who knows. He knows all things. His knowing is sharp and swift and to the dead center of it all: he knows it is all death. He knows it is all nothing. He is a big, sorrowful-looking fellow in excellent American clothes who plays the guitar the way I write.

He reads my stuff. He does not believe I know about my writing.

Each time we meet at a party, this great Russian, this great singer who is truthfully my brother comes to me and very bitterly, in his deep voice, says to me, roaring deeply, very hurt about everything, a truly tragic man, a truly noble one, Wheelyam Sar-o-yan, *you* will understand.

I don't try hard to understand because it seems I almost always understand without trying, and I bust out laughing, and he tells me he cannot understand how I understand, how I write what I write. Sometimes, believing what I say, I say, sincerely but with a smile, that it is true, very often I do not know what I write, what I say, I simply write, like this, as it is here, something perhaps more significant than I know, which falls in place by itself, rather strangely. And oddly enough, or not oddly enough, not half oddly enough, not oddly at all, he brings out his guitar, takes his stance, which is practically tragic, which is truthfully a thing to see and remember, and after a suitable half minute of reverent silence, he begins easily, effortlessly, as I begin each of my pieces, to sing and play the guitar, and before you know it, before you've had a chance to understand anything about anything he's singing and playing like one who was placed in this world to sing, and play a guitar, and in no time at all the room is full of electrical, almost metaphysical, I might go so far as to say holy, splendor, magnificence, tragedy, and comedy; all at once, all together, all of it together in one piece. Eat, eat, eat, he sings in Russian, only the Russian word is not so flat, *kossi, kossi, kossi*. This Russian word for eat is the warm, kindly, gentle one of the mother to her child, the endearing one, *kossi, kossi, kossi*.

I do not believe there is a better singer of this kind in the world, nor for that matter, of my kind, a better writer. This man is possessed. And, unless I am badly mistaken, I am too. Most people meeting me, talking with me, do not get the impression that I am a great writer, and often do not believe me when I tell them so. Very often, even after I have told them six or seven times, they do not believe, and I beg them to read my stuff. I know they will know, while they are reading my stuff and afterward that everything I have said to them is true, and I beg them because I know it will be a splendid and extraordinary and funny experience for them. To hear me bragging, and then to read my stuff and know that I am a great writer. I beg them to read my stuff, so it will be complete.

I admit it. I am possessed. Most of the time not violently so. But often enough. Not haunted, mind you. The presence is not an evil one. It is often angry and bitter and furious, but most of the time it is warm and friendly and amiable and gentle and courteous, and at times a little gallant, even. It is a good presence, and in varying degrees it is with me always. I do not mind it at all, and am on the contrary on excellent terms with it. We sometimes have quarrels. I am sometimes strongly inclined toward one thing, such as loafing and having an easygoing time, and this presence is inclined toward another thing, such as sitting down somewhere and putting two or three thousand words on paper, making a story, or something else. As I say, I do not know a great deal about what the words come to, but the presence is always anxious that I take time out to say something. I say, What's there to say? And the presence says, Now don't get funny; just sit down and say anything; it'll be all right. Say it wrong; it'll be all right anyway.

Half the time I *do* say it wrong, but somehow or other, just as the presence says, it's right anyhow. I am always pleased about this, after it's happened. My God, it's wrong, but it's all right. It's really all right. How did it happen?

Well, that's how it is. It's the presence, doing everything for me. It's the presence, doing all the hard work while I, always inclined to take things easy, loaf around, not thinking, not paying much attention to anything, much, just putting down on paper whatever comes my way.

The Russian singer told me about this. Wheelyam Sar-o-yan, he said, *I know what you are saying, but you do not know.*

This is, unfortunately, or fortunately, true. I think fortunately. Because I like being alive. And being dumb this way allows me to stay alive. By rights I should have died long ago. This is no fancy phrase. It is the truth. By all rights I should have died long ago. I didn't.

Two years ago, at three in the morning, when I fell down a flight of cement stairs into the basement of a Greek restaurant on Market Street in San Francisco and should have been instantly killed, why did I get up and yell at Pete the short-order cook, What the hell's the big idea putting these stairs where the toilet's supposed to be?

How did that happen? How did it happen that I was not even scratched?

I could give seventeen other instances. All them years, all them crazy years, all that crazy stuff, all those years when I had no money, why didn't I die? How did it happen that I didn't even lose my hair?

I have always suspected that what I am doing is not the work of one man, but I have never given the notion much thought. Then I met this Russian singer, and he told me, and now I know for sure.

Death

A very great painter once told me this story of himself: I was on my way from The Universe Restaurant on Broadway, off Columbus Ave, to my room on Montgomery Street where my painting is, "Beginning and End," which I have been painting all my life and which I know I shall never finish when suddenly, walking alone through the early afternoon stillness of an October day, the street, which is the only earth that has ever interested me, *angered* me. I turned, staring bitterly at the Oriental Importing Company Building, and began to shout.

I had seen this building a thousand times, going and coming, and suddenly I was loathing it; loathing every building of every street of every city; the whole idea of these things, places for all of us to creep into and hide, the rotten horror of it grabbing hold of my blood and making me shout.

I began to use the most offensive language any man ever used, and I saw the people of the street stir with deep unconscious fear, something old in them drawing away from me. Then I heard a woman say to a small newsboy:

That's Stone, isn't it? The painter? Is he drunk?

She was one of many women I had met at art galleries when my paintings had been on exhibition and although I did not remember her name I knew she was the wife of a very rich businessman and that at one time she was on the verge of buying one of my paintings for two hundred dollars, but hadn't gone through with it because, she said, my paintings were so violent and might upset her two daughters. I suppose it had been two daughters.

The thought of those two children was as hateful to me as the sight of the street.

If this woman had bought my painting, I would have been able to go up to Vallejo and visit my son Stephen who was working on a farm there, trying to get himself adjusted to living. I knew my son disliked me because of the early death of his mother, a woman I had never loved, but I knew also that he wanted to see me now and then, and that above all things *I* needed to see him. I had an idea that he was going through the same sort of agony I had gone through as a boy of twenty in Ireland, in Dublin, and I wanted to tell him the thing to do was to be patient, to love no one, to hate no one, to fear nothing, and to read great writers like Dostoyevsky and Tolstoy, men who had not run away from life but had gathered all of it into themselves, the good with the horrible.

But this woman hadn't bought the painting and I hadn't been able to visit my son and talk to him, and less than a month later they told me he had been smashed to death under the tractor he had been driving.

The tractor had gotten out of control, they said, and my son had tried to bring it to a stop at a ditch bank, but instead the machine had tipped over on him and he had been smashed a full foot into the earth. This is what they told me, but I know different.

Stephen, my son, the same as I might have done at twenty, had been driving the tractor and everything had gone black and void in his impatient brain and he had let the thing out at top speed and had *driven* it into the bank and turned it over onto himself and been killed, out of sheer despair, angry with me and with himself and the whole world.

Standing in front of the Oriental Importing Company Building I thought of my son; and hearing this woman speaking of me to a newsboy, I hated her and her husband and her two daughters, and I said:

Do you remember that painting you almost bought, the one called "Desolate Landscape," well, my son is dead now.

Suddenly she was shivering, wanting, I could tell, to scream, but being unable to do so. I knew the newsboy well, for he was one of many Chinese boys I had seen growing up and I had always liked him, but now, because he was shivering with the woman, I hated him too.

All this happened in much less than a minute. At the same time many other things happened. I could feel myself getting away from the limitations of my flesh, wholly, with absolute finality. This sudden flight was bitter. I felt, remotely within myself, as from the first day of my life, wholly, immortally refreshed. I could not imagine what next I would do because the doing was out of my power. I was merely the doer. I could not tell what I would do.

I was afraid that it might be something strange, but some thought from my own mind, hollow and meaningless with the meaninglessness of mortal thought, bewildered me, so that I had to laugh at it, and suddenly I *remembered* myself standing in the street, laughing in a way that must seem horrible to people who were not aware of what was going on in me, my death, my son's death, the death of the street, of all streets, the whole world. But this was so. It *was* so. It happened and I *was* of the happening, and because of this absurd thought of mine, I had to laugh.

A crowd began to form, their fearful eyes staring at death. Even automobile traffic was affected. There was a definite commotion in the street because of my anger, and my laughter immediately afterward, and I had enough of normal consciousness about me to realize that if I had caused traffic to become involved, the city would certainly place me in jail. This struck me as being the most amusing and ridiculous thought that had ever occurred to me, and now instead of laughing, since I had already laughed, I began to cry.

But it was impersonal crying. I was sorry for no one, not even for my son Stephen, not even for his mother, not even for the rich woman who had not bought my painting, not even for the Chinese newsboy, not for anything or anybody. I could do *nothing* else. It was simply the *only* thing to do. I felt wholly unashamed and unembarrassed, and cried all the way through centuries of mortal dying, and living. I cried at the emptiness and error and waste.

When I got into the police automobile, and there was nothing else to do, I turned to a young cop and said, Give me a cigarette will you, Mac.

I was dead then, and all I wanted was a cigarette.

The Young Husband and Father

My cousin Aslan was a fellow with a motorcycle. He was from the common side of the Garoghlanian tribe. One day he took and rode away on his motorcycle and didn't come back for two months. He was seventeen at the time. He came back with a girl sitting behind him on the motorcycle and introduced her to everybody. This is Peg, my wife, he said. She was Irish. I don't know where he'd found her, but it was somewhere in San Francisco where he'd gone.

This boy had no education to speak of, no especial talent of any kind, and nothing but a good heart.

Everybody was crazy about Peg, and *she* was crazy about everybody.

I don't remember her well, except that she was lively and full of laughter. She and Aslan used to just sit around in the house and laugh all the time. He had a real loud laugh that somehow made you feel tickled to death to be alive and at the same time made you just kind of awfully sad about everything, way in deep. They wouldn't be doing anything, just sitting in the parlor, and then they'd start laughing together. It was beautiful. Aslan was dark in a way that was fine, and his girl was as fair as anything could be, with eyes like you just didn't know what, they were so blue and warm and good.

I guess I just had to go and fall in love with her, Aslan said.

All the months she was pregnant they would be together in the parlor, when he got home from work at the packinghouse, and full of this laughter.

Then she had the baby; and died; and the baby lived; and Aslan didn't cry. He was the only one who didn't. All the rest of us almost died of grief.

He *did* die of it; that's why he didn't cry.

When it was all over and the baby was all right with its grandmother, he got on his motorcycle and went away. He stayed away a year. When he came back he was bigger and harder and real quiet. He'd been to South America.

He came to see the baby. It was like the girl. He couldn't bear to be near it. He never took it in his arms, but stood around looking at it. He spent a week looking at it and then went away again. He was gone a year and a half this time. When he came back the War was going on and he said he was going to join the War. He talked to the girl in Armenian and then went down and enlisted. He never wrote to anybody and when the War ended we all thought he would come back and see the girl, but he didn't. After two years we decided maybe he was dead, but when we wrote to Washington about it, they said they didn't know exactly what had happened to him although there was no report that he had died.

Then one day in 1923 he came back and apologized for not writing or coming home sooner.

I don't know, he said, I was just always going somewhere.

He was sitting in the parlor with everybody, four minutes after he'd arrived, talking fast, everybody delighted to see him. Then he asked to see the girl, and his mother didn't wait a minute to tell him the girl was dead.

He seemed to know anyhow.

He just stayed where he was. He didn't say anything. He lighted a cigarette, inhaled, and then tears came to his eyes. From his lips you could never tell he was crying, but tears came from his eyes for a long time, maybe five minutes. Everybody left the parlor, except me.

I was fifteen and remembered.

I remembered the way he used to laugh with her, the way her eyes were, what a sweet kid she was, and how crazy he was about her, how crazy she was about him, what a great adventure it was going to be to have the baby.

When he went away that first time I said, But where will he go? Where does a man go when it's that way?

He just sat in the chair and smoked the cigarette and let the tears move out of the crazy ache in his blood and fall down his cheek.

At last he got up and said in Armenian, I don't know. He shook his head and said, How should I know what it is? He shook his head and went around the room touching things and saying he didn't know.

The Hours of Day and the Hours of Night
(A Prose Poem)

In the morning the sun comes up. The sun rises and it is day in the world, the time of wakened limbs, opened eyes, of walking, working, and talking. The time of living, the beginning of the world. This morning the sun rises and the world begins; or it is a morning of a day one thousand years ago, and again the world begins. They waken and rise because it is day. It is light: there is no longer darkness on the face of the void, and the living rise.

The night-dream of man pauses for the hours of day, returns to memory and waits. The day will end and again the dream will continue. It will continue in another universe, a place of even greater beauty than this place. The eyes of the child inhabitant of the earth open to the light of morning, and for a moment the dream ends. The child rises and stands upon his feet, the inhabitant of this place. The dweller here. During the hours of day the child performs his role of inhabitant. He builds and breaks and mends, and builds again, and breaks and mends, and the hours of day come and go, a year goes by, and then another, and then a decade, and then a century, and the child builds a city, he builds a civilization, and the hours of day come and go, and the city falls beneath rain and wind and snow and it falls beneath sand and rock, and the hours of night come, and the child dreams.

In Manhattan, in 1938, or in a city now buried under the earth.

But the dream does not end. It is of the endless beginning, and when it is night in the world the dream continues.

The Body

One thing in life. No, not that, not a thing: wait a minute. What can one call it? How can one name this thing so deep in all men and so secret and yet so real to every man alive, dumb or articulate? How can one place the word over and within it and bring forth this thing so deep and secret and real that nothing, no event of life, one way or another, joyous or tragic, can spoil it? What is the word? Is there a word big enough, broad enough, deep enough to *say* it? The body? Well, yes, but that is another word and nobody will know that the meaning now is not the same, though the word is: *the* body. The *whole* body? The *timeless* body? The *deathless* body? Mangled in wars? Starved in famines? Killed again and again by errors and disease? That body, still whole, still timeless, still deathless, still living?

The *godly* body? Wait. Let's call it the inward flesh. Not the spirit because while it is also this, the spirit, it is essentially flesh; substance, related to substance, made of it, a brief variation of rock and earth and fire and water and air. And space. Don't forget it. A brief variation of substances with weight, density, as fire, the clod flowering with heat and color, the temper of rock.

One thing, though, we must never forget, nor for that matter *can* ever forget, where remembrance is most deep and most secret and most real: that the world cannot touch this inward flesh, this inward body of man.

The outward body which we dress in the clothes of our time can be broken by the world and held pathetically together by the garments we put over the flesh: shoes, trousers, shirts, coats, hats. And the errors can be hidden by these garments, and agony can walk forth into the city in the grandest style of the day and even smile with the safety of good shoes, good trousers, good shirt, good coat, good hat. The objects of the world can encumber the outward body, cause it to trip, to fall, to be hurt, and the outward flesh can bruise and bleed and break and be eaten by disease, and the heart can blacken with pain and bewilderment and hate, and still this inward flesh remains whole, *the body*. And one whole outward body can die, end, and begin to rot, and the sudden and glorious variation of substances can end, the street can end, the house can end, the face of the beloved can end, and the outward body can begin to rot and smell, and worms can eat it, and the earth can swallow it, and still this inward flesh lives. Or a million whole bodies of the outward flesh can end, and a million magnificent worlds can end, and still this inward body will be whole and deathless and timeless and godly. Wait now, wait. Don't read it wrong. Don't get it fancy. Get it plain. Get it simple. Get it as simple as it is: the inward flesh. You know what I'm talking about.

The whole confounded world cannot touch this flesh. It can do many things to the outward flesh, even the final outward thing, kill it, end it, and never touch this other. It can devise the war and place the implements of war in the hands of multitudes and it can destroy multitudes, but not the flesh. You know about the war. There is only one. The place, the scene of battle may change. The men may be of different tribes. The year may be a year long ago, or the day today. It is the same war. The men have died. The men are dying now. The flesh, the inward flesh, is still whole, still living. The earth of many places is rich with the blood and decayed substance of flesh and bone ended, but the inward flesh is still whole.

This is God, I think. This is also the source of our deepest grief and joy. That it cannot end, that even after madness, when all things should end, when all men should die, when the world *should* end, when the universe itself *should* circle away into nothingness and let substance rest, sleep forever, the inward flesh is still whole, men still live, the world is still real, the universe is still in its place. It should end. After such madness, such grief, such pain, it should end. It should be no more. Nothingness should *be* endlessly. But no, the body is whole again, of the earth again. The tragic world is still real, still tragic, and soon there shall be another war and another multitude shall end.

What sense is it? Why is it so? What is the flesh waiting for? When will the inward and the outward come together and be one and when will the world be a place of immortality? Will it ever, as it is written that it shall and must? Will the war ever end? Will the deathlessness of the inward flesh ever reach the outward flesh? What's the idea? Wait now. Don't fly off the handle. Take it slow and easy.

One glory of possessing substance, of being one of many variations of rock and earth and fire and water and air and space, now and a time before, and one delight of having presence in this place, confounded as it is, is this simultaneous presence of the inward flesh here, within the outward flesh, within the earth and the world and the universe, within time and space, related to all things seen and unseen, smile of sky, field, brook, sea, and the quiet persistent and holy belief that one day these two, the inward and the outward, will be one, and the world will be a place of immortality, the inhabitant of the world noble, the earth a garden, the universe God.

This is our glory, and the source of our deepest grief. Will we see that day? Will we know that earth and world and universe? Will we ever know that *oneness* which is within us, or will the outward flesh stumble and fall and end? Will that body ever inhabit this one? Will it ever enter the billion cells of this body and reach to the tips of our toes and fingers and look out upon the world through our eyes? Will the wholeness and deathlessness of that body belong to one, to the man, to me, and to you, instead of to man, the whole living multitude, the whole large multitudinous body, the tribe, the mob? Will it ever belong to one, from tips of fingers and toes to intake of air, to movement through the city, to holy sleep? It is there. We know it is there, within each of us. It has always been there, waiting. It has always been the source of our grief, and our only comfort. Will it ever happen? Will we ever know our immortality? Or are we going to go on holding the broken pieces of the outward body together with the tragic and proud rags of our time, tighten the belt, tie the lace, button the coat, and let it go at that, waiting to end, doing the pointless things, uttering the pointless words, dreaming the pointless dream? What the hell are we going to do? It's there. It's within every living variation of substance, and the belief is there too, that we can be immortal, so what are we going to do?

Or shall we gain the world? Shall we take Europe and Asia and Africa and Australia and Greenland and Iceland and all the islands of the seas and all the cities of the world and all the puny wealth, people and money and jewels and wheat and oil and the growth of vines and trees? Shall we take what is easy to take? Shall we enter every continent and destroy every tribe that dares to stand in our way? Shall we blast cities and burn them and take the money? All we need is a big army. We know two men can overpower one man, and if necessary kill him. It is very simple, and from a certain viewpoint the desirable thing to do. Certainly. Take the world. Send a hundred million against fifty million, and let a quarter of each perish. The womb is fertile and the impulse to plant seed in it is always fresh. There will always be many births of flesh. Infants will always emerge from the womb. Who cares about men? Their destiny is to perish, taking the world. It is written that men must be born again, but death not birth is the destiny of men who covet the world. And those who come one day to be the lords of the world come to be the lords of what is not worth having, the lords of *nothing*, bloody nothing, confounded and rotten and full of the stink of sweat and dirt mixed with blood and foul guts. The lords of the world. Have it, gentlemen. It's all yours. Have it. Have the continents. Rule the waves. Boss the works. Tell them what to do and what not to do. Kill them who disobey. Entangle and encumber the outward body of man. End all variations that stand in your way, and encumber all variations that do not. Gentlemen and brothers, be as great as the number of variations that you violate: men, women, and children, and the wasted unborn. Do it with a flourish, in the name of holy history.

Shall we go on taking the world and having it taken from us, and wanting to take it and *fearing* that it will be taken from us? Or shall we quiet down and remember the inward flesh and our dream of immortality here, in the moments of our days and nights and years? How about it?

The Comic Page and Vital Statistics

Fifth Avenue and Thirty-seventh Street in New York is Tiffany and Company, and in the winter snow; wind at night; at times rain; at times sleet; the windows very bright and warm.

During snow, there is the solacing memory of sunlight in the world.

If you live, there is; if you die, there is neither one nor the other, neither the light nor the memory of warm days and unfearful shadows.

On the pavement, in the city: the smile of the pushcart peddler, the newsboy, the loafer, the beggar, and the street itself.

Under the sun.

If you die, neither one nor the other, and in the winter the street quiet and pious because this (the thought mingling with the smell of city and the sight of the window of Tiffany and Company and the remembrance of the tall unfearful shadow) within yourself is quiet, pious, and wrathful, with love; beloved, you will never die. When the year ends you will live, and when the year begins; and you will live, beloved, when the world ends; and begins; and you will live until the end. This world (the kiss through the long night) is rain and sleet, the roar of the subway under the street; beloved, you will live until the end of everything.

To be near the world a young man, if sufficiently in the image of God, will sometimes go north a thousand miles by foot or wheel, or south, or east, or west, and reach nowhere; and gladly; and be grieved by the memory of her smile, a thousand miles south or north, west or east.

The street is white and the climate severe.

The dime you squander for two cups of coffee is forever lost; beloved, you will live forever.

And then, to be away from ugliness, a young man, now old, if sufficiently mortal, will go around the world in order to be away, during the moment of moving, from both the world and the ugliness of it: and he will never be away.

Beloved, you will live until the end: it is the tiger stalking through the night, sometimes with hate and sometimes with love: the dime squandered, the smile wasted: months and months ago.

And I mean the heart's road: Agony Avenue: where the tiger is: lithe and supple, international.

He turns his face from gloom of winter night to warmth of window light, and does not weep: the tiger stands before him in grace and purity, waiting for the groan or lamentation, and then they wrestle.

Superb power. Nimbleness.

That's the trick of mortality: baby, you will live until the end, and there is no end. A young man will wander up and down the world seeking everything and all he will reach will be forgetfulness: of all gifts of God, this is the noblest, saddest, most godly, most impertinent.

Comma.

The famed six-cylinder engine, with floating power, super-efficient cooling, 6.7 to 1 compression with calibrated ignition, aluminum alloy pistons: your family is safer: the safety-steel body protects them. And the hydraulic brakes. Eleven added comfort features. Inches of new room. New sway-eliminator. New steel springs.

Eighteen to twenty-four miles per gallon of gasoline.

You can be fooled. Nevertheless, you are a guest of honor here.

The big town, New York, finds riding safer, steering safer, stopping safer with Radial Safety Control (patent applied for). America's greatest engineers had *your* kind of traffic in mind when they developed Duo-Automatic Hydraulic Brakes (patent applied for).

Money may not be all-important. Start the new year right.

Won't you let our representative call to discuss your problem?

Those who enjoy fine living.

And if you die, neither one nor the other; and in the winter snow; wind at night; at times rain, at times sleet; the windows of Tiffany's sad with wild electric illumination and remarkable jewelry, the tiger on Agony Avenue.

A comical man is the great Democrat. Another comical man is the great German with the small moustache; the stark-faced Italian; the bovine-eyed Russian; the dissipated Turk; the bouncer of the Reno Club.

The bouncer of the Reno Club is a sad comical man and his name is Amarillo Willy. Forty years ago he was born in Amarillo, Texas, and his father named him William, after Shakespeare. Amarillo Willy is a large comical man, and his ears are swollen from the days of professional wrestling, years ago, in the big cities of the world. In his day Amarillo Willy was famous. He was strong and wealthy. Time not only ages and mellows fine wines: it ripens the comic in men, the great Democrat, the German with the small moustache, the stark-faced Italian, the dissipated Turk, the bouncer of the Reno Club (All right, Bull, outside; I said *outside*).

On his left ear, the giant Bull, drunk, broke, disgraced for half a minute: and on his right ear, the German; on his left, the Italian; on his right, the Russian; and the Turk, on his left. Brothers, what happened?

It's the comic newsreel: it has taken Manhattan by storm. One place in New York where you won't be crowded: in a 1938 Terraplane. Another, the public library. Another, the church. And another, the cemetery.

One of these days each of them will die. One of these days the earth will rejoice with the decay of substance grown haywire: wild flowers will bloom in many quiet places of many quiet continents. There will be no rhetoric to speak of, and the iron gates of old houses will creak with noonday arrival and departure of laborers home for lunch, and the God damn noonday whistles will blow, and the big locomotives will puff out of town, and the wind will blow, and the sun will shine, and rain will fall, and children on the way to school will laugh, and late at night, in parks, in moving-picture theatres, clerks will kiss stenographers, and the newspapers will have forgotten the great and comic who once lived, who are dead: old, rotted, and world-famous.

In no part of the world has it been possible to grow one comic man whose antics delight children: only the soil and the sun of the great lost theatre of the heart and mind have succeeded in producing this prodigy of art and nature and religion and chemistry and so far he has never been seen by mortal eye, though he is the source of all mortal laughter. There isn't a man living, and yet the streets of the world are wretched with multitudes.

Gentlemen, what happened?

What You Get for Trying Your Best, If Anything

For to have tried one's best, or another's, grace, let us say, will have come to us, goodness too I guess, land perhaps, or at least enough of it under foot to enable the feet to walk, and the rest to follow, the heart in its own big way, the eye too, the ear, and all the rest of it. To have labored, as it were, in the orchard or in the vineyard, or late in the afternoon, amid radio music perhaps, swing or semi-classical one may hope, over the years, for the arrival, let us say, of friends from the country, a letter from a book publisher alleging that one may make friends, and having made them influence people, or one may dream, standing at the window, or at the table busy with bread, onions, and water, or asleep on the floor, of the arrival of a large lady with wings of feather, pure white, soft, and after a fashion religious.

For having sat alone one year, through climate of every kind, through all the named days of the week, all the weeks of every month, and all the months of the year, making eternity, one may, we may imagine, rightfully consider the coming of beauty not unlikely fantasy, but in all probability a probability, human and female in form, except for wings of soft feather, with a voice like the best of birds.

For having studied a year the way of things among themselves any man over eighty pounds in weight and under seven feet in height may consider anything inexpensive no more a bargain than lawn in front of somebody's house, and, if not under contract to a manufacturer of movies, believe the necessity to have money nine times out of ten untrue, except for gambling. Or, on the other hand, for having every day of the year seen comedy in the delirium of the living, any young Communist or Christian may be right in understanding that although money isn't everything, it is something, and not having any of it is just as bad, ten or eleven times a year, as being in church without pants or in the picket line in evening clothes. What I mean is, he's got a right, most likely, to feel sorry for the dead who imagined it was heroism when it was no more than what it always has been, comedy for whoever is still watching: yourself, if you are still.

And for having all the time breathed, a good-natured graduate of Yale 1908 may spend long hours remembering one thing or another one day or another one year or another, all the time, as when everybody fought the war and didn't know it, or, even, as when summer ended one year and a number of small birds, visible to the naked eye, flew in a hurry from the north of Boston to the south and promptly perished of cold. One may, in short, be courteous time after time and, if able to stand, not regret the waste of years as well as raw products.

For my part, which is the greater part in this region, one may be steady too. One may wait for the worst and get a letter in the afternoon from somebody in London who has troubles. One may even have troubles oneself. One may have trouble with climate, although there's no profit in it. For having watched them murdering one another, and for having, from a distance of five or six thousand miles, known the effect of their doing so, one may not be rude in going for a walk and at a certain corner saying with no ill-will what I have here said. That is, one way or another, one *may*, so let one do what one pleases, breathe or not, speak or not, or die or not. One always may. And the living *are* one. For my part, now greater than ever, I say one may or one may not. One, named God, let's say, may. One, not so named, may. And for my part I say, Why don't you? What do you want to make them happy for? What do you want to die for them for? For having died for them one may not, any time, so what do you want to do it for? One may let them do it, what does one want to do it for them for? Who are they? They're poorer than the poor heroes who die for them, so what do you want to go to work and please them for? What do you want to go to work and make them feel important for? One may go one's way and *let* one go one's way.

That's all.

A Nice Old-Fashioned Romance, with Love Lyrics and Everything

My cousin Arak was a year and a half younger than me, round-faced, dark, and exceptionally elegant in manners. It was no pretense with him. His manners were just naturally that way, just as my manners were bad from the beginning. Where Arak would get around any sort of complication at school with a bland smile that showed his front upper teeth, separated, and melted the heart of stone of our teacher, Miss Daffney, I would go to the core of the complication and with noise and vigor prove that Miss Daffney or somebody else was the culprit, not me, and if need be, I would carry the case to the Supreme Court and prove my innocence.

I usually got sent to the office. In some cases I would get a strapping for debating the case in the office against Mr. Derringer, our principal, who was no earthly good at debates. The minute I got him cornered he got out his strap.

Arak was different; he didn't care to fight for justice. He wasn't anywhere near as bright as me, but even though he was a year and a half younger than me, he was in the same grade. That wouldn't be so bad if the grade wasn't the fifth. I usually won all my arguments with my teachers, but instead of being glad to get rid of me they refused to promote me, in the hope, I believe, of winning the following semester's arguments and getting even. That's how it happened that I came to be the oldest pupil in the fifth grade.

One day Miss Daffney tried to tell the world I was the author of the poem on the blackboard that said she was in love with Mr. Derringer, and ugly. The author of the poem was my cousin Arak, not me. Any poem I wrote wouldn't be about Miss Daffney, it would be about something worthwhile. Nevertheless, without mentioning any names, but with a ruler in her hand, Miss Daffney stood beside my desk and said, I am going to find out who is responsible for this horrible outrage on the blackboard and see that he is properly punished.

He? I said. How do you know it's a boy and not a girl?

Miss Daffney whacked me on the knuckles of my right hand. I jumped out of my seat and said, You can't go around whacking me on the knuckles. I'll report this.

Sit down, Miss Daffney said.

I did. She had me by the right ear, my most sensitive ear, and one that was getting out of shape from being grabbed hold of by Miss Daffney and other teachers.

I sat down and quietly, almost inaudibly, said, You'll hear about this.

Hold your tongue, Miss Daffney said, and although I was sore as the devil, I stuck out my tongue and held it, while the little Mexican, Japanese, Armenian, Greek, Italian, Portuguese, and plain American boys and girls in the class, who looked to me for comedy, roared with laughter. Miss Daffney came down on my hand with the ruler, but this time the whack grazed my nose. This to me was peculiarly insulting, inasmuch as my nose then, as now, was large. A small nose would not have been grazed, and I took Miss Daffney's whack as a subtle comment on the size of my nose.

I put my bruised hand over my hurt nose and again rose to my feet.

You told me to hold my tongue, I said, insisting that I had done no evil, had merely carried out her instructions, and was therefore innocent, utterly undeserving of the whacked hand and the grazed nose.

You be good now, Miss Daffney said. I won't stand any more of your nonsense. You be good.

I took my hand away from my nose and began to be good. I smiled like a boy bringing her a red apple. My audience roared with laughter and Miss Daffney dropped the ruler, reached for me, fell over the desk, got up and began to chase me around the room.

There I go again, I kept saying to myself while Miss Daffney chased me around the room. There I go again getting in a mess like this that's sure to end in murder, while my cousin Arak, who is the guilty one, sits there and smiles. There's no justice anywhere.

When Miss Daffney finally caught me, as I knew she would unless I wanted even more severe punishment from Mr. Derringer, there was a sort of free-for-all during which she tried to gouge my eyes out, pull off my ears, fingers, and arms, and I, by argument, tried to keep her sweet and ladylike.

When she was exhausted, I went back to my seat, and the original crime of the day was taken up again: Who was the author of the love lyric on the blackboard?

Miss Daffney straightened her hair and her clothes, got her breath, demanded and got silence, and after several moments of peace during which the ticking of the clock was heard, she began to speak.

I am going to ask each of you by name if you wrote this awful— poem—on the blackboard and I shall expect you to tell the truth. If you lie, I shall find out anyway and your punishment will be all the worse.

She began to ask each of the boys and girls if they'd written the poem and of course they hadn't. Then she asked my cousin Arak and he too said he hadn't. Then she asked me and I said I hadn't, which was the truth.

You go to the office, she said. You liar.

I didn't write any poem on any blackboard, I said. And I'm not a liar.

Mr. Derringer received me with no delight. Two minutes later Suzie Kokomoto arrived from our class with a message describing my crime. In fact, quoting it. Mr. Derringer read the message, made six or seven faces, smiled, snapped his suspenders, coughed, and said, What made you write this little poem?

I didn't, I said.

Naturally, he said, you'd say you didn't, but why did you?

I *didn't* write it, I said.

Now don't be headstrong, Mr. Derringer said. That's a rather alarming rumor to be spreading. How do you *know* Miss Daffney's in love with me?

Is she? I said.

Well, Mr. Derringer said, that's what it says here. What gave you that impression? Have you noticed her looking at me with admiration or something?

I haven't noticed her looking at you with anything, I said. Are *you* in love with her or something?

That remains to be seen, Mr. Derringer said. It isn't a bad poem, up to a point. Do you really regard Miss Daffney as ugly?

I didn't write the poem, I said. I can prove it. I don't write that way.

You mean your handwriting isn't like the handwriting on the black- board? Mr. Derringer said.

Yes, I said, and I don't write that kind of poetry either.

You *admit* writing poetry? Mr. Derringer said.

I write poetry, I said, but not *that* kind of poetry.

A rumor like that, Mr. Derringer said. I hope you know what you're about.

Well, I said, all I know is I didn't write it.

Personally, Mr. Derringer said, I think Miss Daffney is not only not ugly, but on the contrary attractive.

Well, that's all right, I said. The only thing I want is not to get into a lot of trouble over something I didn't do.

You *could* have written that poem, Mr. Derringer said.

Not *that* one, I said. I could have written a good one.

What do you mean, *good?* Mr. Derringer said. Beautiful? Or insulting?

I mean beautiful, I said, only it wouldn't be about Miss Daffney.

Up to this point, Mr. Derringer said, I was willing to entertain doubts as to your being the author of the poem, but no longer. I am convinced you wrote it. Therefore I must punish you.

I got up and started to debate.

You give me a strapping for something I didn't do, I said, and you'll hear about it.

So he gave me a strapping and *the whole school* heard about it. I went back to class limping. The poem had been erased. All was well again. The culprit had been duly punished, the poem effaced, and order reestablished in the fifth grade. My cousin Arak sat quietly admiring Alice Bovard's brown curls.

First thing during recess I knocked him down and sat on him.

I got a strapping for that, I said, so don't write any more of them.

The next morning, however, there was another love lyric on the blackboard in my cousin Arak's unmistakable hand, and in his unmistakable style, and once again Miss Daffney wanted to weed out the culprit and have him punished. When I came into the room and saw the poem and the lay of the land I immediately began to object. My cousin Arak was going too far. In Armenian I began to swear at him. He, however, had become stone deaf, and Miss Daffney believed my talk was for her. Here, here, she said. Speak in a language everybody can understand if you've got something to say.

All I've got to say is I didn't write that poem, I said. And I didn't write yesterday's either. If I get in any more trouble about these poems, somebody's going to hear about it.

Sit down, Miss Daffney said.

After the roll call, Miss Daffney filled a whole sheet of paper with writing, including the new poem, and ordered me to take the message to the office.

Why me? I said. I didn't write the poem.

Do as you're told, Miss Daffney said.

I went to her desk, put out my hand to take the note, Miss Daffney gave it a whack, I jumped back three feet and shouted, I'm not going to be carrying love letters for you.

This just naturally was the limit. There was a limit to everything. Miss Daffney leaped at me. I in turn was so sore at my cousin Arak that I turned around and jumped on him. He pretended to be very innocent, and offered no resistance. He was very deft, though, and instead of getting the worst of it, he got the least, while I fell all over the floor until Miss Daffney caught up with me. After that it was all her fight. When I got to the office with the message, I had scratches and bruises all over my face and hands, and the love letter from Miss Daffney to Mr. Derringer was crumpled and in places torn.

What's been keeping you? Mr. Derringer said. Here, let me see that message. What mischief have you been up to now?

He took the message, unfolded it, smoothed it out on his desk, and read it very slowly. He read it three or four times. He was delighted and as far as I could tell, in love. He turned with a huge smile on his face and was about to reprimand me for again saying that Miss Daffney was ugly, when I said, I didn't write the poem; I didn't write yesterday's either. All I want is a chance to get myself a little education and live and let live.

Now, now, Mr. Derringer said.

He was quite pleased.

If you're in love with her, I said, that's your affair, but leave me out of it.

All I say is you could be a little more gracious about Miss Daffney's appearance, Mr. Derringer said. If she seems plain to you, perhaps she doesn't seem plain to someone else.

I was disgusted. It was just no use.

All right, I said. Tomorrow I'll be gracious.

Now that's better, Mr. Derringer said. Of course I must punish you.

He reached for the lower drawer of his desk where the strap was.

Oh no, I said. If you punish me, then I won't be gracious.

Well, what about today's poem? Mr. Derringer said. I've got to punish you for that. Tomorrow's will be another story.

No, I said. Nothing doing.

Oh all right, Mr. Derringer said, but see that you're gracious.

I will, I said. Can I go back now?

Yes, he said. Yes. Let me think this over.

I began to leave the office.

Wait a minute, he said. Everybody'll know something fishy's going on somewhere unless they hear you howl. Better come back here and howl ten times, and then go back.

Howl? I said. I can't howl unless I'm hurt.

Oh sure you can, Mr. Derringer said. Just give out a big painful howl. You can do it.

I don't think I can, I said.

I'll hit this chair ten times with the strap, Mr. Derringer said, and you howl.

Do you think it'll work? I said.

Of course it'll work, he said. Come on.

Mr. Derringer hit the chair with the strap and I tried to howl the way I had howled yesterday, but it didn't sound real. It sounded fishy, somewhere.

We were going along that way when Miss Daffney herself came into the office, only we didn't know she'd come in, on account of the noise.

On the tenth one I turned to Mr. Derringer and said, That's ten.

Then I saw Miss Daffney. She was aghast and mouth-agape.

Just a few more, son, Mr. Derringer said, for good measure.

Before I could tell him Miss Daffney was in the office, he was whacking the chair again and I was howling.

It was disgusting.

Miss Daffney coughed and Mr. Derringer turned and saw her—his beloved.

Miss Daffney didn't speak. She *couldn't*. Mr. Derringer smiled. He was very embarrassed and began swinging the strap around.

I'm punishing the boy, he said.

I understand, Miss Daffney said.

She didn't either. Not altogether anyway.

I'll not have any pupil of this school being impertinent, Mr. Derringer said.

He was madly in love with her and was swinging the strap around and trying to put over a little personality. Miss Daffney, however, just didn't think very much of his punishing the boy by hitting a chair, while the boy howled, the man and the boy together making a mockery of justice and true love. She gave him a very dirty look.

Oh! Mr. Derringer said. You mean about my hitting the chair? We were just rehearsing, weren't we, son?

No, we weren't, I said.

Miss Daffney, infuriated, turned and fled, and Mr. Derringer sat down.

Now look what you've done, he said.

Well, I said, if you're going to have a romance with her, have it, but don't mess me up in it.

Well, Mr. Derringer said, I guess that's that.

He was a very sad man.

All right, he said, go back to your class.

I want you to know I didn't write them poems, I said.

That's got nothing to do with it, Mr. Derringer said.

I thought you might want to know, I said.

It's too late now, he said. She'll never admire me anymore.

Why don't you write a poem to her yourself? I said.

I can't write poems, Mr. Derringer said.

Well, I said, figure it out some way.

When I went back to class, Miss Daffney was very polite. So was I. She knew I knew and she knew if she got funny I'd either ruin the romance or make her marry him, so she was very friendly. In two weeks, school closed and when school opened again Miss Daffney didn't show up.

Either Mr. Derringer didn't write her a poem, or did and it was no good, or he didn't tell her he loved her, or did and she didn't care, or else he proposed to her and she turned him down, because I knew, and got herself transferred to another school so she could get over her broken heart.

Something like that.

1924 Cadillac for Sale

Anytime you think you can go out and pull something over on somebody, like selling them a bad used car, you're kidding yourself because people don't believe lies anymore unless they've got their heart set on having the used car anyway. I used to sell an average of two used cars a week five years ago, but nowadays I'm lucky if I don't sell two a day. People who buy used cars these days would kill anybody who tried to stop them from buying. They just naturally want a used car. I used to try to argue them into believing they *ought* to have a used car, but that was before I found out I was wasting my time. That was before I found out people don't like to be fooled anymore.

All I do now is hang around this used-car lot and wait for people to come around and start asking questions about the jalopies we're showing.

I tell them the truth.

I let them know exactly what they're getting, but it don't seem to stop them any when they've got their hearts set on going for a ride in an automobile. They just naturally insist on making a down payment and driving away. It used to make me feel real proud and smart to sell a used car in the old days, but nowadays I feel a little hurt every time somebody comes up and forces me to sell him one of these out-of-date broken-down heaps. I feel kind of useless and unnecessary, because I know I ain't selling anybody *anything*. I'm just letting the tide of humanity rush where it pleases or must.

They come here by the hundreds every day, men, women, and children, wanting a used car, and all I do is let them have their way. I don't put up any kind of an argument, because it's no use. An old lady who doesn't know how to drive a car wants to buy an old Hupmobile because it's green, so why should I interfere with her wishes? I let her know the truth about the old heap, but she buys it anyway, and the next day I see her going down the street forty-three miles an hour. She's in sports clothes, and the radio's going full blast, with a crooner hollering: "Deep in the heart of me."

My God, it's beautiful and awful.

And then again a small boy, no more than twelve, comes in here with eleven dollars he's saved up, and he wants to know how much is the cheapest car on the lot; and I show him that 1922 Chevrolet we've been offering for fifteen dollars for seven years now, and he hops in, holds the wheel and says he'll go home and get the other four dollars. He comes back with his big brother, who signs the papers for him, and the next thing I know they've got the hood lifted and they're repairing the motor. In my opinion the old heap's got no more chance of moving than a bronze horse in a park; but three hours later something happens, and the whole lot is full of smoke and noise.

It's the old Chevrolet.

By the time the smoke clears I can see them walloping down the street, and I know deep in the heart of me, as the song goes, that either the people of this country are natural-born heroes or that the average used car, for all any of us knows, is part human and will respond to tender and loving care, just as anything else will.

There was a young Filipino came in here last April who'd been doing farm work down around Bakersfield, and he'd saved up a small amount of money which, he said, I wish to purchase a sports model Packard touring car with. Well, I had that great big battleship of a Packard that had been abandoned in the middle of the desert just south of Pixley about seven years ago, and I didn't want to see the boy gypped, so I told him I didn't have a sports model Packard touring car except one old one that had something fundamentally wrong with the motor and wouldn't run.

You wouldn't be interested in that car, I said.

I would appreciate it very much if you would allow me to look at it, the Filipino said.

His name was Vernon. I'm telling you this because I remember how amazed I was when he signed the papers. Vernon Roxas. The other boys who sat in the car with him when he drove out of the lot had names that were even worse. One of the boys was called Thorpe; another was named Scott, and another Avery. My God, them ain't names you ever see attached to people, native or alien, and me hearing them little men calling each other names like that made me stop in my tracks and wonder what the world was coming to. I mean I felt awful proud of them young citizens. I like people just so they're sensible and honest and sincere, and I like Filipinos as much as I like any other kind of people. I was just profoundly impressed by their superb adaptability. Them boys had not only adjusted themselves to our world: they'd fitted themselves out in the best style of our clothes, and they'd taken over our most impressive names. I felt awful proud of that condition in America among the boys from the Island.

Of course I was a little worried about their wanting that old Packard.

I showed the car to this boy Vernon Roxas, and he began crawling all over the car, trying out everything but the motor.

What is the price? he said.

Well, there was no price. I'd never bothered to give it a price because I was satisfied to have it in the lot as a sort of decoy, just to take space. I figured I'd do the boy a favor and name a big price so he wouldn't buy it.

Well, I said, it's pretty expensive. That'll run you about $75.

You mean $75 dollars is the first payment? the boy asked.

Well, right there I guess I could have swindled him, and for a moment I was tempted to do it; but I just couldn't go through with the idea.

No, I said; $75 is the total cost.

I'll take it, the boy said.

He brought all kinds of money from his pockets, and we counted. He had a little over $75. I drew up the papers, and he signed. He said he would come back later that afternoon with several of his friends. He'd take the car then.

He came back in two hours with eleven well-dressed Filipinos named Thorpe, Scott, Avery, and other names like that. Each of them was carrying a satchel containing tools and other stuff. Well, they took off their coats and rolled up their sleeves and went to work. One of them started working on the motor, and the others started working on other parts of the car. In less than two hours they had that old warship looking like the car the Governor rides around in when there's a parade. And they had smoke coming out of it too.

I mean they'd fought their battle and won.

I stood in the lot with my mouth open, because never before in my life had I seen such beautiful cooperation and strategy. They just naturally fell on that pile of junk and tightened and cleaned and greased and oiled until it looked like a five-thousand-dollar job. Then they all got into the car and slowly drove out of the lot with the motor barely making any sound at all, like the motor of a car just out of the factory.

I couldn't believe my eyes. Or my ears, either.

I walked beside the boy at the wheel, Vernon Roxas, while the car moved out of the lot.

Vernon, I said, you boys have just taught me the greatest lesson any man can learn.

It is our opinion, Vernon said, that this Packard will travel fifty thousand miles before its usefulness is exhausted.

Well, I said, I don't doubt it in the least. I'm more or less convinced that it will keep moving as long as you boys want it to.

And don't ever think it's the car. Don't ever think it's machinery. It's people. It's America, the awful energy of the people. It's not machinery, it's faith in yourself. Them boys from the Island went to work and changed that worthless heap of junk into a beautiful and powerful automobile with a motor that hummed.

When they drove out of this lot in that magnificent Packard my heart cheered this great country. People with no money having the polite impudence to want class and get it at no expense and to insist on getting it no matter how run-down and useless it might seem at first glance.

I don't *sell* used cars anymore.

I just stand around in this lot and admire the will of the people, men, women, and children, as they take over a bankrupt and exhausted piece of machinery and breathe new and joyous life into it. I just stay here and admire this great and crazy race of adventure-loving people who can't be stopped by truth or expense. I just watch them throw themselves into a cause and come out with a roaring motor that five minutes ago was a piece of dead and rusted junk.

You're the first man who's come to this lot in six months and not *forced* me to sell him a car. I want to shake your hand. Like yourself I'm an honest man, and I believe as you do that every car in this lot is worthless, useless, and incapable of moving. I believe as you do that anybody who buys one of these cars is a fool and ought to have his head examined. It's my job to let the people have what they want, but I believe as you do that the most they can find here is junk, so naturally I admire somebody who agrees with me. This old 1924 Cadillac you've been looking at, in my opinion, isn't worth five cents, but we're asking sixty dollars for it. I don't think you're the type of man who could bring this car to life; and I wouldn't care to see you try, because if you failed I'd feel unhappy and maybe lose my faith in people.

But if you *want* to give it a try after all I've told you, well, that's your affair. I won't try to stop you. I'm telling you in all sincerity that this car is no good, but if you think you can fall on it like the others who buy cars here every day, and make it go, why go ahead. Nothing can amaze me anymore, and if you've got your heart set on driving a Cadillac, well, here's a Cadillac, and good luck to you.

The First Day of Summer

The first day of summer was cold, foggy, damp, dark, and like a day of winter. He had had no idea it was the first day of summer until the neighbor boy, Jimmy Barcos, now thirteen, told him. The boy was in the street, as usual, this time with an old tennis ball he was throwing against the steps of his house and catching. Sometimes the boy was there with a bat, or with a *Western Story* magazine, or one skate which was usually one that he couldn't get on his left foot, or a borrowed bicycle. He seemed to be in the street every time the young man left the house to go to the store for a package of cigarettes, or to mail a letter, or to go for a walk. The boy greeted him every time.

Hi-ya, he said. Here it is summer again.

Summer? he thought. Where?

Summer? he said to the boy. Where?

Right here, the boy said. Everywhere else too, I guess. Today's the first day of summer. Today's June twenty-one.

This is a hell of a first day of a hell of a summer, the young man said.

School's out, anyway, the boy said.

That's a good way to know it's summer, the young man said. Don't you like school?

No, the boy said. He made the sound of the Bronx bird.

Nuts to school, he said.

The boy tossed the ball to the young man who caught it and began taking turns with the boy, throwing the ball against the steps and catching it.

Joe, the boy said, did you really go to Europe that time? Remember? When I came up and asked you about it?

Sure, the young man said. I went to Europe.

Did you meet any interesting people anywhere? the boy said.

There aren't any dull people anywhere, the young man said.

I don't mean like that, the boy said. I mean important people. Did you meet anybody big?

I met a few, the young man said. They were supposed to be big, but they weren't. They were small.

Did you meet any writers? the boy said.

The boy had heard that the young man was a writer and he had seen a number of photographs of him in the local papers and in a number of the national magazines, but even so he didn't believe the young man was a writer. The young man lived next door.

Sure, the young man said. I met some writers.

Who? the boy said. Did you meet Zane Grey?

No, the young man said. I missed Zane Grey. He wasn't in Europe at the time. I met a writer named Edmund Wilson.

Who's he? the boy said.

He's a little guy who's supposed to be a good writer, the young man said. He's just a little guy who knows how to look athletic in what he writes. He's an expert at bluffing.

Is that the way a writer is? the boy said.

That's the way I found this one, the young man said. That's the way I found him in Moscow. He thought a Russian factory worker who spoke a little English because he had lived in Detroit ten years was a spy. He wrote about that in one of his little books. He thought it was dangerous for me to talk to the Russian worker. I think he thinks everything is dangerous. Even if the worker had been a spy I would have talked to him that way and told him I thought a lot of things in Russia were lousy because that's what I thought.

Was he a spy? the boy said.

Who? the young man said.

The Russian worker, the boy said.

No, the young man said. He was no more a spy than you are. This American writer only thought it would be dramatic to imagine he had saved me from a Secret Service man. That Russian was a guy who'd lived in Detroit once and wanted to talk to an American. He was just a guy who'd grown homesick in Russia for America.

Maybe he was a spy, the boy suggested.

Well, the young man said, maybe he was. If he was, he was still a guy who was homesick for Detroit. Even if he was a spy it wouldn't have made any difference to me. Maybe I'm a Secret Service man myself. Maybe I'm collecting secret information all the time. Part of the secret information I've gathered so far is that writers are dopes.

Did you have any fun over there in Russia? the boy said.

That's *all* I had, the young man said. I met a lot of unknown people who deserved to be known. I took part in considerable secret singing, talking, laughing, and mischief.

What kind of mischief? the boy said.

Counter-revolutionary, the young man said. I met a young Georgian on the train to Tiflis who agreed with me that half of everything everywhere, including Russia, is phony. We enjoyed secret laughter all the way to Tiflis.

The young man and the boy threw the ball against the steps and caught it and then the boy caught the ball and held it.

Are you still writing stories? he said.

The young man lighted a cigarette.

Oh yes, he said. I'm writing one all the time. I'm going to write a new one this afternoon.

What about? the boy said.

Well, the young man said, on the face of it it will be about you and me, but actually it will be about everything.

Don't you ever write a *Western* story? the boy said.

The boy asked this question every time they talked a moment or two. It was because he was a reader of Zane Grey, Harold Bell Wright, and the others who write what are known as *Western* stories.

All my stories are Western, the young man said. Eastern too. Also Southern. Also Northern.

The writer made the sound of the Bronx bird.

My God, he said. All of them. The South. The North. The East. The West. The proletarians. The intellectuals. The whole lousy mob of them.

The boy threw the ball against the steps, it bounced back high, almost out of the boy's reach; he leaped and caught it.

Nuts, the boy said.

That's right, the young man said. Nuts to all of them.

He began moving on down the street.

So long, the boy said.

So long, the young man said.

When the young man was at the corner the boy laughed very loudly and shouted:

Anyhow, it's the first day of summer.

That's something, the young man said.

Of Love and Time

Everything dies, that's all you can know; not anything is out of dying; nothing is free of it; so the boys sit down and write stories; they go along slow and easy and let it be so, everything dying all the time; they take a good attitude and write about somebody coming into a room somewhere and meeting some people and doing something or other; anything at all; anybody at all; they give themselves all the breaks and don't remind you that everything dies; they don't tell you it's more than half dead before it begins; maybe they don't know; that's why I'm going to the trouble.

I've got to tell you nothing is out of dying, no matter what, because I know and pleasing or unpleasing I've got to tell you that nothing endures or was intended to. The making did not provide for the enduring of the things we believe endure. So the boys sit down and let you have a little corner that's glossy and bright for a moment, with the death in it not visible. They go to the trouble to do that because in the long run it's no different from anything else; all that happens is that after everything a man is alone again and knows. He knew from the beginning and he's always known but after everything all of a sudden he knows again and lights a cigarette.

Nothing is worse than the way a man dies in the woman he loves, and the death of the woman who loves him in himself, the way it comes about, each of them suddenly knowing a funeral is going on while they talk the same as ever and all the rest of it and yet know they are at the funeral of themselves; they are burying the dead although each of them is very much alive; that is the awfulest of the kinds of dying there is. That is awful because each of them does not want to die in the other and be alone again and then suddenly it's so and each of them knows it's so and everything they say and do is full of what they know. He tells her she's lovely and means it. She is lovely, she is lovely as no man ever knew her to be, lovely as a flower close to the eye, and yet when he says so, himself in her is dead and his face does not brighten with her loveliness, it is the face of a dead man, and herself in him is dead as he in her is, and then they go away, staying close, talking, reaching out to each other, and this can go on for as long as the years left to their lives. It can go on almost forever, even before each of them is truly dead, almost before a hundred years have gone by and the people of the world have all changed, except she and he, almost before that night is half over, before he closes the door behind him and tries to know and then knows, knowing again, having always known, and says, Everything dies. This is all I know.

It can go on after he has been away from her a month, after he has been away from her a year. After he has been to others, it can go on, and a man can remember over and over again that she was where he came to life, she was where he lived, and he can laugh with others, talk with them, be with them, and always know that everything dies, except *that*, everything dies except that which died. He knows everything he shall ever know shall die while he lives except that which died, and that shall die only when he himself is truly dead everywhere, and maybe not even then, maybe even then he will go about everywhere and regret, maybe even then he will still know that it all dies and not believe.

That is the part of it that gives a man all the things he has: his humor, his kindliness, his warmth: that knowing that the brightest, finest, loveliest, strongest, gayest, warmest, and the best ends the same as all other things.

Piano

I get excited every time I see a piano, Ben said.

Is that so? Emma said. Why?

I don't know, Ben said. Do you mind if we go into this store and try the little one in the corner?

Can you play? Emma said.

If you call what I do playing, Ben said.

What do you do?

You'll see, Ben said.

They went into the store, to the small piano in the corner. Emma noticed him smiling and wondered if she'd ever know anything about him. She'd go along for a while thinking she knew him and then all of a sudden she'd know she didn't. He stood over the piano, looking down at it. What she imagined was that he had probably heard good piano playing and loved that kind of music and every time he saw a keyboard and the shape of a piano he remembered the music and imagined he had something to do with it.

Can you play? she said.

Ben looked around. The clerks seemed to be busy.

I can't play, Ben said.

She saw his hands go quietly to the white and black keys, like a real pianist's, and it seemed very unusual because of what she felt when that happened. She felt that he was someone who would be a long time finding out about himself, and someone somebody else would be much longer finding out about. He should be somebody who could play a piano.

Ben made a few quiet chords. Nobody came over to try to sell him anything, so, still standing, he began to do what he'd told her wasn't playing.

Well, all she knew was that it was wonderful.

He played half a minute only. Then he looked at her and said, It sounds good.

I think it's wonderful, Emma said.

I don't mean what *I* did, Ben said. I mean the piano. I mean the piano itself. It has a fine tone, especially for a little piano.

A middle-aged clerk came over and said, How do you do?

Hello, Ben said. This is a swell one.

It's a very popular instrument, the clerk said. Especially fine for apartments. We sell a good many of them.

How much is it? Ben said.

Two hundred forty-nine fifty, the clerk said. You can have terms, of course.

Where do they make them? Ben said.

I'm not sure, the clerk said. In Philadelphia, I think. I can find out.

Don't bother, Ben said. Do you play?

No, I don't, the clerk said.

He noticed Ben wanting to try it out some more.

Go ahead, he said. Try it some more.

I don't play, Ben said.

I heard you, the clerk said.

That's not playing, Ben said. I can't read a note.

Sounded good to me, the clerk said.

Me, too, Emma said. How much is the first payment?

Oh, the clerk said. Forty or fifty dollars. Go ahead, he said, I'd like to hear you play some more.

If this was the right kind of room, Ben said, I could sit down at the piano for hours.

Play some more, the clerk said. Nobody'll mind.

The clerk pushed up the bench and Ben sat down and began to do what he said wasn't playing. He fooled around fifteen or twenty seconds and then found something like a melody and stayed with it two minutes. Before he was through the music became quiet and sorrowful and Ben himself became more and more pleased with the piano. While he was letting the melody grow, he talked to the clerk about the piano. Then he stopped playing and stood up.

Thanks, he said. Wish I could buy it.

Don't mention it, the clerk said.

Ben and Emma walked out of the store. In the street Emma said, I didn't know about that, Ben.

About what? Ben said.

About you.

What about me?

Being that way, Emma said.

This is my lunch hour, Ben said. In the evening is when I like to think of having a piano.

They went into a little restaurant and sat at the counter and ordered sandwiches and coffee.

Where did you learn to play? Emma said.

I've never learned, Ben said. Any place I find a piano, I try it out. I've been doing that ever since I was a kid. Not having money does that.

He looked at her and smiled. He smiled the way he did when he stood over the piano looking down at the keyboard. Emma felt very flattered.

Never having money, Ben said, keeps a man away from lots of things he figures he ought to have by rights.

I guess it does, Emma said.

In a way, Ben said, it's a good thing, and then again it's not so good. In fact, it's terrible.

He looked at her again, the same way, and she smiled back at him the way he was smiling at her.

She understood. It was like the piano. He could stay near it for hours. She felt very flattered.

They left the restaurant and walked two blocks to The Emporium, where she worked.

Well, so long, he said.

So long, Ben, Emma said.

He went on down the street and she went on into the store. Somehow or other she knew he'd get a piano someday, and everything else, too.

The Job

Felix came into the O.K. Lunch on Kearney Street where I was having a hamburger and a cup of coffee and said, Guess what happened, Fritz? I got a job.

I nearly choked.

The waitress came running with a glass of water and Felix slapped my back.

He was humming *Les Preludes*, the part where Liszt really got going.

Are you all right? the waitress said.

Thanks, I said.

I swallowed some water.

I'm fine.

What happened? the waitress said.

He says he got a job, I said.

Felix was going to town on *Les Preludes.* He was tickled to death.

The waitress, who was a large flabby-armed German girl with eyes that were barely open, looked at Felix and listened to him humming.

What is he? she said. A singer?

A sad-looking little Greek gambler came into the place and sat down and the waitress hurried away to take his order.

You're kidding, I said to Felix.

He was playing the trombone now: "My Ohio Home."

I want to wake up in the morning, he sang, and the little Greek gambler turned to look and said something to himself.

Sit down and shut up, I said.

Felix sat down and began to drum on the counter with a knife and fork.

Where'd you get a job? I said.

Some lousy little building on Geary Street, he said.

What kind of a job? I said.

The waitress came back and began looking at Felix all over again. She just couldn't figure him out. She just couldn't figure out anybody human being so happy.

Is he a singer? she said.

Tell her, Felix said. Go ahead, Fritz. Tell her.

Well, I said, I don't want to shock you or anything, but this young man is a composer of music.

I thought it would be nice to please the waitress.

What the hell, Felix said. *Tell* her. Don't be conservative.

Well, I said, this young Jew is probably the greatest composer of music in America.

Jesus, Felix said, is that the best you can do for a pal? Listen, he said to the waitress. Listen, sister, he said. My name is Isadore Schwartz. That don't mean anything. All right. I was born in the Bronx nineteen years ago. That don't mean anything either. O.K. My father was a pushcart peddler from Vienna. That don't mean anything either. O.K. He died when I was five years old. That don't mean anything either. O.K. My mother died when I was two years old. O.K. I had two older brothers and an older sister. My sister committed suicide when she was seventeen and I was seven. One of my brothers is in Sing Sing. O.K.?

Take it easy, I said.

The waitress was getting pretty scared. The short-order cook was listening carefully, and the Greek gambler was listening too.

Wait a minute, Felix said. I don't get a chance every day to tell people who I am. I want this girl to know.

There was a piano in the Jewish orphanage, he said to the girl.

I finished the hamburger and swallowed all the coffee in the cup and lighted a cigarette.

I was playing Chopin when I was seven, Felix said to the girl. He was happier than he'd been in months.

He began to hum a little Chopin.

I have composed three symphonies, two operas, four ballets, seven concertos, eleven tone poems, and forty-six songs, he said.

That's fine, I said. Let's get going.

The waitress was almost trembling.

Isadore Schwartz, Felix said to the girl. We walked up to the cash register. The Greek gambler's eyes were almost popping out of his head. He was scared too.

Isadore Schwartz, Felix said to the Greek, and shook his hand vigorously.

I dropped a dime and a nickel on the counter beside the cash register, stuck a toothpick in my mouth, and we walked out.

In the street I had to smile about him.

Wow, Felix said.

What did you want to go and tell that poor girl all them lies for? I said.

What lies? Felix said.

What did you want to go and shout at that poor innocent girl for?

Who shouted? You told her I was a composer, didn't you?

Some day, I said, some sensitive person is going to get so awful excited while you're telling lies about yourself that he's going to bust loose and kill you.

What the hell, Felix said. I'm happy. Can't I have a little fun?

Is that your idea of having fun?

I like music.

Lots of people like music, I said.

I *could* be a great composer, Felix said. If I could *write* music, I could be a great composer. I wasn't lying *much*.

We walked down Kearney to Market, and then up Market to Eddy, and then up Eddy to the poolroom. There were chairs in the poolroom. It was a cool dark place. It was a pleasant place to be. It was only a small place and we knew the night floor man. He was a nervous man of fifty who had a very kind heart. He used to leave the back door open for us and after the place closed we used to go in through the back door and sleep on the pool tables. We used to make pillows out of crumpled newspapers and put our coats over the paper. It wasn't bad. We had been sleeping in the poolroom five nights. In the morning we used to go out the back door before the poolroom opened, so nobody would know we had been sleeping on the pool tables. We used to walk around town till around eleven or eleven-thirty and then we used to go back and take a seat and stay there most of the day and night. We used to earn coffee money helping the day floor man any time he needed somebody to give him a hand. But our best friend was the night floor man.

We went into the poolroom and sat down.

What kind of a job? I said.

Elevator, Felix said.

What do you mean, *elevator?*

I'm supposed to run it.

Do you know how to run an elevator?

It's an old-style elevator. It's an old-style building.

How much are you going to get?

Eight dollars.

Eight dollars a *what?* A day, a week, a month, a year, or what? A week.

It's an old-style salary, too, I said. But it's better than nothing.

I'm an old-style Jew, Felix said. Wahoo. Am I happy?

Do you get Saturday afternoons off?

No.

Sundays?

I don't think so.

How the hell did you do it?

I don't know, he said. I was walking down Geary Street and I saw this sign in the doorway of this little building: *Elevator Boy Wanted.* So I went in and rang the elevator bell and after a while the little old-fashioned elevator came down and an old man opened the old-fashioned door and I told him I wanted to apply for the job.

That's great, I said.

I start working Monday, he said. Today's Saturday.

He went back to the old mood of triumph in *Les Preludes.*

Well, I said, I guess I'll be going along now.

What the hell you talking about? he said.

I don't like Frisco, I said. It was all right when I had money and was gambling and winning. It was all right six months ago. I guess I want to try Seattle for a while. I think maybe my luck will pick up again if I go to a new city.

You ain't got a dime, Felix said. Next Saturday I'll have eight dollars *cash.* You can do plenty with eight dollars.

I ain't lucky anymore in this town, I said. I don't want to take your money.

It ain't my money, he said. I owe you plenty. You kept me going six months, didn't you?

You brought me a lot of luck.

Sure. I brought you so much luck you ain't got a dime to your name now.

That was my own fault.

Your own fault, my eye, Felix said. You kept me going six months. I got a job now and you can do plenty with eight dollars next Saturday.

My luck's no good anymore in this town.

What the hell am I going to do with them lousy eight dollars next Saturday?

Well, I said, you *could* do plenty. You could rent a room with a bed in it and sleep in a bed for a change and you could eat a few decent meals for a change and maybe buy a new shirt and maybe after a week or so a new pair of shoes.

You kept me going six months, Felix said. I don't want that lousy money. How the hell are you going to get to Seattle without any money?

I can get along.

I don't want the lousy money.

Listen, I said. I want you to get some sense in your head. Jobs are not easy to get.

You're a hell of a brother, Felix said.

I want you to keep that job, I said. I want you to get a room with a bed in it and I want you to get some decent meals.

All right.

We walked together to the street.

I'll be back here in a couple of months.

All right.

Take it easy.

O.K.

He stood in the doorway of the poolroom while I walked down the street. I wouldn't let myself turn around, but I knew he was standing there and I kept saying, All the luck in the world, kid, you'll need it.

At the Chop Suey Joint on Larkin Street at Two-Thirty in the Morning

This was a place that didn't do a nickel's worth of business till after ten o'clock at night; mostly low-lifes of the region; five not-very-Chinese-looking Chinese, that is, not truly Chinese any longer, kind of spoiled after too many years in that neighborhood, a little too close to American tragedy and scum and vulgarity; that is, they'd lost the East in themselves, they'd become Western, kind of snappy in a way, kind of efficient, talkative, which is not the true Chinese way. In the Chinese restaurants in Chinatown of Frisco, where the Chinese are truly Chi-

nese, the waiters aren't that way, they're quiet, self-respecting, unhurried, partly deaf, and yet at the same time, not at all offensive, they don't
make you dislike them, like the boys in this joint do, who, to all
appearances, are the friendliest souls in the world. It just doesn't seem to
work, some reason or other.

Anyhow, Terranova and I had just walked a friend home, after a night
of dull conversationally brilliant people who had griped Terranova, and
much drinking, and now he was hungry, so when he saw the Chop Suey
sign he thought he'd like some tomato beef which when cooked right is
something good to eat.

It was half past two in the morning and when we got to the door we
saw the good-looking young man and the smart Chinese waiter making
a commotion. You could just tell trouble was going on, so Terranova,
who was feeling disgusted on account of the lousy conversation all
evening, went in and we took the table next to the young man's.

Look at the poor guy, Terranova said. He's so lonely he's got to make
trouble about the price of something he ate in a joint like this.

The Chinese waiter was growing severe, in a sort of American bouncer
way, and he said, You pay thirty-five cents or I call police.

The young man got more indignant and said, Go ahead, call the
police.

He wants to see them, Terranova said. He wants *them* to see *him*. It's all
on account of loneliness. Who wants to argue about thirty-five cents?
Ten to one he's got more money than you and me put together.

How do you know? I said.

You're dumber than the people you introduced me to tonight, Terranova said. He's lonely, can't you see? It's not the money. He wants
them to make a fuss over him. Look how pretty he is.

I looked, and sure enough he was pretty. He was soft all over and
indignant like a woman with trouble going on in her.

The Chinese waiter came close to grabbing the young man by the neck
and the young man kind of challenged him to do it, but he didn't after
all.

You pay, he said, or I call police.

I won't pay, the young man said.

So the Chinese waiter stepped out to the sidewalk and in less than two
minutes two big cops came in, kind of businesslike. They had been in the
beer joint next door. They were like the Chinese too, kind of spoiled by
the neighborhood, easy work, and lots of money from the joints.

They were big, though, and that was what counted.

All right, the biggest one said to the young man, you ate, so pay or I'll
run you in.

Well, said the young man, you can see for yourself from these dishes
on the table that I didn't have thirty-five cents' worth.

The big cop looked over at his friend and smiled and the other one smiled back, then made one of them faces that means, Well, shut my mouth, look what we've got here.

Oh, the big cop said. Oh, I see. You didn't have thirty-five cents' worth. Well, what is thirty-five cents' worth? Come on, give this young Chinese boy his thirty-five cents and take a walk.

Well, it isn't fair, the young man said.

Come on, *pay*, the cop said. Come on. Come on, he said like a comedian.

He didn't touch the young man and for a moment the young man waited.

Then he got up and brought some currency from his pocket.

Terranova hit my arm and said, See? I win.

He gave the Chinese waiter a five-dollar bill, and the cop said, That's a good boy.

The two of them went back to the kitchen to eat something free.

The Chinese waiter came back in a moment with the change. All of it was silver, the way it is in Frisco always. The young man put the money in his pocket, but dropped a half dollar.

The Chinese waiter picked it up and offered it to him.

Keep it, the young man said.

It wasn't easy to figure out why. The Chinese waiter couldn't figure it out either, and the young man went away. The waiter giggled and went back to the kitchen and then the cops roared with laughter.

A Flash of the Flashlight and the World-Shaking Question: "Joe?"

Next to having a revolver (which of course you could never get; which you would never really *want* to have; which, nevertheless, it was always pleasant to imagine you wanted more than anything else in the world), having a flashlight was a wonderful thing and marked you as a boy of the world; modern, and aware of all the latest scientific developments, the progress of industry; and, much more important, a hero: eleven years old and not afraid of darkness, not afraid of the world, the strange people who peopled it, the strange shadows they made, or anything else strange. You were a boy with a flashlight. That meant that you went around in the darkness, flashing light upon dangerous and dark things.

You could never have a revolver or a horse. You might make a crazy mistake with a revolver and kill your cousin Joe instead of Mr. Davis, the principal. You might not be accurate with the thing and you might shoot off somebody's nose. Somebody real nice; somebody you liked, standing

on the corner, at high noon, with his hand over where his nose used to
be, and your heart full of regret, and your mouth trying to say, Honest,
Mr. Wheeler, I didn't mean to shoot your nose off. I was shooting at the
chicken hawk flying over the roof of the Republican Building. I'm sorry,
Mr. Wheeler. I apologize.

Or you might get bawled up, trying to take a quick second shot at a
circling chicken hawk, turn quickly, and shoot off your own nose.

No good. Too dangerous. It was the same with a horse too. It would be
all right if the horse had some sense and knew how to behave, but it
didn't; have sense or know how to behave. All it did was want to go
somewhere where you *didn't* want to go, so that after six or seven years
you had no private life to speak of, and were living the life of a horse,
getting to sound like one, and look like one.

No revolvers and no horse. No shooting off anybody's nose, and no
growing up with the manners of a horse.

A flashlight. That was another story. Pure light at night; controlled
and sent where you pleased. Press the button and flash: light. Lift your
thumb off the button and the light went out.

Marvelous. Great age. Beautiful world.

Your cousin Joe's real name was Hovsep, but this was America.
Hovsep? What did they know about that? They thought it sounded
funny. Not Hovsep; Joe. A natural change. Hovsep is Joseph in Armenian; you shorten Joseph and it becomes Joe. Hovsep. Put a J where the
H is; put a small h after the p and you get Jovseph. Then take out the v,
and you get Joseph. Throw away half of that and you get Joe. Your
cousin—no matter how you spell it, what you do to it, what it stands for
in Armenian, or what it sounds like in American. He's the same kid. Like
yourself eleven years old, only funnier. A month and a half younger too.
Which means that—well, you were first. You were ahead of him. You
arrived a whole month and a half before he did. Forty-five days or so you
were in the world breathing before he came in, too. Great age. Beautiful
world. Hovsep in Armenian; in American Joe. Great kid. Funny as they
came.

Play? Like a wild Indian. Run? Like a deer. Laugh? Like nobody else in
the world. Your best pal; Joe. Joe Hagopian. Hagopian in Armenian—
well, you couldn't do anything with that. You could take the H away and
put an L or some other letter in its place, but what good would it do you.
You'd have Lagopian, which was no good at all. Nobody called anybody
by his last name anyway, except Mr. Davis when he was sore. So it was
just plain Joe Hagopian.

Afraid of the dark? Joe wasn't afraid of anything. When he got sick
with the flu even, he didn't think it was anything. I got a headache, he
said; I'll be out to play tomorrow. So you went in and asked his mother
how he was and she said, The doctor's with him; and then you got real

scared. You knew it; you just knew it. Poor Joe. Poor Hovsep Hagopian; better known as Joe. Poor Joe was going to die.

You went out to the street, out into the darkness of November, and began to walk home, and by God you were sore. You wished you had that revolver and that horse, so you could jump on the horse and go galloping over the cold winter streets to where the doctors were, and draw the revolver and from the street, on the horse in front of the house they were in, holler out to them, Come on out here, you cheaters. And after they came out, run them in front of the horse and holler, You're going to keep Joe from dying or I'm going to know the reason why. And after you herded all eighteen of them into the house where Joe was sick, turn the horse around and go for the preachers, and do the same, hollering at them: Come on out here, you liars. What about Joe? Never mind all that talk about heaven, and get over to Joe's house and start praying, and see that you make it good, you guys who live forever and whine about heaven all the time, while kids like Joe, eleven years old, die of flu.

Even when the big flu epidemic had everybody dying like flies, Joe wasn't scared. It's nothing, he said; I just feel weak; I'd come out and play but Ma won't let me. And you knew it; you knew he was dying; you knew he'd be dead in no time, and you couldn't do anything about it. All you had was the cockeyed flashlight. You went down the dark street, thinking it over, thinking everything over, and all of a sudden you yourself were the eighteen doctors in the room, and boy what you knew about saving a life; boy how you eighteen doctors went to work and started making arrangements for that boy to stay in the world a while longer; and then you were the troop of preachers, the Catholic priests, the Baptist ministers, the Presbyterian preachers, the old ones and the young ones, and you all went into the house, got on your knees, and began to pray; and boy how you prayed; six of you prayed in Armenian; four of you in bad English; and one of you in Russian. (That was that Russian priest of the Russian Catholic Church across the tracks that you once got chased by for letting them crazy Russian kids convince you that what you were hollering was, Hello, Father; how are you? when actually it was cussing of some kind.)

It was terrible. The whole thing was a nightmare. Joe had no business being sick with the cockeyed flu and if he died—well, by God, you'd get even with him. You'd get even with everybody else too. If Joe dies, you said on the way home, you'll get yours, you cheaters and liars. It was a clear cold night and it was the greatest time in the world to be alive and eleven years old, with the dozens of years ahead, all the wonderful years of adventure coming, and you didn't want any cousin named Hovsep Hagopian to be dying, that's all. You just didn't care to have any cockeyed thing like that happen, so get that straight, you guys.

You were too busy being sore about Joe to remember how scared you were of the dark, and then all of a sudden you remembered: and for a minute you were real scared, and then you said, Yeah? Well, who are you? You can't scare me. And you pressed your thumb down on the button and the light went on, shooting forward; then you flashed the light all around; down to the ground; up into the branches of the trees; left and right; north and south. And then suddenly, as you walked, it was all over, and Joe was dead, and you were walking down the street all alone, and the years were going by at the rate of two a minute, and it was a night in November again many years later, and you were still sore and you still couldn't believe it. You flashed the light to the trunk of a tree and said, Joe? but nobody was there; and a moment later you turned the light to the dark steps of a porch, thinking he might be sitting there, smiling, and you said, Joe? but he wasn't there either. So you went home and swore at them all until you fell asleep.

The next day you couldn't wait to run over to Joe's during lunch hour. Was Joe dead, or alive? When the noon bell rang, you jumped out of your desk, got to the door first, got out of the building first, and began running up L Street, then down San Benito Avenue, until you got real tired and couldn't run anymore. Then you got scared about Joe. *Real* scared. Please, you said. Please don't let my cousin Joe die. Do you hear me? You got out the crazy flashlight and turned it on, but the daylight was brighter than the light of the flashlight, and you could see everything, so what good was a flashlight now? You kept hurrying and flashing the light at everything you passed, as if it were night, as if Joe was in the last night of life, and you were looking for him, and you kept asking the world-shaking question: Joe? The tree: Joe? Is he alive? The face of the boy in the billboard advertisement: Joe? Oh Joe. Are you alive, Joe? Sky, is he alive? Sun, is Joe alive? Street, is my cousin Joe alive? World, is Hovsep Hagopian (Joe to you) alive?

At last you got to the house and stood on the sidewalk and looked at it, asking, Joe? Was it a house that had a dead boy in it named Joe? Was it a house full of the amazed, frantic, sorrowing mothers and fathers, grandmothers and grandfathers, great grandmothers and great grandfathers of Joe Hagopian, the eleven-year-old American whose family arrived seventeen years ago from Bitlis? Was it a tribe? Did the house contain the forms of the living and dead of a tribe just cheated of its son?

Breathing hard, you cracked the whip over the heads of the preachers and said, Come on now, you guys, get going with them prayers; pray hard now, you preachers.

Then you went to the back door, quietly on into the kitchen, and saw his mother, and oh boy you knew, you knew they'd prayed hard, you knew the doctors had given Joe everything they had, you knew the light from the cockeyed flashlight had found his heart in the darkness of the

November night, and in the brightness of the November day, and you knew he was alive. You knew he would go on being alive all the years that roared by your ears the night before. You knew the dead grandmothers and grandfathers were all smiling, and you sat down at the table and didn't say anything; you just looked up at Joe's mother and smiled and watched her fill a dish with lamb and vegetables for you, and sitting on the horse you said quietly to the eighteen doctors, Look, boys, I'm throwing away the revolver; I don't want it. And then to the preachers you said, Look, boys. I'm throwing away the whip. And here you: horse. I'll take off that heavy saddle, and I'll take that cockeyed bit out of your mouth. See? Now you're free. Go ahead, run up into the hills where you belong; this is no life for a horse. Get up there into the hills and really do some healthy running for yourself.

He's sleeping, Joe's mother said. He's all right now. He'll be up in a few days. Come back after school. Maybe he'll be awake.

Sure, you said. Here, when he wakes up, give him this flashlight. It's the only thing I've got. Joe's always wanted one. He can flash it in the night at the walls and the ceiling. It's lots of fun.

And then you got up and said, All full; and went walking slowly back to school, with the world wonderful again and full of all sorts of mechanical devices of extraordinary cunning that came in handy for all kinds of beautiful occasions.

The Ride on the Great Highway in the Sky of the Sinking Sun

The way it is now the sun goes down around five-thirty in the afternoon. This afternoon it went down at five thirty-three or five thirty-four. From my house on Carl Street to the ocean it is three miles, maybe four. Anyhow, walking through the park, I cover the distance in about fifty minutes, sometimes less, sometimes more. It all depends. If I walk steadily all the time I make it in about forty-three minutes. If I loaf around along the way it sometimes takes me an hour.

If the gophers are puffing out of the ground as I go by, I always have to stop and watch them because that is a thing I can never get tired of being delighted about: the quiet way the gophers push up the soft moist earth and get ready to eat a little grass. I just stand there and wait to see the face of the gopher. There's something about the gopher puffing the soft earth up that pleases me very much. They are very fearful, though; every time one of them sees me, he disappears into the earth, and then I have to wait two or three minutes before he'll stick his head out to see if I'm still hanging around.

There are other things that break into the timing of my walk to the ocean, through the park. Flowers sometimes; to look at closely and smell. Little odd leaves that I'd never noticed before. The ducks, which I sometimes ignore and sometimes go down to the edge of the lake to really have a time with. I listen to them squawking at one another; quacking; and I watch them as they float on the little lake; sitting on the water and just not caring about anything. Just sitting there at the end of day, and nobody unhappy; the little ducks just sitting there the same as their parents, quiet and at peace with the world, and only occasionally quacking—saying nothing more than, Well, it's all right; it's all fine; it's a beautiful body of water; the people come with stale bread which they don't like, but which we do; the sun comes up every morning; the sky is beautiful; it is all fine. Truly it is all a dream of loveliness. Quack. Quack. Quack.

Then of course there are the little fluffy cottontails. It is pleasant to see three of them nibbling the fresh green shoots of grass; they come out at the end of day. That's when they love to come out and eat. They aren't afraid of automobiles going by, but people on the walk—no; they run and hide, but if you're very quiet, they come out again and stay out, even though you stand only three yards away and watch. They don't mind just so they know you aren't nervous and aren't figuring on killing them, out of nervousness.

I also waste time now and then just looking up at a tree because all of a sudden I see how truly wonderful it is, what a magnificent thing it is. Or I stand and look at a road in the park, the road empty, silent, and going away, as if to some wonderful place, with the day ending; and then quietly a small boy coming down the road on a bicycle, going home and not making a single sound; not whistling or singing or humming; just going along quietly home to supper because day is ending and everything in the world with any sense knows the time has come for stillness.

The sky, and the clouds in the sky, never make me stop because I can always see them; the sky is large and walking along I can always see the sky and the clouds before me. I even hurry, so I can see them over the water, over the great ocean, and then it is truly a thing to stand and look at, with the setting sun putting fire into the clouds while the waves of the ocean come pushing one another onto the land, and then slipping back, and the earth real big, endlessly big, a place of wonderful bigness, a place of great room, great size, great depth and height, far away north, far away south, and far far away west.

I try to work it out so I can get out to the ocean a few minutes before the sun disappears into the water, because that is a thing I can never get tired of watching and feeling wonderful about. I just stand there on the beach and watch the sun go down as if it just couldn't happen any other way. I just stand there and laugh and say things to the world while the sun keeps sinking into the water, and the clouds are in flames. And then the sun is gone, but not the light; for minutes longer the clouds are still on fire, the light of the sun is still in them, and I just stand there and wait and watch the color of the sun's fire in the clouds change, grow dim, until the clouds are black, and then I turn away from the ocean, go over to where the streetcar stops, get on, and ride home to supper, which always tastes wonderful after I have seen the sun go down. No matter what it is, it always tastes wonderful if I've seen the sun go down.

This afternoon, as I say, the sun went down around five thirty-three. This is October the seventeenth. Tomorrow the sun will go down a little earlier, so if I plan to watch it go down I've got to leave a few minutes earlier, or walk faster, or not stop on the way to watch gophers or anything.

Clouds are funny. They are full of all sorts of moods. They are wild or peaceful, crazy or pompous, peaceful or restless, or any number of other things. But they are never uninteresting. They are always fine to look at. And with the sun going down among them, they are whatever the best in you is, or can make them: they are music; mighty, gentle, roaring, generous, smiling music. They are also the players on the stage of the sky which no man can be deprived of watching, if he wishes. All he need do is lift his eyes. They are continents, nations, mountains, meadows, the dream and the dreamer.

This afternoon the clouds were all these things, but another thing too. They were a great highway which began where the sun was sinking and, sloping upward, went far away to the south. It seemed very strange. It was truly a highway from the sun, south; no artist could have painted a highway in the sky more dramatically than the highway which was there this afternoon as the sun was sinking, and afterward. Starting from the sun it swept along beautifully in the sky, with a tremendous lift in it, as if it were a highway to the greatest and only destination.

So of course I got on the highway in my little green roadster, with the top down, and began speeding along the great highway. What a highway; what a view from it; and not another car on the highway to clutter up the way. A whole highway in the sky all to myself. So I drove along for hours and days and weeks and years, and years, and years. And there was no end to the beauty all around to look upon; sky and water and clouds and land; land full of meadows and valleys and hills and rivers and lakes, and wonderful animals.

It was a great ride, but it just couldn't end. The highway kept going forever, so what could I do? The sun was gone; the sky was darkening; so I went to where the streetcar is, and rattled back into the small, tight-packed wilderness that we call the world.

Seven Easy Ways to Make a Million Dollars

Many people have written me confidential letters asking me to tell them seven easy ways to make a million dollars. Nothing could please me more. All my life I have wanted to tell poor people how to get in on the big dough and start living the life of Riley.

The best way to begin earning your million dollars is to rise in the morning and shave. Get right up out of bed, and shave. Care must be taken, when one uses a straight-edge blade, not to cut off the right or left ear because nothing is more dangerous to the prospective millionaire than the absence of one or another of his ears. One spends precious hours explaining to one's wealthy friends how it happened and how one felt at the time and whether or not one can hear just as well with the remaining ear. Also, the appearance of the head becomes odd and to some people irritating. People are used to seeing two ears on every head and when they see only one, it burns them up and they take the situation as a personal affront, being neurotic.

On the other hand if *you yourself* are neurotic and take the loss of an ear as a personal affront, then of course everything is perfectly balanced and you may say to your wealthy friends, Don't think this pleases me (Mr. Rockefeller or Mrs. Whitney, as the case may be). It happens that I too am disgusted.

And then proceed to the matter of oil or horses.

Nine men out of ten will shave without losing an ear, but I wish to furnish information for the exceptional child, or genius, no less than for the ordinary child, or riffraff, and the next step is a cheerful cup of coffee with bread, if it is available. Any kind of coffee will do, provided it is available, and if there is no bread, whatever you do, don't get down in the mouth and blame it on the system, or Capitalism.

Statistics show that nine average men out of ten who want to make a million dollars and go to Paris for a vacation haven't a nickel for carfare, so naturally, unless you are the exception to the rule, you will have to walk to where your wealthy friends are spending their time and money.

Unfortunately, some people, like myself, live away over to hell and gone in San Francisco, while our wealthy friends live across the continent in the East somewhere. Whatever you do don't write a letter to one or another of your wealthy friends because in nine cases out of ten he will not make a prompt remittance of one million dollars and no cents, but will drop your letter into the wastebasket and ask somebody what the hell the world is coming to and why aren't people satisfied with what they've got?

In some cases (but only rarely) your rich friend will turn the matter over to the government (rebel). An automobile will stop at your door.

Three small, elderly men will ask to have a talk with you. These are men from the Department of Public Health. They spend their time trying to determine if somebody is crazy. If such a thing happens, if these three men visit you and begin asking you a lot of questions, don't get alarmed and try to be witty because they have a name for wit and it means you're crazy. Just act dumb and they will go away and try to find out if somebody else is crazy. Then you can have a quiet laugh to yourself because you fooled them all the time.

In eighty-two thousand cases of poor people writing confidential letters to their rich friends, asking for money, only one poor man has turned the matter over to the government when the money did not arrive promptly and asked that Mr. Rockefeller's head be examined. This man didn't get to first base of course, because if there is anything a rich friend doesn't like, it is having his sanity questioned, and invariably the rich man will refuse to speak to the poor man and the poor man will have to go back to his lower-class friends who are always willing to speak to him.

Your face clean, coffee in your belly, you are now in the street moving in the direction of your rich friends, no money in your pocket. Naturally you hitchhike, hop a freight, or walk. It is a long way from Frisco to New York. Take a small book and read when everything seems hopeless, and remember that it is darkest just before dawn.

I have no desire to misrepresent anything involved in the attempt to get hold of a million dollars in a hurry, and I tell you frankly it is no easy thing to do, and at times rather dangerous. Last year a fifty-seven-year-old boy from Lawrence, Kansas, was bitten by a small spider while riding in an empty boxcar, and upon reaching Manhattan, where he was to have put the cards on the table with J. P. Morgan, died of cold and starvation. Three months ago another young man, this time from El Paso, Texas, while running to catch a gondola, slipped and severely bruised his knee and chin, besides spilling a handful of small coins, all of which he succeeded in finding, except three. These things happen and there is nothing you can do about it. If you aren't big enough to take it, stay where you are and try to invent some small item of everyday use, something preferably new, something different, something that might, with proper advertising and financial backing, revolutionize everything.

Personally, I feel that such an invention should retail for not more than fifteen cents, and should be small in size, brightly colored, attractive to the eye, portable, and should either make an agreeable sound when blown into, spin swifter than anything else like it on the market, or completely disappear when thrown any distance at all. Of course a catchy trade name for such an invention is very important. Without overtaxing my imaginative powers I can think of at least one catchy trade name for such an invention: *Joe Stalin's All-Fired Three-Piece Multi-Purpose*

Hey-Hey, after the manner of the once popular and now extinct Yo-Yo, which was nothing more than an odd-shaped brightly colored ball-like piece of wood attached to a piece of good quality twine, three feet in length, which when turned loose immediately returned upon the twine and struck the performer on the chin, delighting children. The man made a neat profit of two million dollars and died in Philadelphia of old age. So why can't you? You may say of course that you are not old enough. That is nonsense. Children, babes in arm, have invented items useful to man and important to civilization. Don't make alibis.

Once you get to the East where your rich friends are killing time and riding around in expensive automobiles, the tempo of your work increases and consequently the possibilities of being killed in the attempt to get your money rise from one in a million to one every five minutes, unless you find a dime and buy a hamburger right away.

I refer again to statistics. These clearly show that nine average hungry men out of ten seldom if ever find an American dime in the course of a whole lifetime, and that if you intend to get a hamburger you'd better figure out some other way.

In short, a million forces will begin to act upon you and try to keep you from sticking to your original plan to join your rich friends, chat with them intelligently, get your money, and take the next boat to Europe. For one thing, you will think of trying to find a job. This tendency is a survival from the old (or conventional) order of life, and if you ever let it get the best of you, you might as well give up. It will get you nowhere, maybe not even across the river to Brooklyn. Nine people out of ten born in Manhattan have never been across the river. If you let the idea bother you enough, the first thing you know you'll be going around to different places asking different people if they haven't some kind of a job, and if the idea grows at all, you will keep this up until some unkind person will break down and hire you at a salary of twelve dollars a week to start.

Let me stress this: Don't look for a job because things are picking up and some thoughtless person is liable to hire you.

This bitter inward struggle of the apprentice is technically known as *The Tragic Stage of Questioning & Answering*. Most apprentices of sixteen years and over furnish their own questions, but not one in a hundred is able to come through with his own answers, consequently Dorothy Dix receives many letters. Heart-Broken From Walla Walla writes her as follows, under date of December 17, 1936: "Sweetheart, I am alone in New York. I want to meet Andrew Mellon and other rich friends, but have no decent clothes. What shall I do?"

It takes from seven to fourteen days for the average apprentice to emerge from *The Tragic Stage of Questioning & Answering*, if he lives; if he doesn't live, he probably never emerges, since no one knows what happens after the body gives up the ghost. My own theory is that when the body gives up the ghost, the ghost gets sore and gives up the body, and then friends have to step in and assume the responsibility and expense of a funeral.

Once you emerge from this *Stage*, however, you are all set. Nothing short of violence can kill you, and your ideas are all intact. The next step is to get into the private homes of your rich friends and electrify them with your personality. This step is technically known as *The Poverty-Stricken Capitalist Hop* and is very popular with all the orchestras in the country, blending, as it does, the best features of the old polka, the waltz, the fox-trot, the tango, the rumba, and the hunger stagger. The dance begins at your door and ends in the parlor of your rich friends where you collapse. Everyone will be delighted to see you and the minute you are revived it is a good idea to start talking about oil or horses or art. Nine average apprentices out of ten will make the mistake of saying, What happened? Where am I? This is no way to begin a gay sophisticated conversation, and I am glad to tell you how to begin such a conversation.

Rising on your elbow from the floor you smile cheerfully and say, Charming weather, isn't it, for December? and then lose consciousness.

No one will be able to misunderstand, and in the morning after breakfast the conversation will naturally proceed to the matter of pocket money, and unless I am badly mistaken Mr. Rockefeller will be delighted to present you with a million dollars. Not at all, he will say. Glad to do it.

So you take your hard-earned money and hurry right over to Europe just in time to see the beginning of a new war, and once again the rich prove their nobility, and one more hungry man of the world has been made happy and useful to society.

Genesis

Never in the history of the world (or after, or before, or at any other time) was there ever a small man named Harkos whose left eye was glass from birth and who had a horse's tail, but there is now. This amazing child of God was able and is still able to be every place in the world and anywhere else at the same time, so that no matter who else happened to be alive, and no matter what year or day or hour of day it happened to be, Harkos was there, probably in the remarkable disguise of somebody else, maybe yourself.

The manner in which this furious young man came to be is a long story, beginning appropriately enough with holy nothingness, pious emptiness and religious silence, in the glorious year zero, day before yesterday.

One melancholy January morning the emptiness of the universe became so vast and uneasy that small fragments of matter, invisible to the naked eye, nervously leapt out of it, leaving the emptiness refreshed, and the silence began to roar with storm: thunder, rain, hail, sleet, and after each of these, in order, pious snow and sleep. This, the snow and sleep, continued for a moment of centuries, during which these small fragments of matter came together, without thought, until finally there was a place somewhere (though God knows where) in which existed a great number of somewhat large bodies of matter. All in darkness. All immobile. And everything everywhere perfect.

Then something went haywire, and nobody knows why, not even me. It was just one of those things. One holy error after another.

Late one evening in December the biggest of these bodies of matter began to glow, making heat and light, and then began to move.

The tremendous heat of this body set in motion each of the other inert bodies of matter and these bodies began to move in vast circles, and have been doing so ever since.

This glowing body of matter has come to be called the sun. Another glowing body of matter has come to be called the moon. The body of matter we ourselves inhabit has come to be called the earth. It is one of the least significant bodies of this place which is everywhere, and if it has any importance at all, this is so because of Harkos, the man with the glass eye and the horse's tail. God's only begotten son.

The heat of the sun became immediately *cause* in all things, no matter what, especially when the heat was combined with the other basic things involved: the pneumatics of space and air, suggesting breathing; the composition of earth, water, and so forth. And the effect of course was nothing less than change, or mortality, or growth, the magnificent beginning of beginning and end, forever and ever, by God.

Substances of every kind began to change, and out of this change came *newness* and what we call hi-de-ho, as in the American song, I can't dance, I got ants in my pants.

One thing was born and grew and died upon another thing dead, and out of the decay of many things dead came new kinds of things alive, so that nowadays you can see some people in cutaway coats and top hats, and others in gas masks. One kind making conversation and the other artificial sound.

The manner in which this furious young man came to be, as I say, is a long story, beginning nowhere and everywhere, with nothing and everything, during no time and every time, and certainly never ending, though millions of him die in a million different ways every year.

One pleasant August afternoon a melancholy molecule was walking aimlessly along a lonely street in a rotted tree twig when suddenly it observed near a brook an electron of such charm that the molecule fell upon the electron in the most immoral manner. There was some half-hearted resistance on the part of the electron, followed by a movement of the two which thoroughly combined the elements of the tragic and the delightful, making love forever after in the world a mood and activity of the profoundest complexity, being at one and the same time good and evil, gay and melancholy, ugly and beautiful, noble and base.

In short, while the impulse of the lonely molecule was altogether of the spirit, or energy, the actual form of the impulse, or act, was somehow only of the flesh, or matter, causing in each of the early lovers a most painful sense of frustration, which in turn caused the beginning of what is today known as articulation, or language, or The Word, from which has emerged, as anyone knows, everything anybody can think of, or consciousness, the beginning of sin and innocence: God and religion and philosophy: time and space and science and statistics: everything you can think of, amen.

Problems of Writing

Every man who wants to write has to find out for himself how to do it; otherwise his work will not be his own. I am speaking technically. The story he tells may very well be his own, but unless he has found out how to write in his own way, the way he writes is apt to be the way any number of other writers write. Which is a thing to try to avoid, and which can be avoided. All of us are pretty much alike in basic things, but each of us is *special* in all things, too. Every man has his own identity, his own understanding, his own temper, or quality, and his own way of expressing himself. The thing to do is to discover that way, after it is discovered, to cultivate it, sharpen it, and take advantage of all its potentialities.

A few things that have been helpful to me may be of help to others, too. I have found that the best source of material is my own experience. *Stay at home for your subject matter.*

I have found that it is undesirable to be literary; to write with words. *Bring the words into being to make your story live—don't use the story to make words.*

Listen to your writing and make sure that it reads and sounds well.

Be brief.

But most important of all, be alert all the time, wherever you go, whoever you see; listen carefully, look carefully, try to notice everything; try to understand everything deeply. And try to keep your writing balanced: that is, remember that everything has its opposite: evil is balanced by good, ugliness by beauty, darkness by light, and so forth and so on.

This is only a hurried note, not an essay, but it may be of some help.

The Empty House

Night was coming on. Slowly gray shadows came down from above and took their places on the walls of the room. The elder brother stood on a chair and turned on the electric light. The globe, bought at Woolworth's, deepened and magnified their shadows.

The younger brother sat, with large, frightened, unseeing eyes, at the bare table, turning the pages of a five-cent magazine with pictures. The elder brother sat opposite him with a book of arithmetic before him, a pencil in his hand. The house was so still, the night so calm, that when the pencil slipped from his hand to the floor it made a racket, and the brothers grasped the bottom of their chairs.

The elder brother picked up the pencil, wondering how it could have made so much noise, and with the movement was encouraged to speak.

"Shouldn't we eat?" he said.

"I'm not hungry."

A long silence followed, growing in terror as the moments passed, and the brothers looked at one another.

Then the younger brother whispered softly so that there would not be too much sound, "Where is Ma?" he said.

The other stared at the shut front door, as if he expected their mother to open it and to step into the house.

"I don't know," he said.

Then, while his eyes were still on the door, he went to it and slid the bolt across. A front window was partly open; he shut it. Next he went to the back door and locked it too.

There were no blinds on the windows of the house. When an automobile turned the corner to pass down the street its lights came flying through the windows into the room, throwing a spotlight on the brothers. Shadows appeared on the walls, racing one after another. They sat stiff and cold, glued to their chairs.

Every now and then the footsteps of a man walking on the sidewalk could be heard, and it seemed to them someone coming to their door. They sank in their chairs until the sound of the footsteps died away. Then the little brother asked, "Who was that?" as if it might have been some monstrous, evil thing.

"I don't know who," the other said. "Some man, I guess."

"I'm scared," the younger brother said.

"So am I," the elder brother said.

A long hour passed, and still their mother did not come. It was eight o'clock, almost time for them to go to bed, and they had not yet had their supper. The younger brother whispered, "I'm hungry. My insides are groaning."

"Shall we eat?"

"Is there anything to eat?"

"I'll go in the kitchen and see. You stay here."

"I'm afraid to sit here alone."

"I'll be in the kitchen if you want me."

The elder brother went into the kitchen, and the younger brother could hear him lifting the lids from the pots and pans on the wood stove. One of the lids fell to the floor.

"What was that?"

"A lid fell. It's nothing."

"Anything to eat?"

"Some boiled potatoes and French bread. Shall I bring it in there?"

"All right, we'll eat it here tonight."

The elder brother brought out the cold boiled potatoes in a large dish and half a loaf of bread. They sprinkled salt on the potatoes and broke the bread into chunks. The elder brother crammed a lot of food into his mouth and swallowed without mixing saliva with it. The younger brother nibbled some bread.

"Ma will be here pretty soon, won't she?" he said.

"I hope so."

"I'll eat when she comes."

"Why don't you eat now?"

"I can't. It tastes funny. When Ma comes I'm going to ask her to make some tea."

"I hope she gets here soon."

The elder brother finished the potatoes alone, took the dish back to the kitchen, and sat down again.

"I feel funny in here," the younger brother said.

"The doors are all locked. No one can get in."

"I feel funny just the same. I feel like someone was watching us through the windows."

"Watching us? What for?"

"I don't know. I would feel better if we went out of the house into the street."

"Where could we go?"

"Just walk around till Ma came home. I'm scared in here."

"You'll be more scared outside."

"No, I won't. There's lots of room outside. We can run if someone comes after us. In here we've got no place to go."

"Shall we go out?"

"No," said the younger brother. "We better stay here, after all, I guess. We've got to stay with the house."

"All right."

Two men walking together passed by talking loudly as if in argument. For a moment the brothers couldn't breathe, and when the men had passed on the younger brother asked, "Suppose they came up the stairs?"

"What for?"

"I don't know, but suppose they did?"

"We could go out the back way and run up the alley."

"Let's go out now. Let's not wait till someone comes up the stairs."

"All right. Shall I leave the lights on?"

"I don't know. What do you think?"

"I've got a key. I can lock the door from the outside. The house will be safe. Shall I leave just this one light on?"

"I guess so. We couldn't come back if it was dark in here."

The elder brother slid the bolt back, opened the door, and they left the house with the front door locked from the outside.

For a moment they stood before the house, and looked in at the empty room. They could see everything. "You see; anyone could watch us in there," the younger brother said.

"Come on. Let's get away."

They hurried down the street. When they had gone two blocks the younger brother said, "Do you think Ma's home yet?"

"I don't know."

"Where shall we go?"

"I don't know."

"Let's go back and see if Ma's home yet."

They turned back and walked toward the house. A man was walking alone behind them. He walked fast, gaining on them all the while.

"Let's hurry. Who is that coming?"

"I don't know," the elder brother said.

"Why don't you turn around and look?"

"Shall we run?" the elder brother said.

"No, I can't."

Finally the man caught up with them. He passed them without so much as noticing them. They stood on the sidewalk until he passed their house. They had expected him to go up the stairs and pound on their door.

It was growing cold, the lights in most houses were being turned off.

"Where shall we go?" the younger brother said.

"Back home, I guess."

"I'm afraid."

"We'll just pass by and see if Ma's come back yet."

They passed the house slowly, as if it was not where they lived. Then they returned and stood before the front window looking in at the bare, empty room. Not a sound came from the house.

"Maybe she's in the kitchen," the younger brother said.

"I don't think so."

"But maybe she is."

The elder brother called out, "Ma! Oh, Ma!" For a moment it seemed that all the world stood still to listen.

But the house was empty. The brothers would not believe it, and stood waiting.

Then the elder brother said, "She's not in there."

"What shall we do?"

"Let's go back in and wait."

"I'm afraid in there. If we only had a gun."

The oldest held his brother's hand and together they went up the front porch stairs. He opened the door with his key, they slipped into the house, bolted the door, and walked through every room to see if anyone had entered. It was several minutes to nine.

"If we only had a gun or something," the younger brother said. The elder brother went to the kitchen and returned with the meat and the bread knives. One he handed to his brother, the other he kept for himself.

"These'll do, I think," he said.

"But you can shoot a gun, and you don't have to be close."

"These are better than nothing. They're pretty sharp."

They took firm holds on the handles of the knives and sat waiting.

The younger brother began to nod with sleep. He came out of the dream with a shudder.

"Is Ma here yet?" he said.

"Not yet."

"I dreamed she was home again."

"Do you want to go to bed?" the elder brother said.

"I'm afraid to."

"I'll sit up and watch."

"No, I'll sit up too."

"If it were only morning," the younger brother said.

"I wish it was too."

"How long before it will be morning?"

"Tomorrow."

"How many hours?"

"Seven or eight, I guess."

"Then it will be daytime again."

"Yes."

"Then everything will be all right?"

"I guess so."

"Ma will be home then?"

The elder brother did not reply. Suppose she did not come home again?

"I'm getting sleepy," the younger brother said. "I can hardly keep my eyes open."

"Why don't you undress and get in bed?"

"Undress?"

"Sure."

"I'm afraid to undress. I don't want to take off my shoes. Suppose somebody came and I had to run in my bare feet?"

"Well, you can go to bed with your clothes on if you want to."

"Shall I?"

"Sure. I'll sit up till Ma get here."

"But suppose——?"

"What?"

"Ma will come home tonight, won't she?"

"I guess so. Go on, get in bed."

"I'm afraid to get in bed with the light on. Anybody could see we were alone."

"I'll turn the light off."

"No. I won't go to bed until you do."

"I'm sleepy, too."

"Let's go to bed together."

"All right."

The elder brother got on a chair and turned off the light. Together, without taking off their shoes or any of their clothes, they slipped into bed, their knives under their pillows. They cuddled close, and the elder brother put his arms around the younger.

Then it began to rain.

"It's raining," the younger brother said. "Where is Ma now?"

"I don't know," the elder brother said. "Go to sleep. Ma will be here in the morning."

The younger brother began to cry. The rain became heavier and then they began to sleep, waiting for morning.

Notes

What interests me most? Everything, especially me. That is, you. That is, people. That is, the world. That is, time; space; energy; matter; order; disorder; adventure; religion; music; movies; marble games; everything.

The Pool: a story. Out of the pool comes mystery, beauty and love.

I'll See You in My Dreams: a love story, with the boy dying, the girl dreaming.

The Inner and the Outer.

Introducing Battling Kate.
A Romantic, Tragic, Humorous Man, Above All Things Human.

There's Nothing in This World I Wouldn't Do for You. (He was going down the street. Dead. Dead to the world and busy as a bee.)

The Sixth at Arlington: Anywhere you go, you just go. That's a good thing, like a horse in the sixth that's a cinch to win and then runs seventh in an eight-horse race. A sure thing, as the tout says, and says, What's your name? And you say, Sam; what's yours? And he says, My name's Sam too. Anywhere you go at all, you just go and unfold the morning paper and take it all in: everybody involved in the sixth at the sign of the world, three o'clock, weather clear, track fast. There's nothing to it, and all I want back is my life, not my money. I want no traffic with the owners, the jockeys, the trainers, the bookies, the handicappers, the reporters, the touts, or the suckers.

I am a writer, and I don't mean a writer of short stories, essays, or anything else. I make form; form doesn't make me. I'm too big in every dimension to be limited by the smallness of other men. My ignorance of what is useless and unimportant is as great as my wisdom of what is useful and important.

The Hero of the World. Scene: A large elevated drawing room, with a balcony, anywhere. Time: The present, two or three hundred years ago, two or three hundred years ago now, or two or three hundred years ago two or three hundred years from now.

If You Get What I Mean.

The Man with the European Manners.

At New Joe's. The Lady: You make your money in this city; why don't you speak English? Joe: If you cannot speak Italian, please do not eat in my dump.

The weight of what's to come (that would be two tons tomorrow). This weight is heaviest in my sleep where the circus is, where everybody has his chance to tumble, walk the wire, or rise like an angel without wings as high as you please. And where nine times out of ten the top is very near the bottom, with You and I in between, near top and bottom. What you say to me is what I say to you: Before grace, all we need is money. Have you got any now? As out of a dream I bring coins out of my pocket, count them, and say: I have forty-five cents; we will marry tomorrow. There will be war tomorrow, you say. Let's marry today. If there is war tomorrow, I say, let's have no children, for the sake of their memories.

Just a Moment Please.

In art, in life, in religion, in politics, in everything, a man of integrity.

Remembering Parties. It was last night. Wasn't that a wonderful party? Lucy, your party was wonderful.

The Failure and the Success: a story of success that doesn't ruin the young man; in fact everything good comes with success: love, women, ease, energy, poise, good food, good clothing, money, comfort, and his work improves all the time. The failure is a failure all the time, not a genius.

Inside Out: a book.

Yesterday at the beach I found a small flat round pebble, almost the size of a dollar, that is the yoke of an egg beginning to grow to life, red, green, white and gray, with red veins. I do not know who to give it to who will see it as I do.

The Word of Mouth Advertising Done by our Good Friends.

My love, warm, warm, and fragrant, young as the moment coming, and still—still, still, mouth quiet as a rock's, and shy, for waiting all the years for me.

Nine Kids and Laughter: (in the spring), the way suddenly they are possessed with godlike delight with life and the world, by the comedy of health and clear air, and the strange pious clowning of all things in the world suddenly.

The Beautiful Women on the Pages of *Harper's Bazaar* and *Vogue:* a story.

You Take a Girl by Surprise.

He Grew Up in the Business. (His father was with us.)

You fooled around till you got my goat; I got a razor, honey, you got a throat. (The song.)

Order and Adventure Are Enemies.

The Winners and the Losers.

Writers should look at movies, not write them.

Of Love and the World.

From Seven to Seventeen.

The Proud and the Lonely.

What makes a play? Character, more than anything else; story comes out of character. A variety of moods, behaviors, sadnesses, methods of gaining confidence; liquor, love, talk, weeping. A situation, broad and dramatic and yet funny.

The Streets of the World Ten Years Ago.

Elegy, the story of the young Italian prizefighter and his dead girl, the night of the big fight, that I never finished. It saddened me too much. I was in New York, and I was he.

A Fine Feathered Friend.

You Only Live Occasionally.

Give me my integrity, you take the money.

Abstinence Makes the Heart Grow Furious.

A Perfect Gentleman to the Nth Degree.

Daisy, How Come I Don't Hear From You? A story. They meet; separate; he goes back to find her; she's gone; he looks for her all the time, even in his sleep; in the meantime she's sold to street men, taken into a house, and with a disease driven an automobile over the side, alone and in sunlight; and he keeps looking and in his sleep asking; Daisy, Why don't I hear from you?

Laugh if you like, or if you like cry.

In the garden the rose will fall and the bird will fly. (Oriental, but badly translated. Perhaps: The red rose will fall, the red bird will fly.)

I go haywire when I ain't got no work to do; boredom; we've got it powerful; our tribe.

THE STORY

If the people are right you are likely to go along, listening and talking, and all of a sudden see in the world of the story a whole work, with everything a whole thing is supposed to have. There are always stories just beyond every man alive. They are part of him and part of everybody else. At The Cinaloa, which is a Mexican Restaurant in San Francisco, there is a Mexican woman who plays a guitar with two others with guitars, one fat man and one small lean one. She is tall, gaunt, and her face has lots of hardness. It is full of bones, instead of feminine softness. Then she sings and becomes the most desirable and lovely woman in the world. And a whole story. There is the one about the man who ran into Indians who didn't know America was changed; they were kind of cut off in Michigan somewhere and hadn't heard. Etc.

Can I Have Another Beer, If I'm Awfully Nice?

Optics: the apparatus I've thought of creating for the past nine or ten years: to magnify, multiply, and give dimension to the vision of the beholder: through reflection, repetition, variation, etcetera, through mirrors, at various angles, and so on; I believe something that would be exciting could be done and when I get some money, I'll get an authority on optics to work with me on the idea and a good craftsman to build the apparatus; the idea is thus, one, two:

One, the ball, of stainless steel, containing an opening through which the beholder may look, and on the inside are an infinite variety of images which come into focus at the beholder's wish, or: Two at the same time, revolving, as he wishes, by a thing of entertainment, as well as a pleasant means of enrichening vision and broadening understanding of matter, color, form, etc.

I am only a writer, not a doctor or a lawyer or an engineer or a thief or a Capitalist or a truck driver or a labor organizer or anything except a loafer and a writer. I have nothing to do but loaf and write. This isn't a time that has any great respect for either a loafer or a writer. To be saved, I've got to get a job of some kind or begin trying to acquire an education of some sort. My contact with people is casual; I know gamblers and others of the low life of cities. I do not go to people in pain and heal them; I do not open a door to people in trouble and get them out of it; I do not build bridges or highways or buildings or great machines; I do not run a business and accumulate millions of dollars; I do not organize workers; I loaf and sometimes I write. Is that any kind of a way of life?

Ma calls Willie, Willie, and I think it's something important, so I leave my writing and go to the parlor where she's listening to Herbert Hoover over the radio.

What? I say.

Hoover's talking from the Opera House, she says. Don't you want to listen?

No, I say and go back to my typewriter; then I figure I'll make it an Armenian joke and go back and very seriously ask:

Is he talking about me?

So she laughs.

Sometimes there is nothing to say. That is when you've got to try to understand writers, and others. Of course everything is spirit, how much of it you have, or haven't, and what kind it is. Sometimes there is none, there is only inner silence, poise, and mournfulness which unlike much mournfulness does not impel one to do something. Sometimes one endures mournfulness which makes no demands to act, creates no impulses to grow intense, if that's talking sense. What I mean is, there is a kind of mournfulness which rests in a man like an enormous sleeping tiger, powerful and savage, but at the moment asleep, with no dream. I feel this mournfulness now. Another year is coming to an end. I have behaved furiously and stupidly and sadly most of the year. I have been ambitious and eager and fretful and energetic. I have moved in many directions, for myself, the spirit, the race in myself; and for myself as man, one who lives, impersonally, the writer. I have seen the coming of error and waste and misfortune where I least expected it. I have been angry and at times physically ill, and several times overcome by anarchy of spirit: a compulsion, though finally willful, to be altogether heedless about the future, feeling the absurdity of everything, the hollowness, the futility, and unimportance. I have traveled, with absurd consequences: to New York and back with some good luck, some bad. I think I was lucky to get out of everything without any serious damage. On returning to San Francisco my behavior changed and with this change my luck seemed to change too, so that now I have come again to this mournfulness which is peaceful and I think my true nature, and man's too. The best things of man have been made or done by men not too pleased with themselves, their fortunes, and so on.

I want to sleep. In spite of the mournfulness, I feel joyous and glad.

The Mouse

He was a little man with a sad look in his eye; an uncertain posture, as if he were held together only temporarily and might at any moment break into all sorts of ridiculous, surrealist fragments. He was not nervous as very strong people sometimes are. He was on edge, but friendly. That was because he was afraid; a mouse among many cats. He was hungry and so were the cats, so he was friendly and good-natured.

He called them all killers.

Hi-ya, Killer, he would say to Sam. Sam wouldn't even look at him. Look, Killer, he'd say to Dopey, I got a horse in this next race that's a cinch. He'd try to smile and seem one of the cats, but Dopey would give him a dirty look and say, All right, Mouse, you've got a horse in the next race that's a cinch, so bet him to win, or ride him, or eat him. You're hungry, so eat the horse.

Ha ha, Mouse would say, I could eat a horse at that.

Sam himself, though, and Dopey too, were no better than Mouse. They just happened to be less temporarily held together. They just happened to be able to take it better than the little fellow. If no one talked to them they didn't feel lonely and scared. If they didn't eat they didn't suffer the way he suffered. If they gambled and lost they didn't feel like falling down somewhere and dying.

In a way they were his inferiors. He was at least critical of the world. He only wanted to be one of them, the ones who were no good in the world. He didn't want to be making up to the world anymore because he knew it was no use. He'd tried long enough to get by as a clerk or something in some corner of the world, some corner of commerce or industry or something. There was no place for him out there, so he wasn't eager to go out anymore and try to make a place for himself. He talked about it a good deal whenever he found somebody who would listen and he swore a good deal, spitting at every opportunity, being one of the boys, turning around suddenly to see if anybody was going to play a joke on him again. He'd always laugh, and try to be one of the gang. Blackie or somebody else big would lift him off the floor by the seat of his pants and trot him out of the place and drop him in the alley and he would stand in the alley a moment, trying to decide what to do, and after a while he'd come back in, talking at the top of his voice while everybody roared with laughter.

The others of course were stupid, not strong. They didn't understand that in a way he was the best of them, the gamest, and the one who was having the most trouble and taking it better than anybody else. They didn't realize that when they were unfriendly to him they were behaving like the smug ones in the world, the ones who had kicked *them* out and told them to stay out. They were enjoying a vicious and wretched kind of superiority. He was a little brother and instead of being kind to him they hurt him all the time and wouldn't even do him the favor of letting him be useful to them once in a while. He was always eager to be helpful to any of them. He was always the first to offer to go on an errand, but they always pushed him out of the way and sent somebody else. They didn't even want him to feel useful. He took it all and showed up every day and stayed until the races were over, and even though he never seemed to have a nickel to his name he managed better than the others to keep from coughing.

One day a big lout named Harry won eighteen dollars on a race and felt so superior that he began to pick on the little fellow.

What do you eat, Mouse? he said. Where do you sleep?

The little fellow was scared to death because of the money Harry had in his pocket and didn't know what to say.

If Harry hadn't won all the money he would have said, I eat the same things you eat, and I sleep where you do, in empty stores. But now he didn't know what to say. It wasn't easy for him to lie. He stood uneasily, fidgeting, trying to think of a good answer and then he said:

I eat Irish stew and sleep in a bed.

This was too desperate a reply not to be funny and everybody busted out laughing. Everybody knew that what the Mouse was saying was that he wished to God he could eat Irish stew and sleep in a bed for a change.

Then Harry asked a question that made everybody laugh.

Somebody goosed the little fellow. He jumped and tried to get into a corner while everybody crowded around him, pretending to want to touch him, making him shrink and bend and put his hands in front of him and then in back. When he was safe in the corner everybody waited for him to talk. Everybody was all primed to bust out laughing no matter what he said. He looked about fearfully and when he spoke his voice cracked.

I've got a girl, he said.

The laughter was hysterical. Everybody went around shoving and striking one another, saying, He's got a girl.

One of them who wasn't much bigger than Mouse himself and a good deal more of a weakling tried to embrace the little fellow. The little one pushed the other in the face. It was all an accident. He just didn't want anybody with a face like that to kiss him. The other one stopped being funny and smashed a hard fist into the little one's face and the little one crumpled into the corner and sat down. His eye began to swell and his lips were trembling and before Harry lifted the other one off the floor and ran him out into the alley, the Mouse, almost crying, said, Well, I have. I can show you her picture.

Everybody was a little disgusted with the whole episode now, and

Harry pushed through everybody and took care of the other little guy
who knocked the Mouse down.

Who the hell are you? Harry said. This was my joke.

He ran the other fellow out into the alley, and the other fellow never
came back to the place again. The next day, though, the little one was
there the same as ever. That made everybody have a little respect for
him. His left eye was badly swollen, but at least he was there. He was
very quiet of course, but so was everybody else.

Harry was the richest one in the dump for three days. Then he had his
normal run of bad luck and once again he was broke. He went on being
broke for four days, and it looked like he was going to be broke for a long
time to come. One day, just before post time on the last race, the little
fellow, who was standing beside Harry, said quietly, I really *have* got a
girl. Do you want to see her picture?

No, Harry said. I believe you. *I* haven't got a girl and neither have any
of these other lugs.

California

The sunsets are standard and we enjoy watching them from afar through
the eucalypti, but just about the finest thing of all about California is the
ocean, anywhere you care to go, and we usually get a big kick out of
sporting around near where the water comes and goes. As we say out on
the coast, there's nothing like it, unless it's the same thing somewhere
else, which it is down around in Florida and all around in there. There's
nothing like it except the same thing, but we are especially proud of the
sea gulls. We take pride in the seals too, and six or seven dry martinis
before supper. After supper we take pride in the skyline and an easy
chair or a walk, or if the worst comes to the worst a casual attitude about
economic conditions and people. The noble thing about the coast is the
sky which is visible nine times out of ten and better than standard. Nine
times out of ten the writers are lousy. Sporting around near where the
water comes and goes, a visitor from Iowa or around in there isn't apt,
on even the brightest day, to encounter anything but what's been here
from practically the beginning. He'll meet no writers and no door-to-
door salesmen. (I'm speaking of the ocean near where it touches the land
of San Francisco, or Frisco, as we say out on the coast.) All I need now is
a plot and some good heart-to-heart dialogue.

The coast is where bad writers are born and where worse ones come
to.

Nine times out of ten.

Around lunchtime we take pride in the waitress, a girl from Texas and
down around in there.

Stranger, this is the West.

By God, I always wanted to get west and here I am here, right smack at the edge of it, and down around in there, near where seven sunsets every evening, through eucalypti.

Ever hear of Hollywood?

Can't say I have, stranger.

Down around in Hollywood and all around in there you certainly meet actresses.

I suppose you certainly do. Is that good?

Good? Brother, it's upper.

Brother?

Comrade, I mean. Take down around in Moscow and all around in there. Marx. Dialectics too, Tovarish.

Pardner, I reckon I'll smile when you call me that.

Lots of folks go to work on bicycles too, and numerous workers take their lunches while others visit lunch counters where they admire the waitress and figure on romance, some way or other. The best of all, though, is what's been down around in here from practically the beginning and if it weren't for everything else crowding in all over the place the best would be fine. It's the crowding that meanders in and out of the talk and leaves it horror-stricken on the one hand and mouth-agape on the other.

The coast is wonderful. The sunsets are lovely, the ocean is magnificent, the eucalypti are beautiful, the climate is excellent, and the writers are lousy. On top of that, nine times out of ten, the well-to-do are pathetic. I know because one evening I met a well-to-do. He was an elderly well-to-do and he was pathetic.

How are tings going, Sam? I said, and he said, My name's Wallace.

That's all right, Sam, I said. What I always like to do is go around and spread a little cultured conversation.

What tings? he said.

That's where I knew I'd come in, so I went out, and there in the west sure enough was the sun going down for the seventh time, eucalypti, two bricklayers coming home on bicycles with empty lunch pails, a fair to middling sky, good air, citizens, strangers from Michigan and down around in there, and a young door-to-door salesman who that day, in 1929, hadn't sold one lousy piano and turned out to be me, turned out near where the ocean comes and goes.

A Moment of Prose in Kansas

Critics are beginning to criticize me on the ground that I am always writing about myself, but everything I write is about man, not one word of it is about myself. No matter what happens to me, I remain the writer of stories; the one who is watching.

I remember how I made good prose of a little accident that happened in the state of Kansas, during August of the year 1928.

I was seated in a motorbus that was traveling along a country road about forty miles an hour. It was a little after one o'clock in the morning, and I was singing. There was a girl in the seat next to my seat and she was singing too. We were in love.

The bus tipped over, turning a corner, and fell on its side, making an ugly noise, smash of glass, and so on. Everybody in the bus began to scream: everybody but this girl and myself. It was because I had been alert, a writer of stories, and had felt the bus rising and falling on its side, losing its balance, and because I had said to the girl, quietly but swiftly, while it was happening. There is going to be a small accident now: please do not let it alarm you. Then the bus smashed on its side, and I fell over the girl, keeping myself from hurting her by supporting myself, and she looked into my face and said, What shall I do? And I said, Above all things remember everything. This is an accident. Listen to the men and the women, feel the fear, the panic, and the amazement, but *do not be* a part of it.

Then the girl laughed. We were the last to crawl out of the bus, still talking about it this way. An old woman was stunned and ill, but no one was seriously hurt; a few had bruises and so on, but nothing ghastly, and twenty of us stood in the darkness of the road, trying to figure out something to do, something orderly and sensible. The girl came to me and she said, Everyone is bewildered: what are you going to do?

You will see, I said. I will make a story of this. Watch how I do it.

I went to the driver of the bus and I said, It was unavoidable, Max. Don't worry about it. All we have to do is lift it back on its wheels and go on. There are eleven men, two of them United States Marines, and we can do it.

We did do it, and the bus continued its journey through Kansas. I sat beside the girl again and I began to sing again, carrying on from the place where I had been interrupted by the accident. The girl said, How do you do it?

It is my style, I said. It comes from my being a writer.

The next day the girl got off the bus and disappeared into Kansas. I myself disappeared there and remained aboard the bus at the same time, and it was a story because, while my heart was breaking for the girl, I was watching how it was happening. It was prose, and I said to myself,

Well, how do you do it, anyway, for you know that more than life itself you want that girl, so how do you do it?

And I said, speaking as a writer of prose, It's very simple; it comes from being yourself and man at the same time; it comes from ceasing to be yourself and becoming only man when death occurs, in yourself and darkness comes over the earth, and that is how it is now, but you will be resurrected, and all you have to remember is to go on watching, go on keeping your mind alive, and never bury yourself in grief, and always remember everything. By the time the bus had rolled out of Kansas, the young man who was sick with love for the girl was resurrected again, and this now is the prose of that moment, just as it happened, nothing added, nothing subtracted, the small and everlasting truth of art, of artful living and artful watching.

A Holy Silence

Arrangement of black vase and room: face in electric illumination: piano keyboard against early evening growing dark and quiet: surface of table and stance of four books: three chairs.

It is Maud, who was a child in a field of Kansas wheat, higher than her head: arrangement of movement across room, from window to table: cigarette and flame: unmeaningness of smoke inhaled, exhaled.

There is a presence, unseen, in the arrangement: Ben of the newspaper: headlines: Ben himself a shout in contemporary unreality: I said, he said, everything is lost, and we are maggots in a rotten carcass: I said there is nothing for us to do but weep, and instead we get drunk and talk, and sometimes laugh, only our laughter is diseased, like everything else about us. I'm tired, he said, and he went to sleep on the davenport, as if it was the proper thing.

When he woke up, he yawned and said, It means that I love you, my sleeping in your house: I cannot sleep everywhere.

Without stopping even to touch her hand or to look into her eyes he took his hat and went out of the house, not even saying good night. She walked up and down the room.

She sits, the unpresence of Ben falling about her like a warm cloak; and smiles. There is no knock at the door and no ring of the telephone bell and no letter upon the table: he is drinking himself to death in some stinking hole, she thinks, or he is walking swiftly along the waterfront, looking at everything and hating everything: maggots in a rotten carcass.

Arrangement of telephone mouth and her own: no sound: a moment of industrial staring: the instrument black and clean: precise: and her own mouth imprecise with need to speak.

She does not say, Ben, for God's sake, why don't you come to this house and be here and sleep here and let me see you and let me know that you are here and let me know that you are alive?

Arrangement of unthought and motion of weary hand.

Ben, she does not say.

Combination of early evening quiet and neighborly radio unquiet: *Boulevard of broken dreams: where gigolo:* and combination of cloud in corner of window and leaf: outside: the dirty lousy good-for-nothing disgusting life: and the whole goofy joint: this age and this day:

Arrangement of blasphemous inward pulsing of blood and historical earnestness of effaced identity: Maud herself: the day when: alive once before: and a better place.

And then the other time when he knocked at the door at two in the morning:

She awakened from a dream, shuddered with the harsh return of reality, leapt from bed and went to the door: arrangement of door opening and heart opening: the words: I shall not send him away, he may come here, and stay here, and I will give him my bed and my body and my heart, and I shall not say that he is drunk and I shall not be angry with him: the door opened, and there he was, unsmiling, hurt, angry, apologetic:

I have been walking, he said.

Ben, she said.

He came in and stood, wobbling, by the piano and said, I'm very drunk: but sober too. It is this, he said: we are alone: every confounded one of us: and there is no place to turn. I come here because I slept here once and part of myself is here: but I do not love you.

He didn't laugh: it was no joke.

I know, she said.

And you love *me*, he said undrunkenly.

Yes, she said.

God strike me dead, he said. Let me be dead: and he kept saying it undrunkenly for a long time: until she said:

Ben, go to sleep.

She took off his coat. He fell face down on the davenport, saying into the cloth words that she could not understand.

That time too.

Arrangement of weary smile and face of clock: twenty minutes of seven.

Combination of thought of swallowing food and thought of impossibility to do so:

Ben, she did not say: gesture of wiping out the world.

If she telephoned him, hearing his voice, hearing her own, he would laugh, say that the only hope for man was to destroy the whole thing, not the government alone, but the whole blooming thing, the whole basic idea and begin again, and then:

He would say, How are you, Maud?

That would be all: he would not say, I am coming right up, I am taking the streetcar and coming right up: he would say no more than that man was to kick over the whole works.

Arrangement of need and unneed, love and unlove, time of breathing and untime of it, time of seeing and of unseeing: and arrangement of:

Maud in holy silence: unwaiting, saying, He will come again late some night, drunk and garrulous with anger and I will love him: holy silence everlastingly, arrangement of universe and earth, vase and room, silence of space and clamor of inward silence: some night, saying: it is the end.

The Europa Club

In 1918 one of the gambling joints I used to loaf around in, pretending to be selling papers, was The Europa Club on Tulare Street, across the Southern Pacific tracks, near China Alley, in Chinatown.

The Europa Club was supposed to be a gambling joint, but actually it was nothing more than a place where men with no money sat around and talked, and during the War I used to walk over to Chinatown and visit this place. The ugliest men in the world were loafing in The Europa Club in 1918. Italians, Greeks, Negroes, Chinese, Japs, Hindus, Russians, and Americans. Every kind of American, from big dumb Indians and sad-eyed Mexicans to old white-trash gamblers from Texas.

The place was full of tables and chairs and spittoons. There was a player piano in a corner, a bar along the back wall, and over the mirror was an oil painting of a man who looked a little like Woodrow Wilson. It was a great big painting, the work, no doubt, of a loafer who had painted it for drinks.

The place stank. The air was polluted with the wasted hours of many men, and every time I went into the place with a dozen papers under my arm I used to try to figure out what kept them going. I used to figure maybe it was the silent player piano in the corner. Maybe they were waiting for some spendthrift to show up and drop a nickel in the slot. Maybe the men were waiting for music. Or maybe it was the big painting of Woodrow Wilson, the great man of the bad years. Maybe it was the dumb force within themselves, centuries old, demanding to grow centuries older. Maybe it was nothing.

One day the little Jap called Suki swallowed a big fly.

He was a very melancholy-looking man. Any Jap who is loafing is a melancholy-looking man because it's not in that race to loaf. He was disgusted with everything, and nobody would be his friend. He tried to get along with his countrymen who were loafing in the dump, but they wouldn't have anything to do with him. He tried to laugh with the Negroes, but he couldn't laugh that way, and they didn't like the disharmony of his giggle mingling with their guffaws. They bawled him out every time he tried to laugh with them. He tried to be friendly with the Indians and the Mexicans. But *nobody* wanted to be friendly with him, so he gave it up and just sat in a corner.

One day in August Suki noticed that everybody in the room was aware of the flies. Not bothered; just aware. It was very hot and very still in the room and the big flies were flying around and lighting on noses and making the noise flies make. Suki got up from his chair and waved at a couple of them and didn't catch one. Everybody noticed him. He waved at another group of flies and this time caught one. The fly was furious and tried to get away, buzzing loudly, but Suki held it by its wings.

Then he swallowed it.

His countrymen went over to him and spoke in Japanese with great dignity and great seriousness. It seemed they wished to know why he had swallowed the fly. He told them he had swallowed the fly because he was going crazy, from loafing. His countrymen were very upset and at the same time very proud. They thought at first that he was showing off. He had no labor to perform in the world, he said sadly. They asked what labor he wished to perform, and he said he wished to plant and care for strawberries. They told him the season for the growing of strawberries was ended long ago. He said he knew that.

His countrymen told the other loafers why Suki had swallowed the fly.

For weeks during the last days of the War the loafers at The Europa Club talked about Suki and the fly he swallowed. Part of the time they looked upon him as a fool and part of the time as a hero.

Before the War ended, Suki swallowed four flies. I saw him swallow the first one and the last one. The Negroes told me about the others. They said he liked flies. They roared with laughter about Suki and the flies.

He was a very melancholy-looking man.

The loafers waited patiently, and at last the War ended.

When the soldiers of our town came back from the War, The Europa Club was sold to a soldier who kicked out the loafers and put the place in order. The soldier himself dropped nickels into the slot of the pianola and every time I walked into the place I heard music. Men were at the tables, really gambling, for money. At the bar were men who were drinking. It was all illegal and all that, but the soldier was a hard guy and he knew all the ropes. His best friends were cops.

One afternoon in February while I was in The Europa Club I saw Suki come in and buy a drink. He was disgusted, and after he swallowed the drink, he caught a fly and swallowed it. The soldier almost went out of his head when he saw Suki swallow the fly. He took Suki by the neck with his left hand and by the seat of the pants with his right hand and lifted him out into the street.

The little Jap walked away without turning around.

The soldier came back in and dropped another nickel into the slot.

Then he turned around and saw me.

I want you to get the hell out of this place, and stay out, he said.

The Unpublished Writer, Rain, and His Daughter

It is raining, and for the first time in months the pavement of our street is sad with the reflections of houses in it, illuminated now and then by the light-flash of a passing automobile moving up the street with a wet hissing sound. I am sitting in the front room of our house with my daughter Joanna. She is a small child of three with her mother's large eyes, and the same quietness, and she is standing at the window, staring at the sadness. Because of her presence in the room, and her silence, I feel with her a child's wonder of the world, and it seems to me that her wisdom is the only wisdom of man. To see, to be deeply moved by the picture of life, and yet to say nothing. When it is this way with her, looking and not speaking, I seem to understand much about language I have never before understood. Still, it is impossible for me to place in words what I mean. I seem to feel, Silence is everything.

I cannot be more lucid about what I mean, because the feeling is not ordinary and does not lend itself to language. The child is silent. The sadness of the street is her own desolate sadness, yet she is silent.

Now and then, however, she says something in words, and for one reason or another what she says seems so intelligent and final to me that I, a writer, feel ashamed, and wonder how it ever happened that I came to use language so ineffectually.

It is night, but we are sitting in the darkness of the front room because darkness and silence seem naturally to blend, and each of us seems to feel that this is what we want: to be in the darkness, to be in the quiet: to move not, and to speak not. I have tried to be as quiet as the child. I have not moved from my chair. Somehow, nevertheless, my daughter seems infinitely more quiet than I. Silence seems a more valid part of her identity, for she is quiet effortlessly, whereas I am so because I am forcing myself to be so. God knows, except for the presence of the child, I might now be walking back and forth in the room, and perhaps shouting, although I know it is foolish to do either of these things, and really do not want to, but feel I must.

She turns suddenly and speaks in English. It is sad, hearing her voice: darkness and silence and rain and life and sadness being related, my life and her life in the darkness, my child speaking to me: another child, though with the ugly distortions of growth, the deep scars of pain and experience.

It is crying, she says.

In all my miserable writings I have said nothing more profound or artless. I want to take the child in my arms, but I dare not. I make a sound, midway between a sound of laughter and a sob, and I wonder why my life should be so dark.

She turns again to the window, looking up the street. Her mother will soon be coming home, and we are sitting at the window waiting.

You get penny, the girl says. Buy me skate. Two of them skate.

Yes I say. I get penny and buy you skate.

Lord Jesus, my child wants skates and I have no money. A whole month I have promised to bring her a pair of skates, and have not done so, and my child cannot forget the need to have the toy. You get penny, she says, and I say, Yes, I get penny and bring you skates. And every day she accepts my lie with faith. I have no money. Shall I steal a pair of skates for my child?

The Word

So far as man is concerned (and the kingdom of man: the world, built on earth, and confounded as it is), I think we may assume no beginning *was* before the Word, though a universe was: our earth, its seasons; space, darkness and light, heat and cold, air and water and fire, matter and energy, growth and change; and *time*, insofar, at least, as time may be *said* to be an element of day and night, the steady flow of energy miraculously in substance, the steady cohesion of substance, the beginning and end, birth and death, inhale and exhale, of all animate beings, beast or man.

If we are naturally religious (and of course we are, and could never by the farthest stretch of imagination not be religious and still endure), we must believe in the reality of God *before* the Word, and in the reality of the Word before the Word came to us and was translated into the languages of the several tribes of the earth.

That is to say, the Word (essentially timeless, essentially without beginning or end), for us is only the symbol of the *thing*, the vast and complex *one*, timeless or multitudinous or fleeting or variable as it may be: the convenient and necessary and noble substitute. It is the *means* of breaking into small units of *one* the *only* one, all, enabling communion and understanding (at least of a sort) between man and man, without the need every time one wishes to open his mouth to go to the beginning and to articulate everything which *is;* enabling communion between man, one, and the other one, God or the universe or the void, or God in time, or the universe; enabling the question and answer; enabling consciousness, the willful thought, the willful act; establishing freedom of choice.

If the Word were not the symbol of the *thing,* and its convenient and necessary substitute, a man would have to be an eloquent orator in order to greet his neighbor in the morning, and something of a poet to go to the store and exchange a coin for a can of beans.

The trouble of course is this: that the word is misused, especially by scientists and philosophers who go stumbling after absolutes, and who, in using the symbol, multitudinously, travel far from the object of the symbol, so that finally truth (even tentative truth) becomes a trick of grammar or prose style, and the consequence less of earnestness and clear vision than of labor and stubbornness.

In reading the prose of several living and dead scientists and philosophers I have been both amazed and amused by the extraordinary and often fantastic manner in which the Word is used.

And I have been unable, in these works, not to observe the ultimate meaninglessness of almost every word used.

This is so, I have earnestly come to believe, because the language of the scientist, unlike the language of the poet, is without form. And the basic truth of all things, as nearly as we may ever dream of determining and knowing this truth, *is* form, that which is, *as* it is. The way and shape of the thing no less than the thing itself. The universe is form, wholeness, one, and a poem is beautiful and truthful and satisfying insofar as it inhabits its form, and is whole, a universe. Instinctively, the reader of such a poem is momentarily healed of dispersion, momentarily restored to godliness, and momentarily made whole because the poem *is* the *thing.* The reader can feel himself being returned to the beginning, to timelessness and innocence and perfection, and with the last word of the poem, he is there again, though only momentarily.

It may or may not be the same with the writer of the poem while the *poem* is being written, but if the poem has form it will be the same for the man who wrote the poem *after* the poem is written. If the poem has form, it will have form forever, although the man who wrote the poem will not. That is why he went to the trouble of writing the poem. After the poem is written it will be of itself, whole, and the writer of the poem will know that it was he who was once godly, and any number of men who do not write but are able to read will know that since the writer of the poem was once godly, they too are now godly.

I think this is pretty much the function of the writer: to gather together again the fragments of man.

Form is inhabited by substance, which is not necessarily matter: it is often energy, mood, remembrance, temperament, etcetera. And everything or anything is substance. It is impossible to write about nothing because there is no such thing as nothing. When Chekov said he could write a short story about anything, he meant he could give anything form: he could *relate anything* to *everything*.

Style is the man of course, but only as the man *is* at a given time, within a given form, in relation to a specific problem, and a writer would perish in the attempt to write again in the same manner in which he once wrote. The difference may be little, but there will be a difference. This is the reason a poet does not abandon the activity of writing after he has written a good poem, or story, or novel. Style, I think, is also the integrity, or the lack of integrity, of the man, but not this alone. It is many other things, many of them seemingly irrelevant, if anything is ever irrelevant.

To me the Word is holy, and the only force capable of restoring order to the world, and man to godliness. Unfortunately it is the same force which has confounded the world and disintegrated man. It is primarily *yea*, but it will probably go on being *yea* and *nay* forever. This is so not because men vary, but because the *man* does. In the beginning the Word was God, invariable; now it is man, and only rarely God.

1933

1932 dwindled, fell. I stood at the window, watching the year:
another cigarette:
January:
the body is cold, the mind sunless and bleak.
Prose:
a young man walks through the city streets reading a book. Suddenly I am aware that it is myself. Somehow this is strange: to be still alive. How is it that I am again in the city, walking, holding a book before me?
A book:
that is what amuses me, to be still in love with print.
Short story:
no place to sleep: (the remote horror, the horror of the remote; the ear's own whispering, vaster than any real sound.)
Ten mintues to eleven, coughing:
if you will stand to one side, for the sake of objectivity, you will not fail to perceive that in a certain sense no man lives who is not a disease: for

that matter you will understand that to be alive is to be ill, since life itself is a continuous quarrel with death, a quarrel we always lose, sooner or later.

Story:

we are between the hills, in the valley, and our climate is good, though at times the atmosphere is apt to be sultry. Our churches are many and our streets are wide and well-paved. Ten years ago there were only two skyscrapers in our town, but today there are six, and the Pacific-Southwest Building is fifteen stories in height. Our police department is fairly efficient, and our crime is largely petty; murder and suicide are rare. We have a fine county hospital and our people live good lives. There is a class, however, which is swiftly spoiling our reputation. These are the loud people and the ill-mannered. Of ugliness, which is everywhere, we have our portion, and of beauty, which is rare, we have our share, so that whatever may happen in our city, our lives must be both good and evil. (To catch, if possible, the essential identity of the whole population of a small city: climate, social events, social mischief, etc., etc.)

A story ramified by the news of the day: headlines: war in Manchuria, so many killed, names if possible: events in Europe: fires, storms, shipwrecks, kidnappings, robberies; the whole picture: awareness: and a delicate appreciation of those events unrecorded in newspapers: conversations, very youthful love affairs, very subtle, no touching of hands, in some cases no expression at all; also a sermon, very pious.

Fire interests me.

A unique style of prose: technically simple, by implication both complex and profound: not what is said but what is meant, etc.

Program: rise at six, walk half hour, finish breakfast by seven, begin working on novel, 1,000 words daily; complete these by ten; read or relax till noon; light lunch; afternoon devoted to the composition of short stories or criticism; (plays, etc., all forms); religion in the evening: sing loudly, "Nearer, My God, to Thee" also no mockery.

Our silence was music before.

Silence now is grief.

With wind old terror stalks along the street, lifting yesterday's papers from their graves and sweeping them with dust to meet an army of whispering brown dead leaves. With rain the city towers send down their tears.

A book relating to heroism: fearlessness, blind self-sacrifice: personal incidents, war and peace.

Art & Politics: France and England continuously warring, continuously communing through art; other nations.

A Cry to Arms.

William Saroyan

Born August 31, 1908
Alive April 23, 1933
24 years 8 months 23 days
8984 days
8984 nights
215,616 hours
12,936,960 minutes
776,217,600 seconds

Thurber: I'd give my right arm to play the violin like you do, Mr. Bolenska.

Mary Petty: male and female, very old: Then came the Boer War and you.

W. Steig: Write that dirty dog a nice tactful letter.

Again: attorney to convict: Everything's all right, Spud. I can prove you're a low-grade moron.

Again: hightone home: butler: How about that dime you owe me, sir?

And the walls shook; the doors fell to; the earth rolled, Jericho. The houses swayed; small boys ran for life, crying, Jericho. Jericho, Jericho, thou livest, livest, livest, Jericho.

The New Arrivals

Act One. Scene One. Time: the present, twenty years ago. Place: the foreign section of a small or rather middle-sized town of the San Joaquin valley, California. It is the mixed-foreign section. There are many nationalities. Poverty is the main nationality. It is early morning of a day in Summer. A Saturday. Near the alley, beyond the alley, beyond the houses is an empty lot, the playfield of the kids of the neighborhood. The backporch of the Melikian family is visible. A boy of nine or ten, Joe Levy, is in the alley, calling to his friend, Gregory Melikian.

Joe: (like a cock crowing, thrusting his head out as he speaks, the way a crow does) Greg, can you come out? (Pause.) Can you come out, Greg? (Pause.) Greg, can you come out? (Pause. This seems to take on the sort of abstract insistence we associate with traditional things; Joe continues to ask the question, there is no answer, he is dreaming even while he asks the question, but he is very persistent.) Can you come out, Greg? Greg, can you come out? (There is nothing comical to Joe in what he is doing. Apparently his friend, as well as his friend's parents, are still asleep. Joe goes on crowing anyway.) Can you come out, Greg? (Pause.) A window opens somewhere, there seems to be life stirring at last in the neighborhood. The boy listens, but indifferently, as it were. Hmmmm? he says, as if Greg himself were responsible for the noise.

Joe: Can you come out, Greg?

There is foreign talk, angry and sleepy, in the Melikian house, then hurrying, and Greg comes tearing out of the house, only half dressed, with his father tearing after him, swearing in Armenian. He is an enormous dark man, with an old-country moustache. He is very angry as he stands in his nightgown in the doorway, hollering at his boy, and his boy's friend. His anger subsides gradually, but rather swiftly, he shakes his head at the sight of the two young friends, yawns, and sits on the backporch steps.

Greg: Hello, Joe. I didn't hear you. My father woke me up. What time is it?

Joe: I don't know.

Greg: Did you eat? (Quickly spoken of course.)

Joe: Long ago.

Greg: Did your father get you up?

Joe: No. He's still asleep.

Greg: Who got you up?

Joe: Nobody.

Aram Melikian, Greg's father, from the porch, in Armenian: What are you talking about?

Greg, in Armenian: Nothing. I just asked him how he got up so early.

Melikian: Hmm. Who is he?

Greg: He's my friend, Joe Levy.

Melikian: He's a Jew.

Greg: (indifferently) I guess so.

Melikian: He crows louder than a rooster.

The old man goes back into the house.

Joe: What'd you say?

Greg: He just wanted to know what we were talking about.

Joe: Don't he understand English?

Greg: Just a little.

Joe: You can hardly tell my old man has an accent.

Greg: My father doesn't get much chance to practice. He sees Armenians mostly, and they always talk Armenian.

The Song

He went down the street toward where the men were shouting at one another, his mother's brother Melik, the Sourabian brothers Toumas and Hovak, and the Assyrian Tato Vahali.

It was the pleasantest afternoon he had ever known and out of everything music was flowing, warm, hearty and clear. He could hear the men talking, their voices like roars, even though each of them was at ease, not really shouting, just pleased, as he was. He felt a sudden gladness about being one of them, of their world, a joy in knowing the secret language they knew, the strange, rich, warm, comic language which was theirs alone, his alone, which he delighted in speaking, although they told him he spoke it no better than a peasant.

Listen to the boy? his mother's brother often said. How naturally he says the crude peasant words. You'd think he was born in the old country. You'd think he was still there. You'd never guess he is an American.

Boy, his uncle often said, of what place are you?

I am of Bitlis, he always replied, and then his mother's brother would roar with laughter.

Truly he is, he would say. Truly. He is truly of that place.

It was the livest afternoon he had ever known. It was hot, but the heat was the kind that made you feel you could do anything you wanted to do. It was the kind of heat that brought everything good in the world. Even the drab streets seemed full of health and laughter. The sky itself seemed intimate. The sun seemed as close to the heart as father to a son. The people one did not know seemed to be brothers. Even the unlikable ones seemed likable. No, they seemed to be variations of one's self.

As he came closer to the men he wondered if he should hurry by unnoticed and let them continue their enjoyment, or pause for the glance of his mother's brother and be taken into the group, as one of them. He didn't want to intrude, but at the same time he felt so glad about them and so eager to say something that he hoped he would be allowed to do so.

His mother's brother was talking. It was a joke. He was speaking of Torosian, who was pompous and could never get to the point, but always hemmed and hawed as if he had something very important to say, in the strictest secrecy, and then finally said nothing.

Let me tell my brother, Melik said, speaking for Torosian. One knows there is a way, and a *way*. How to say it. A man cannot go barefooted too quickly. Of course it may be no more than the gossip of enemies. Tongues come and go. It is a man. Perhaps ill, perhaps troubled, there is no telling. How shall I know?

What is it? Melik asked, telling his story, drawing his portrait of the pompous man. What is it? Tell me.

What shall I say? he answered for Torosian.

The men roared, the Assyrian losing his breath, bending, squirming, cackling, holding his head in despair.

Melik, he said. Melik, Melik, how you make up stories.

It's true, Melik said. The man is always talking and he never says anything. What shall I say? he says, and he keeps talking and says nothing. He says, It is a man. It is the world. Who can understand one or the other? He says, There are men, and *men*. That's all he says. Nobody knows what fire is burning him. And he's so slow. He is so cautious about his idiocy.

Suddenly his mother's brother saw him, turned with words still in his mouth, and laughter, and without changing the tone of his voice said, Where are you going? What are you doing?

The boy smiled shyly. He understood. No answer was required. He paused, waiting to know if his mother's brother wanted him to stay a moment.

This is my sister's youngest son, he said to the others.

He took the boy playfully by the ear.

Of what place are you? he said.

The boy could not resist the temptation to join in the game.

He pretended to be uncertain, confused, embarrassed. The men watched with amusement, knowing that he was of that tribe.

It is a man, the boy replied, talking like Torosian.

The men roared with laughter.

One does not go barefooted too quickly, he said. It is perhaps no more than the gossip of enemies.

You see, Melik said. He is the same as all the rest of us. How's Mama?

What shall I say? the boy replied, going on with the performance. He gestured, moving his fingers about.

Go, Melik said, speaking with comic haste. Go, go, go.

The boy hurried on down the street, while the men roared with laughter.

Before the laughter stopped the song had taken possession of him and was pouring itself out into the afternoon. Where am I going? What am I doing? Brother, nowhere and nothing, but with laughter and leaping, as it is with all of us.

Life, the Magazine, and Harry, the Polo Man Who Didn't Make the Team

You know how improved American life has been since the publication of the picture magazine called, bluntly, *Life*—which, as you know, *had* been for years what is known as a humorous magazine. *Life*, humorously as it were. *Life* gayly—trippingly as it were—wittily, but pronounced sharply, wittily pronounced. *Life* as it is to forty-year-old dull men with memories of dull boyhoods, members of Clubs of one sort or another, payers of dues, fraternal, overfriendly, clean-shaven, well-dressed, married, children, wives, men about, watchers of football games, loud in speech, born dull and stupid and grown to the heights of dullness and stupidity, college men, members of fraternities, from moneyed families. *Life* as it is to these. The first magazine called *Life* is now scarcely a memory. The drawings were all dull. The writing could not have been more lifeless, more artificial, or more unreal. Dentists had the magazine in their waiting rooms. Now, with this new *Life*, there is a new attitude toward life itself—American life, European life, international life as it were. All life. You get a good variety for ten cents. The photographs are fine. They are clear and sometimes dramatic. You see pictures of people, places, animals, fish, bacteria, objects of all kinds of all kinds of worlds, parties, strikes, storms, meetings, funerals, births, and anything that can be photographed. It is a good magazine, but I had better not forget the color-reproductions of paintings, old and recent. These are also fine.

However, what about life? What about the real thing? It's a wonderful magazine. It's improving American life all the time. It's fine for the children. Excellent for the forty-year-old bores everywhere. Educational for parents who were not fortunate enough to get much schooling. Marvelous for debutantes, their mothers, their grandmothers, and others. But what about the real thing?

Where does the outsider come in? What's his rating? You know. The forty-year-old one who has no horse and doesn't play polo. The one who isn't dull, whose boyhood wasn't dull, who belongs to no Club, who knows too much to be fraternal or friendly, who is not clean-shaven, who is silk-clothed, unmarried, no children, and so on? How about Harry? How about the American who didn't make the dull grade? Whose parents were unmoneyed. Who didn't go to high school for more than a year, let alone college. Is he living, or is only dullness the life *Life's* interested in? How about The Failure? Could that by any chance be life too? It's very educational and you get a lot for your money. It's very wonderful and quite a show every week, but just because the magazine's full every week we shouldn't make the mistake of imagining it's getting everything. It's doing wonderfully and we are all grateful. Friday is a good day because Friday is *Life* day. It's a new magazine and it needs time. All it needs to remember is not to repeat itself with the interesting dull things of which once is scarcely too much, but twice is bound to be absurd.

It takes money to do these things. Large staffs of competent workers. Expert photographers. Intelligent arrangers of programs. Men with good manners who know how to enter a fine house and fit into the scheme. Which is to be delighted. Who know that that is all high society insists on. That you be thrilled to death with everything. Music? It's wonderful. Books? They're simply simply. Painting? It's really the the. Sculpture? How barren living would be without it, we all feel. Religion? It's charming and the foolish dictators who are trying to do away with it are trying to do away with a thing very solacing to the people, we feel. Philosophy? So comforting. Such a source of comfort in times of trouble, we feel. Sport? It's such fun. The theatre? It's our world, really. The opera. Charming. Politics?

Anything at all, just so you've shaved, bathed, in fresh fine clothes, healthy, smiling, and simply delighted. They're a lovely people, dull of course but quite nice too. They really are fine. But even tragedy when it comes to them comes with all its greatness spoiled because they are so awfully awfully delighted and busy with parties for people who really matter. Several of them have spoken to Spanish and Russian royalty. Several others, young women, have danced with Spanish and Russian and other royalty. Several others, also young women, have had experiences with Russian, Spanish, Georgian, Greek, Roumanian, and other phony royalty. But even when tragedy comes to them it is wasted.

The magazine, though, is all right. It's because it's called *Life* that we are fascinated by the pictures of people and places and things it publishes every week. That is such a blunt name for it. We are not hecklers. We are grateful, but is it that?

We don't want anything done about anything or anything like that because we don't believe anything can be done about anything. We just thought we'd wonder if it is that, as bluntly as that. Is it *Life?* Or life? Or a chronicle of part of it? Or what?

How about the American, the individual, not the worker, not the union man, who has no horse and would have loved a horse? How about the polo man who didn't make the team?

The Fable of the War Between the Old Complex and the New Culture

My son, clip this coupon and start getting a little background for yourself, so you can walk right in among the best of them and put the cards on the table. You're not dumb, you're uninformed. The Yale boys haven't got anything on you. All you need is fifteen minutes a day, and five feet of books. Old Doc Eliot's books, and the plan; the fifteen-minutes-a-day plan. It's better than the five-year one. Out of the twenty-four hours in every day, what's fifteen minutes? You can take one along in the morning and read about ancient India on the streetcar; and coming home in the evening you can pick up a little information on architecture in the days of Rome. A year later you can go right in among them and with all that information about Rome backing you up, you can put the cards on the table and know they won't be jokers. They may not make a royal flush, a full house, or a straight, but at the same time they may make a pair of deuces, instead of five wild jokers, and nothing to go with them.

You don't have to be backward all your life. You can clip the coupon and send away for the booklet, which comes free and without obligation. And out of the twenty dollars a week they're paying you you can make a small down payment on the five feet of books, and after they arrive you can start right in getting a little background. You can go to work right away and start getting rid of that foolish complex that's been eating you seventeen, eighteen, nineteen, twenty, thirty, forty, or fifty years. You can buckle right down and begin reading old Doc Eliot's Harvard Classics.

You don't have to have money to be the equal of any of them. Son, or Father, as the case may be, this supreme library of 418 immortal masterpieces is unified into a living, powerful educational force by the marvelous working index containing 76,000 entries, guiding the reader to an understanding of world culture. (Yeah man.) (And now.) (And how.) And so forth and so on. And now or never. And tomorrow is another day. And art. And aesthetics. And agriculture. And politics. And poetry.

And everything.

Every little thing you need in order to become a success, to be well informed, to have a mouth full of wit, a head full of ideas, a pocket full of money, and at least, and by all means, a shelf full of five feet of Harvard Classics, which, if the worst comes to the worst, you can throw at the bill collector, or whosoever it may concern.

What you need is culture, that's all. You can get that in no time at all at the rate of fifteen minutes a day. As culture starts coming in, that old complex of inferiority starts going out: they meet on the stairway and exchange a few words, the old complex speaking right out, and the arriving culture, speaking softly and with all kinds of elegance.

O.K., the old complex says, you can move in, brother, but let me tell you it's a pretty miserable house and you're not going to find the ventilation any too good; the lighting is lousy; the furniture is broken-down; the food is the worst in the world; but it was O.K. for me. I was used to it; but I won't mind being out in the street for a while. I can always get back in. Let me wish you luck. I'll be out in the street when you're ready to go back where you belong.

You're very kind, the shining culture replies with a fine Oxford accent. Thank you.

Never mind that kind of chitchat, the old complex says. Just keep your eyes open and don't fall down anywhere. You'll find the terrain interesting, anyhow.

So the old complex moves out and the culture moves in, and the fellow with ambition goes to work in earnest reading Father Eliot's five feet of 418 immortal masterpieces, with the marvelous working index containing 76,000 entries, etcetera. Doc Eliot himself was a pretty bright boy back there in the good old days when he was president of Harvard for forty years. Forty years, that's all; fifteen minutes a day, that's all. Son, what's going on around here?

So the culture moves in and tries to inhabit that house. Little by little the poor culture begins to get homesick, and after six months at the rate of fifteen minutes a day, late one night it tiptoes out of the house, stumbles over the old complex out in the street.

So soon? the old complex says.

So soon? the culture says. It's been ages, my dear man.

And how was it? the old complex says.

Lousy, the culture says. It's all yours.

Sure, the old complex says. Nothing like trying, though. No hard feelings.

And in the middle of the night, the old complex moves back in, and although the distance covered by the books is still five feet, the fellow himself knows it's no use kidding himself anymore: culture and poverty and years of democratic slavery just naturally don't mix, that's all.

The Long Way to Tipperary

At least twenty years ago a small boy with mobs of freckles all over his face came walking down the street of a little town whistling what a long way it is to Tipperary. He is now dead, and not more than two days ago, which was Friday, another boy, now seventy, sat on a porch in a rocking chair and remembered that it's a long way to go, and sighed. Maybe it wasn't twenty years ago that the boy whistled. Maybe the song wasn't written twenty years ago, but that just goes to show what I mean.

What I mean is that the Irish are not a people, they are a nostalgia in the living. All sorts of people are Irish whose parents are not. All sorts of them weep inwardly to the sorrowful adoration of the young man singing of The Rose of Tralee. How the pale moon was shining. And how it was not the beauty of her face alone that took his heart, but the truth ever dawning in her eyes. Irish? There is no man with a beating heart in him who is not partly Irish. As for myself, I am at least three parts Irish to one of anything else. This is the truth. My long journey to Tipperary began before I was born, and even though I have been in Europe, in England, in London, in Scotland, and in many other places, I have not yet set foot on Erin, a place I love, strangely, more than the valley in which I was born. In Edinburgh I arranged to go to Dublin and from there seek out Tipperary. But at the last minute I decided not to go. If I go to Erin, will I be truly there? If I find Tipperary, will it be truly the place I have hummed of reaching all my life? Of course not. The Tipperary to whom the people of the world are loyal is the great, green, delightful, lovely Tipperary of the heart. It is the Irish heaven and the boy with the mobs of freckles all over his face went to Tipperary when he died, or just before. His last breath most likely hummed, It's a long way to go. And then his heart went.

How the Irish came to be the providers of the ultimate destination for the living may or may not be a difficult thing to determine, but difficult or not difficult, I shall not try to do it. I am satisfied that the Irish heart is the heart of a people full of the good song. And the song is the life. The song is as much the life as breathing is. The songs of all peoples are great and good, but not nearly as many as the songs of the Irish; not nearly as close to the inward journeying of the living either. ·

The long way to Tipperary is the long way to the last minute, and the farewell to Leicester Square is the farewell to the world. It is the farewell to all things of life, all warmth and laughter and delight and health and dreaming and walking about.

So naturally at the last minute I changed my itinerary. No Itinerary can take you to Tipperary.

That wasn't the only reason I didn't go, however. That reason alone would have been childish. I didn't go also because at the most I could afford to stay in Ireland not more than two days, and I did not wish to insult my heart with a visit so unsatisfactory, so wasteful, and so likely to be saddening. I shall go to Tipperary. I shall actually go, and it shall not be a long way to go at all. I shall actually be in Tipperary some day. I shall be there alive and walking about, but even there, even in Tipperary, I know it shall still be a long way to Tipperary, a long way to go, and I shall be delighted to continue the solemn and gay going.

The Life

It's the life all right. (People I met this summer.) Well, how is it the life? What do they do that makes it the life? What is the reason? How does it happen? Well, for one thing everybody has money. There is always liquor. There is always food. There are women and girls for men and boys. There is time for everything.

Only one thing is always lacking: not intelligence, not wit, not goodness in the people, not good intentions, not any number of other worthwhile things; only this: a sense of life. This is the thing that is lacking: a real sense of life. They haven't got it, but have many other things, so in the effort to live, what happens is essentially horrible. Nothing bluntly horrible happens, but what is happening all the time is horrible, and then suddenly something actually horrible happens. Even then, however, nobody can quite understand it, and the horror itself has happened uselessly, wastefully, and does nobody any good; nor for that matter, or, for that matter rather, that is, nay especial harm; which of course it should do.

They are always maudlin because of over-drinking, over-eating, and over-fornicating, or intending to. They are always foolish and unsexed. They are always chattering, the male and the female alike; sighing and not knowing what to do next.

What next? for the love of God, is the question they ask one another in polite words over and over again; all of them not drunk with energy, not drunk with power, but overflowing with torn nerves, weeping blood, wretched hearts, unhinged senses.

And yet they are the revelers; the ones who live. Dinner is always an event. A social event. Lunch is too. Breakfast too, often. And in between times drinking is an event. It is all social, all tragic tribal stuff.

I'm too busy to go into it at greater length. They are all charming and likable, as the saying is, and at their best not really stupid and absurd, as they seem to be. They just haven't been born; don't know whether they're going or coming; because they're too busy with what they call The Life. Which is actually The Death. The pointless ineffectual unsatisfying Death.

Cuba Libre

The headwaiter wanted to know what he wanted. I don't want anything, he said. He never did like that guy. I'm looking for Joe, he said. Joe ain't here, the headwaiter said. The headwaiter loved to be that way.

He went back to the bar and saw who was tending. The young Italian behind the bar asked with his hand, palm up, how it was. He told him. I've got these two people at the table over there, and no money. I thought Joe would be here. Well, that's all right, the Italian said; you just drink and I'll put it on a bill when you are through. All right, they want beer; I'll take one too. Don't you want brandy? the bartender said. I think I'll drink beer with them, he said.

After the first bottle, though, the girl began to order a drink called Cuba Libre—it came to the table looking like a Coca-Cola. Every five minutes or so, the girl would say, And I'd like another Cuba Libre. And they talked all the while; the young man with noble impulses, and with great hopes for the world; and the girl, not talking baby talk anymore; just listening and sipping Cuba Libre. And the bartender, Bill Roma, listening to some of it; and the waiter Lupo coming over and saying, We got a small argument. Is Armenia half-Turkish and half-Russian, or is it Armenia? So of course that was all he needed to jump up from the table and go into a huddle with the boys and explain the whole thing—explain it even to the boy at the old Viennese instrument, hitting it with two hammers, flexible ones; the stringed instrument, called czimbalom. Explain it to the headwaiter too. Is Armenia half-Turkish and half-Russian, or is it Armenia? Listen, boys; listen, Bill; listen, Lupo; Frank— Gazis, listen a minute: half-Turkish? half-Russian? Well, let me tell you.

And he stood at the bar fifteen minutes and explained the whole thing, point by point, showing that Armenia isn't half-Turkish or half-Russian, and that although it isn't a country by itself anymore at all, Armenia is, and always will be, a whole country by itself.

And I'd like another Cuba Libre, the girl said.

The Last Supper

He entered a place of silence and piety when he entered the room. In the darkness he saw the crowd standing about the man, making ready to humiliate him. He felt deeply grieved and wanted to utter some word. Brothers, he thought. He was tired and confused and physically cold. He stood bewildered at the center of the walls, by the small hard bed. The door of the room was open on the hall for air. He heard the floor creak under the burden of someone passing.

It seemed that Peter, whom he loved as one loves a dead brother, was speaking, and although he could not hear Peter's words, their meaning, which he gathered from the pathetic expression of Peter's face and from the manner in which Peter labored to seem devoted, moved him to shame, for he knew what was to happen.

Already the cock was fluttering.

He looked into the brown paper bags on the table by the small gas range. They contained onions, potatoes, a head of lettuce, and a small portion of a loaf of bread. He sliced the bread and sprinkled salt on the lettuce. When he sat down to eat he saw the men at the table, looking mournfully, as he was looking, at the food.

He stared at the food a long time, and then began, silently, to pray or swear. Once again the hall floor creaked.

Swiftly, so that he would not be seen doing so, he stood up and pointed in anger across the table, as if someone were there. He did not know at whom he was pointing, and it did not seem to matter. He could not hate Judas; poor Judas was a bewildered fool. He was angry at the crudity of man, the senselessness, the pathetic pride, the lack of grace in man's emotions. If their senses had not been so blurred, it could not have happened. They would have known everlasting life *then*, where they were, and therefore now, where *he* was.

It was because of this that he pointed across the table, less at Judas than at himself.

He was about to laugh when he heard Paula, the girl who lived in the room across the hall.

Hello, she said.

He turned happily to the girl.

I am having supper, he said, and to himself he said, It is the last supper.

The girl sat across the table from him.

A dozen men, she said, came to the office today. They asked if I would buy stockings, shoestrings, postcards, windshield wipers, or if I would subscribe to *The Cosmopolitan*. I couldn't buy, so they went away. I sent them away, watching them turn and go, closing the door behind them.

I know, he said. They come to my office too, dozens of them.

He chewed and swallowed a mouthful of dry bread. He heard the man say, My body, eat of it. He became bitter with shame because it was so, and still no good had come of it. Now the men were deceiving themselves, saying they would go with him even to death. He knew they would forsake him, since they could not tell for sure if he was not unbalanced.

He saw the man walk away from the men, fall on his face, and pray. After he had prayed the man found all the men sleeping, even Peter. Three times he found them sleeping. The third time he told them to take their rest, it was ended, the time had come.

He heard the girl speak.

Isn't it a beautiful night? she said.

He knew she would like to walk through the city with him. He felt grateful, knowing he would be sad all night and would need her.

Yes, he smiled.

He began to be sorrowful, and knew that when the cock crowed he would be deeply pained, since it was still the same, then and now.

He heard the siren of a passing automobile in the street, clear and tragic in the stillness of the night.

The cock crows, the time of betrayal has come.

Again the siren of the automobile cried out.

He turned away from the girl and knelt at his bed.

He heard the girl laugh, then heard her become silent. He knew she was frightened, so he straightened his face, pushing aside the heaviness in his heart, a clerk in America, preparing to make a remark that would amuse her, restore her to amusement, and suddenly he was on his feet again, smiling, pretending that it had been a performance of vaudeville.

You didn't know I was religious, did you? he said.

He put on his coat and hat, and took the girl's arm.

We'll walk to the North Beach, he said, and have supper at The Universe. I know the headwaiter.

Walking down the hall with the girl, hearing the creaking of the floor beneath their weight, the miracle of their substance in the blurred dream of life, he saw the man before the multitude with swords, and he saw Judas kiss the man, betraying him, and when he was in the street he saw them mocking the man as the man walked with the cross, and while he saw these things, he spoke to the girl. When they reached the restaurant it was all over and again the man was humiliated and dead, it was ended, and the heart of man was still black. He smiled at Guido, the headwaiter, hanging his hat, and the man called out to him loudly, Bring us everything, brother, we're very hungry tonight.

The Three Instructions; and the Evil Step-Mother and the Beautiful Step-Daughter

My grandmother, Lucy, one Sunday afternoon, told me the story of the husband who sat at home all the time and wouldn't leave the house.

His wife went to a wise man and asked what she should do. The wise man told her to drop a raisin just out of her husband's reach. He would get up, bend down, pick up the raisin, and eat it. Then she was told to drop another raisin, and in this manner to keep her husband moving toward the door, and finally out of the house, which happened. The wife then shut the door on him and told him to go away and not come back until he had made a lot of money.

During all these years all he managed to save was three pieces of gold. It was money, so he decided to go home to his wife.

On his way home he found a wise man sitting on the steps of a public building. The wise man was offering, at the rate of one gold piece each, instructions for living.

The poor man thought to himself that three gold pieces was very little money anyway, so he decided to buy one of the instructions, which he did. The instruction was: *To the bad say not that it is bad.*

This was not enough instruction, so the poor man paid a second gold piece for a second one which was:

In all affairs do not fear water, whether rain, stream, river, lake or sea; dive right in and swim; the good Lord will carry you to safety.

This was only mystifying, so the poor man paid his last gold piece for a third instruction which was only one word:

Patience.

The poor man thanked the wise man and went on his way. He began to walk across the desert, inasmuch as he had no animal; donkey, horse, or camel. He hadn't walked ten miles when he saw a caravan of camels, with its men in a state of excitement.

It seems there was water in the small desert pool, but the water was out of reach, so that neither the men nor the animals could quench their thirst, and the animals were so tired they couldn't move.

The poor man remembered the wise man's instruction about not fearing water.

He told the men to lower him with a rope and then to lower urns, pitchers, and jars to him; in that way he would furnish them with water.

He did so. He was very happy about having bought the instructions, and when the animals had had all the water they wanted, and the men too, he called up to them to keep on drawing the water. They didn't know why he wanted to go on drawing water, and asked what they should do with it. He told them to bathe first and after that to bathe the animals and after that to make a stream of the water, which they did.

After a while, as the level of the water sank, the poor man saw a gold door of extraordinary beauty. When the water had descended sufficiently he opened the door and entered the most beautiful room he had ever seen. A throne room. On the seat of the throne was an old man, and on one knee of this old man who was a king was an enormous warty, moist green frog; on the other knee was a coiled fat snake.

It seemed very strange to the poor man that such vile things should be in such a glorious place. The old man lifted his eyes and looked at the poor man.

He said, Welcome to him who has entered where not even eels have entered these hundreds of years.

The poor man was awed by the wealth and splendor of the room, but rather bewildered.

The king said, What are these on my knees?

The poor man remembered the first instruction of the wise man, not to say bad to bad.

The poor man said Youth and strength.

At that instant appeared a multitude of the most handsome, strong young men the poor man had ever seen; the frog and the snake disappeared.

The king, who had been waiting several centuries for the arrival of such a man as this poor man, was very pleased.

For this, he said, I shall give you anything you wish, anything at all; name it.

The poor man told the king the story of the last eighteen years of his life.

The king gave him gold, and jewels, enough for ten kings, and told the poor man to return to his wife. The poor man purchased the caravan which was five miles long and paid well for it, and returned to his home.

Before going in, he said to himself, I will see if she has been faithful to me.

He climbed the roof, and, looking through a crack, saw two beds, his wife's and his own; his wife was in one bed and a man in the other.

This grieved the poor man very much.

His wealth seemed useless now, according to my grandmother. At any rate, he decided to climb down from the roof, kill the man, his wife, and himself.

Then he remembered the third instruction: *Patience,* and decided to lie on the roof looking up at the sky.

After several minutes he heard the man stirring in his bed. The man sat up and said, Mother, I am thirsty.

Just like that.

Then the poor man knew that the man was his son.

He got down from the roof just as day was breaking. He knocked at the door. His wife opened the door but didn't recognize him.

I am your husband, he said. You sent me away eighteen years ago and told me not to return until I had wealth. I have returned with wealth.

The wife saw the caravan of hundreds of camels, laden with all manner of wonderful things.

She welcomed her husband home, embraced him, introduced him to his son.

My grandmother thought this was a wonderful story, but to me it was very sad because the woman was no good, and the man was a fool. What sort of a dope was he anyway? Even in mythology?

My grandmother told me also the story of the girl and the stepmother, a truly beautiful story.

My grandmother, in all innocence, has gone on telling me this story every year, at least once and often twice, for the past twenty years. The gist of the story is this: that the evil stepmother made the beautiful girl stand in the tower of a magnificent structure and serve as the tower's foundation, while the stepmother mortared stones about the girl, until at last the girl was covered, but not dead. Before she died something happened, in the universe I suppose or in the hearts of all living, and the beautiful girl became swallows, nightingales, and all manner of lovely flying things, which forever after flew about the tower making the saddest and loveliest and most heartbreaking of sounds.

The Theater of War

This is a play. As writers sometimes say of their novels, This is fiction. There are no actual persons here, living or dead. The whole thing is imaginary, even the situations. If the name of any living person appears here, it is a coincidence. And so on.

Pure fiction.

A play. The Theater of War.

For twenty-one years they fretted about it, or pretended to. In reality, they were waiting to get home at the time so they could take off their shoes and relax, have supper, listen to a little music, talk with a friend, notice the growth in their children, the beauty or ugliness of their wives, grow sleepy, and go to bed. That's all they were doing at the time, although they pretended that they were working toward a world in which peace would be enduring, in which war would be impossible. Their minds weren't on their work at the time. A couple of them were thinking of women, and smoked cigarettes just to keep them going until they could get to a telephone and make arrangements for the night. They all had other things to think about. One of them was going insane and knew it. Another had a bad heart and was always curious as to when it would be apt to stop beating. They were all bodies, although one of them claimed that more than anything else in the world he loved the music of Mozart. They were all busy with the irritations of bodies growing old and dying. They spoke a good deal of the future of mankind, but they spoke with words. They didn't mean it when they said they loved humanity. They didn't know they didn't mean it because they didn't know anything. They fretted about themselves, not the world, not the people of the world, not the future of humanity.

After 1918 they really got busy fretting.

Some of them grew old and died believing they had left the world a better place than they had found it.

Pure fiction. Absolute fantasy.

Some of them retired and took up the philosophy of sawing wood, reading newspapers, and refusing to see reporters, admirers, or sympathizers.

Absolute hooey. The Theater of War.

A play. Nothing real.

Each was a body. There were conferences. The men took turns at talking. It probably made them feel good. There is so little any man can do about anything that a chance to get up and talk is always welcome. There was an idea that had something to do with establishing a league of nations.

Hooey. A league of nations. A league of idiots. There are no nations. There are no leagues. There can be no organization beyond the organizing of mortality into the body, which happens by itself at birth, by the grace of God.

There were treaties.

Baloney. Had they signed treaties with themselves to be honest about their bad manners toward their wives, beggars, and street children? They had not. They were fiction.

They talked and they wrote.

It was all malarkey.

They prayed, too.

That was the biggest laugh of all, and that character of fiction was the most coincidental of the lot. He might have been eight or nine other people, with or without the costume.

They made movies.

It was all fantasy and cinema.

All they said they wanted was no war. Peace. And while they wanted peace there was no peace. It was because they were fiction, characters in dime novels, nobodies, idiots who had learned to appear impressive.

They worried heroically, always remembering the matter of talking to the gardener about the lawn. And if possible someday: an affair with somebody glamorous for a change who might be impressed, all the way down the line.

They said another war would be horrible. They said it would be the end. They said it would be the final ruin of Europe and western civilization. They were old and not on talking terms with their grandchildren. They were dying and it was too late for that kind of an affair. They were bodies, and their bodies were taking on the shape of age and ugliness.

Three times seven is twenty-one. For three times seven years they fretted about it, and then it happened again.

It was fiction, but it happened again, and there was another war.

Pure fantasy. The Theater of War. Germany. Poland. England. France. Russia. Europe. War.

O.K. War. Bang. Bang. Bang.

This is war. The war they fretted about twenty-one years is now being waged.

The war is a play. It is being staged in what is known as The Theater of War. Every person involved is fictitious. Nothing can possibly be lost. As many as seven million fictitious characters may be destroyed, but actually nothing—nothing at all—can be lost. Like any play this play must end, after three, four, five, six, seven, eight, nine, or ten acts. Sooner or later it must end, even if after six thousand acts, or six million. It will end. It will be a lousy play and there will be no applause. The first act is now going on. The price of sugar is now going up.

It is all malarkey. Ignore it.

Old Country Stories, Part I

1. THE POOR MAN

A man who was always unwashed, his nose always running, his eyes unclean, his breath foul, was asked why he was so slovenly.

I am a poor man, he replied.

All right, he was told; clean your nose and still be a poor man.

2. THE WATERMELON-EATER

Another poor man stole a watermelon, placed it in a brook until it was cool, then ate all but the peelings; after which his good feeling was so great that he watered on the peelings and took a nap; when he wakened he was hungry again for watermelon; he looked about to see if anybody was nearby, and as no one was, one by one he lifted the peelings, saying, The water did not touch this one, and ate it. In a few minutes he had eaten all the peelings.

3. THE SOCIALLY AMBITIOUS WIFE
AND THE SIMPLE COBBLER

An ambitious wife whose husband was a simple cobbler became envious of the fame of the wives of wise men and went about saying that some men might be wise, but that the wisest, the most all-knowing of all, was her husband, Musa.

A woman said, I have lost my bracelet, which is old and priceless; bring your husband to me, so that he may tell me where it is.

The poor husband was taken to the wealthy lady and stood before her embarrassed, bewildered, and stupefied. Not knowing what to say, he thought he might praise the tassels of her coat, and did so. The wealthy lady touched the tassels and beneath them found the lost bracelet.

This is truly the wisest, she said to the man's wife, and gave the man much money.

A wise man from India came to the city and said, I shall speak without words to the wisest of your wise men and we shall see if he can answer me.

Again the poor cobbler was sent for; on the way he found an onion which he placed in his pocket.

The wise man from India drew a circle on a blackboard with a piece of chalk; the simple cobbler thought, That is a watermelon. He drew a line through the middle, thinking, Half for him and half for me.

The wise man of India was satisfied and much impressed.

Out of his pocket he placed an egg on the table. The cobbler said, That is half a breakfast; with the onion it will be a whole breakfast. He placed the onion beside the egg, and the wise man from India was amazed.

The wise man next brought out his fist and placed it before the cobbler. This was altogether too much and the poor cobbler who was terrified, began to curse his wife. Her name was Rose.

Rose, he said. Rose.

The wise man jumped and said, It is true; he *is* the wisest of the wise. I drew the world, and he drew the dividing line through it. I placed the egg on the table, as symbol of the earth, and he placed the onion, showing that the earth is made layer on layer. I placed my clenched fist before him, in the dead of winter, asking him to tell me what is in it, and he replied that it was a rose.

The wise man opened his fist and tossed a rose on the table.

This man is truly the wisest, he said.

The simple cobbler became very famous for his wisdom. The king was robbed of fabulous wealth, called the cobbler to him, and said, You know all things. You know who the thieves are; tell me or I shall know *you* are one of them. I shall give you forty days in which to tell me who the thieves are, and where my stolen wealth is.

Very well, the poor cobbler said, and went home.

He told his wife what had happened.

Inasmuch as I have only forty days to live and cannot count, he said, please place forty dates in a jar so that each morning I may eat one, and when they are all gone I shall know my time is up.

The thieves also knew of his fame and were curious to know what was going on at his home, so they sent a man to climb onto his roof and keep watch. The man was on the roof when the cobbler took the jar and dropped one of the dates into his hand, saying, The *first* has come.

The thief said, Yes, he knows everything; and began to go; and the cobbler, placing the date in his mouth said, And the *first* has gone. And the thief also believed that the cobbler was truly wise.

The thief returned and told the other thieves, of whom there were forty in all, what had happened. They were of course very much upset and fearful; and yet they wished to verify the one thief's story, so the next day they sent another man with him to the roof of the cobbler.

The cobbler went to the date jar, dropped another into his hand and said, *two* have come; the thieves turned to go; the cobbler tossed the date into his mouth, and said, *two* have gone.

The two thieves returned and told their story. The next day they sent *three* and of course the cobbler spoke the third; in all they sent thirty-nine, and the cobbler believed the next day he would be dead, but the thieves came down from the roof and begged for mercy.

You know everything, they told the cobbler; we will return the king's wealth, and ten times more that we have stolen from others, if you will only ask him to spare our lives.

I will, the cobbler said; where is the wealth hidden?

You know, the thieves said; why do you play at games? It is on the hill at the foot of the third tree, on the road to Teheran.

The cobbler went to the king, told his story, the wealth was unearthed, the thieves were set free, and the cobbler was given much wealth himself.

He took the wealth and hurried away to another city, leaving his wife, knowing that the next time he faced a problem, he would not have the good luck he had been having. His wife married a bookkeeper with social ambitions. The cobbler didn't gamble his money and throw it away on loose women or anything like that; he just hid it in a hill somewhere and opened another cobbler's shop in the faraway city because he knew how to mend and make shoes and liked the work and enjoyed sleeping at night. For three centuries nobody found the wealth; then three centuries more went by; then the language of the people changed; another century went by; the cobbler had been dead all this time and nobody knew where the wealth was, so it just stayed there, and harmed no one.

Two Old Armenian Stories, and One New One

1. THE DISHONEST TRADERS

The present war, the political systems involved, and the way of the world at the moment is pretty well understood by remembering this little old country story.

A couple of crooks agreed to make a trade. Honest people knew them for what they were and refused to speak to them, let alone enter into relations with them. So the crooks, a little absurdly, and more by way of keeping in form, rather than to cheat one another, agreed to make a trade. The objects to be traded were negligible, so they could afford to be casual.

One had tobacco, the other a horse. They traded.

Now about the tobacco, one said to the other. I may as well tell you, it is old, moldy, and might, for all I know, be poisonous. If you must smoke it, don't inhale. That won't be easy to do anyway, as the tobacco is wet. You must hold a flame to it all the time.

That's all right, said the other. Now about the horse. Whatever you do, don't try to ride him. He's vicious. He's also blind and feeble-minded. In going downhill, hold the horse by the tail, so that he won't fall and roll down. In going uphill, hold the reins in your hand and lead him. Hold tight, or he'll fall backwards.

In this light, the trade appeared to be honest, and therefore unnecessary. Everything balanced perfectly. The whole transaction seemed rather absurd.

The man with the tobacco decided, however, that what the other had told him was nothing more than exaggeration, intended to confuse him and make him feel that he had been cheated. Consequently, he rolled a cigarette and began to smoke. The tobacco was wet. It was old and moldy, but still it was tobacco, so he inhaled. The result was that he was deathly ill for the rest of the night, and for a week very feeble.

The man with the horse, on the other hand, reasoning in much the same manner as the man with the tobacco, leaped upon the horse and very soon found himself flat on his back, which appeared to be broken, but was only fractured. With great effort he got up and traveled by foot to his home, holding the horse by the tail going downhill, and leading the horse uphill. He also decided to sell the horse.

The transaction had, in reality, been an honest one. Neither one nor the other had profited by it.

The crooks sat alone for weeks, troubling and brooding. At last each of them got to his feet, almost simultaneously, and said, Heygidi, I am an old man. Heygidi, I shall soon die. Heygidi, I must be honest from now on. Heygidi, in the last transaction, I cannot cheat. I get death, and death gets me. I get nothing, and death gets nothing. Heygidi, cheating, I was cheated. Heygidi, if I could only live again.

Death took the bodies of the two crooks and spread them deep into sterile earth. The following Spring the earth flamed with flowers.

Heygidi, said Death, even the carcass of a thief is food for hungry earth and color for the eager flowers.

Children came and picked the flowers. Heygidi, they cried with joy, this year God sent us flowers.

Thus, in ever deepening truth, the trade was a good and honest one, and nobody and nothing was cheated.

2. THE MAN WHO ALWAYS SAID PRAISE THE WISDOM OF GOD

A simple, smiling man once lived in a world no better and no worse than our world, so that, naturally, many unhappy events took place, some of them to him, who was so unimportant and humble. The simple man, however, was never distressed or spiritually destroyed by any event, no matter how cruel or unjust it might be. The first thing that would occur to him in the midst of tragedy, small or large, was to remember God and say, Praise the wisdom of God. He knows what He is doing.

This he said no matter what happened.

Consequently, he was regarded by idiots as a stupid man, whereas actually, he was simple, not stupid. In fact, in a quiet way, he was very wise.

Those who regarded him as fool decided one day to give his faith a real test. The man had a donkey. Next to his wife and nine children, it was the most valuable thing he had. With the help of the donkey he was able to earn enough money to support his family, to satisfy his hunger, and theirs, to sleep in a simple house, and to be pleased with the goodness of God.

So they took his donkey into the hills and tied it to a tree. When the simple man returned, he asked humbly, Where is my donkey?

Kurd thieves on horseback came and stole it, he was told.

The poor man saw his whole life now changed, and perhaps ruined, but nevertheless he said, Praise the wisdom of God. He knows what He is doing.

The others moved on with their donkeys, and the faithful man walked. After an hour he caught up with the others. Now, they too were without donkeys. Every one of them. Eleven of them, each without his donkey.

What has happened? the poor man said.

The others now appreciated the beauty of his faith, and told him the truth.

Kurd thieves on horseback came and stole our donkeys, they said.

Then we must all praise the wisdom of God, the poor man said.

Yes, said the others. We must all learn from you. Your donkey is safe, because you have always had true faith. Go into that hill. Your donkey is tied to a tree. We, in scorn, tied the donkey to the tree, and proved the power of your faith.

The poor man went into the hill and found his donkey, and rode home praising God.

3. THE MAN WHO PRAYED CONFIDENTIALLY

Prayer-meeting night in California twenty years ago always brought an old man to the Armenian Presbyterian Church, and there every Wednesday night this old man prayed, while everybody else listened carefully. This man prayed in a very powerful voice and with great— almost unbelievable—faith in his nearness to God. He gave the impression of being a close friend of God, perhaps a nephew. It was all very beautiful, and it is a pity that the man is now dead, and that nobody else, not even preachers, pray the way he used to pray.

Oh God, he used to get up and say, I have come to this little church again to put everything before you just as it is, not too much on one side and not too little on the other. I am still in good health, thanks to You. No complaints. On the way to the church, a thought occurred to me. I was walking in front of Mompreh's store on Santa Clara Avenue—with all the flies in it—flies on everything. Now don't You think a man like that, twenty-two years in this enlightened country, would get a fly-swatter and kill some of the flies? I thought to myself, oh Heavenly Father, is it true, or is it not true, that all things, all men, all living things come from You? Even flies. If this is so, and we believe it is, then don't you think a man, even the tenderest-hearted Christian, should not go too far in his interpretation of how to behave nobly in Your eyes? For instance, he could kill the flies, and it would be no harm to anybody. It would be a little trouble for him, but a man could go into the store for ten cents worth of sugar and not be attacked on all sides by flies. Oh God, we are all lost, ignorant souls, and except for Your wisdom to guide us, we should all die by morning, but don't You think the price of raisins is just a little bit too low? I'm not saying farmers should all get rich. I mean one can't help wondering if they shouldn't earn enough by the toil of their hands and the sweat of their brows, day after day and month after month, to earn enough money with which to buy bread enough for themselves and their families, and shoes for the children, and a little tobacco, and the other necessities of life? Oh, Most Generous Heavenly Father, all things come from You, I know. I was telling my friend Gorgotian about it this afternoon. As You know, he is an unbeliever, but a kind man. He loves music and is generous with his tobacco, but he doesn't believe. His sons send him money every month, so he always has tobacco, while I, Heavenly Father, sometimes run out of it. He is always glad to ask me in for six or seven cigarettes and a few cups of coffee, after which we tell our fortunes, but he is not a believer and hasn't set foot in any church, Presbyterian or any other kind, in fifteen years. I was telling him this afternoon, oh God, how all things come from You, and he said something that I hesitate to repeat to You, although of course I'm sure you know about it anyway. He said, All right, Mano, if all things come from God, pray for half a pound of Izmir tobacco and we'll have enough for a week. Well, of course, Oh Heavenly Father, I knew he was a good man. Otherwise, I would have been offended. I don't think you could find a nicer fellow in the whole Armenian neighborhood, but as I say, Oh God, he doesn't believe. There are surely others and You no doubt know them each by name, but they are most likely not as honest as he is. But Gorgotian isn't what I came to speak of. Like myself, he's passed seventy and in twenty or thirty years he'll be dead, but, Oh God, what about these kids growing up all around us? Don't You think their parents ought to take more pains with them? Of course everybody is busy in the summer working in the packinghouses, but even so, don't You think the mothers ought to spend at least a half hour every evening teaching the kids how to speak Armenian? Dozens of them can't answer a simple question, except in

English, which I don't understand. And about this war in Europe, Oh God, don't You think it's about time everybody stopped? Don't You think they've killed enough innocent young men already?

On the theme of war, and in this intimate manner, the old man would pray for at least forty minutes, sometimes an hour. The preacher of the church was not exactly pleased with this confidential kind of worship and one day said to the old man, It is good to pray, but perhaps you could be briefer.

How? the old man asked sincerely.

Well, said the preacher, when you come to big things like the War, pass over them quickly. Don't try to solve every problem in the world in every prayer you make.

No, the old man replied, that is impossible. If you insist that I shall not pray at all, then of course I shall not pray at all. But if I am to pray, you shall have to let me pray as I must. Prayer is an ocean which grows larger and larger as one swims in it.

So this wonderful old Christian was allowed to swim in the beautiful ocean every Wednesday night until finally eighteen years later, he died and at last reached the shore where, no doubt, God was waiting impatiently for him, so that they could talk everything over carefully, point by point.

AXIS

By the time he was through work, he was talking to himself on account of (a) the heat, (b) the lousy war, (c) Mr. Pragg, the maniagg, (d) Helen, and (e) everything.

The work was to get out all the lousy letters they were sending to people who owed them money, the ones in which the vice-president said, Now, we know this is merely an oversight on your part, even though you have ignored twenty-seven letters during the past eleven months. However. However nothing. The people are broke or something, so leave them alone. Believe you me.

The heat was super super super, and super. How can you work when it's so hot all you want to do is lie down under an apple tree and go to sleep while mockingbirds sing? Apple tree? Lie down *anywhere* and sleep.

And I do mean you, he said. Yes, you. He was referring to himself. Also to Mr. Pragg, the maniagg. The slave driver. All right, Charlie, shake a leg. What's the matter? Dreaming? No, Mr. Pragg, you maniagg, he said, I ain't dreaming, I'm lazy.

And the war. The great big beautiful war. Pfooie. What are you going to do with a guy like that with a pfooie moustache like that, nervous all the time? Me, he said, and I do mean *me*, I shall put the cards on the table.

Mr. Hitler?

Yes?

Shut up.

That's all. Not another word. Get your little toys out and play soldier on the linoleum. Ah—ah. Not another word. No more speeches.

Shut up.

Blitzkrieg your left eye.

Axis.

And Helen, the bright-eyed, the magnificent, thy beauty is to me. Helen, this is telling. Will you marry me, or won't you? Helen, the one and only.

And everything. Work, heat, war, Mr. Pragg, Helen. Everything.

Now, Helen, how about a Rome-Berlin axis somewhere down around in here where we are? How about blitzkrieg and a swift defeat of the license bureau, and a quick peace. The world's waiting. Everybody's listening to the radio waiting for the good word.

In the street, he ducked into Moran's and ordered beer.

Beer, he said. Blitzkrieg.

What? the bartender said.

Axis, Nemo, axis, he said. He swallowed the beer. All of it, and sighed, feeling better. Certainly cooler.

What are you talking about? Nemo said.

Now, Mr. Hitler, the young man said, that'll be enough out of you.

Mr. Hitler? Nemo said. *Who?*

Beer, the young man said. Nemo, he said, I love a girl named Helen. Hitler talks to Chamberlain. Chamberlain talks to Daladier. Daladier inhales on his cigarette. Helen moves fifty-seven miles south to Gilroy. Germany invades Poland. The *Athenia* is sunk. The *Bremen* is captured. Beer, my friend, beer. We're sending letters to people who are broke. If they don't pay this time, we're going to execute them.

What's the matter? the bartender said.

Axis, the young man said.

What?

Treaty, he said. Non-aggression . . . Russia and Germany. Seen the paper?

Sure, Nemo said. It's hot, yeah, So what's a little heat?

Blitzkrieg, he said.

Mr. Hitler, he told Mr. Hitler, I don't want to hear any more about it. One of us has got to go, and it ain't going to be me. There isn't room enough for *both* of us in this romance, and I was here first.

Beer, he said to the bartender. That's all I want.

He decided to drink a long time, go home, sleep, get up in the morning, tell the landlady to phone Pragg and say he was sick, get on a bus and go to Gilroy, find the street, the number of the house, walk up to the door, knock and when Helen came out, smile, and put the cards on the table. Helen, I hate war. I love you.

Not another word.

The old bartender looked at the young man while he drank beer and swam out into the big sea, zigzagging to avoid submarines and things like that. The old bartender smiled, because he was pretty sure it meant something, even if he didn't know what, exactly.

Four Little Armenian Stories

I

The priest turned to the man who had stabbed him in the back, studied his face carefully, and, dying, said, Why do you kill me? I have never done you a kindness.

II

A man had a cello with one string over which he drew the bow for hours at a time, holding his finger in one place. His wife endured this noise for seven months, waiting patiently for the man to either die of boredom or destroy the instrument. Inasmuch as neither of these desirable things happened, however, one night she said, in a very quiet voice, too, you may be sure: I have observed that when others play that magnificent instrument, there are four strings over which to draw the bow, and the players move their fingers about continuously. The man stopped playing a moment, looked at his wife wisely, shook his head, and said, You are a woman. Your hair is long, your sense short. Of course the others have four strings and move their fingers about constantly. They are looking for the place. I've found it.

III

When the cow came from the meadow busily swinging its tail, the hen said, Ho ho, by the time *you* arrive, I have already sent the guests on their way. Ho ho.

IV

An unhappy boy, visiting the home of his father's friend, was given a toy sword and a toy pistol to drive away his sorrow. The boy raced about the house, destroying enemies of many kinds and making so much noise that it was impossible for his father and his father's friend to talk to one another, which they wanted very much to do. The father asked the boy to quiet down a little if possible. It was not, however, completely possible, so that, beginning quietly, the small boy gradually returned to his loud slaughtering of the enemy, and was again asked to quiet down. Same result. Quiet for a moment, noisier than ever after a moment. Another request. Same result. Finally, the father, who had heard that severity is a good thing sometimes with children, not realizing that his son was not children, but a personality, a real person, snatched the toy sword and the toy pistol away from the boy and put them out of reach. This irritated the boy and revealed to him that his real enemy was his father, which was a terrible thing to realize, and definitely something to cry about, which he did with great power and some beautifully losing of breath and so on. This, of course, was still worse than the battle racket of the boy.

Oh, give him back his toys, the boy's father's friend suggested.

No, the father said.

Please do, the other said. How the poor boy cries. My goodness, he is truly brokenhearted.

No, the father said. I shall not capitulate this time. I came to talk with you.

Oh, give him his sword and his gun and let the boy destroy the world if he wishes, the friend said.

Well, all right, then, the father said.

He offered the toys to the boy, but now the boy had no use for them. This irritated his father very much.

Here, he said. Here is your sword. Here is your gun. Fire away. Cut away.

No, the boy said.

He began to cry worse than ever.

The friend decided to help out, if possible. The boy was standing at the window, with his back turned, sobbing tragically and vigorously, Six years ago the friend had gone to a carnival and had tried to win a pearl-handled automatic revolver, but instead had won a kewpie doll. It was made of chalk and was the most ridiculous image imaginable, neither human nor anything else. An absurdity. For some reason he had decided, however, to keep the thing on the chance that it might come in handy someday, somehow.

The time, apparently, had come.

He hurried to the closet in which he kept all the debris that accumulates over the years around a man, and brought out the kewpie. He hurried to the crying boy and said, Please do not cry anymore. If you will stop crying, you may have *this*. Here the friend brought the kewpie from behind him and thrust it out to the boy. The boy took the ridiculous doll and stopped crying. For fully two minutes he studied the doll in absolute silence, while his father and the friend studied *him*. The tears dried on his cheeks, he looked up critically at his father and his father's friend and, in the most powerful Armenian in the world he said simply, I'll take it home and break it.

This last story is my favorite Armenian story, and I tell it as often as possible, both in English and in Armenian, but nobody so far has laughed at it. Therefore, I explain the story. This also gets the story nowhere. Nobody thinks it's funny, that's all.

I think it is very funny.

The Great Day Coming
(A Fragment of a Play)

The corner of Grant Avenue and Jackson Street, Chinatown, San Francisco.

An American saloon with swinging doors.

About nine o'clock at night.

A group of street revivalists, not members of The Salvation Army, are concluding the Evening's Service by playing and singing the famous old Protestant song, "Leaning on the Everlasting Arms."

The group consists of a girl of eighteen who plays a saxophone. A paunchy man of fifty or so who plays a cornet. A woman of forty-five or so who sings loudly and wiggles a tambourine. An old Chinese who beats a drum and sings. A fat Mexican woman with a spiritual face who just stands, probably a little confused and embarrassed. A young man of twenty-three who plays a portable xylophone and sings. A tall evil-faced old man who keeps saying, Glory. Glory to God.

The young people of this group are shabby, unimpressive, and ineffectual. The old people are dull or deranged.

The group's constant and faithful audience consists of three small Chinese boys in overalls, almost squeezed together in a combination of fear, amazement, horror, and delight; and a small Chinese girl, who stands a little apart from them.

They are all wide-eyed, not amused, but surely fascinated, and definitely unconvinced. The eternal heathens, pure, superior, whole, and beautiful to behold.

Men coming out of the saloon are:

Three American sailors. They drop money on the small drum for the revivalists, who gratefully acknowledge the generosity by singing louder for three seconds.

A small, well-dressed man, epileptically cockeyed, but brilliantly under control. He spends half a minute listening to the revivalists, staying under control, and disbelieving. He then turns and goes back into the saloon.

A bewildered young man, probably unhappily involved in an impossible romance, who listens a moment, joins in the singing a moment, and then walks away.

The song ends. The revivalists begin to pack up. The Chinese children break away from the morbid spell, and say a few words to one another in Chinese. A Chinese newsboy, aged forty-seven, arrives in great excitement with the first edition of the Chinese morning paper and calls out the news in shrill Chinese.

The revivalists move to go, in silence.

Tyler Maxwell, a magnificent figure of a man, comes out of the saloon, notices the revivalists about to go.

TYLER: (booming, sharp voice; dynamic expression of face; ferocious and accusing gesture) Just a moment. (The people come to a halt as one body, scared to death.) Dearly beloved. Just a moment. (He goes to where they had stood. They become the audience. He becomes the preacher.) I shall preach to you. (Swiftly) Precious one. (Pointing at the Chinese children.) And to you, sweet and gentle heathens. (Back to the revivalists.) With neither horn, tambourine, nor drum—for you—since you are inarticulate and lost—lost in ignorance, that is—I shall praise God. Listen. (Pause, while he appears to commune. He speaks slowly, sharply, effectively.) The Lord. Is in his holy temple. Let all the earth keep silence before him.

The old Chinese newsboy calls out the news in Chinese.

TYLER: I said the Lord is in his temple. (Shouting.) Quiet. I have news myself. Quiet. Quiet. (The Chinese stops singing the news, comes over and stands behind the children.) Listen. All of you, whether you understand or not. Let the meditation of my heart be the words of my mouth. My words, your solace and delight. (He places a hand on the head of one of the Chinese boys.) We shall make straight in the desert of ignorance a highway. Walk out upon it and move forward into the light. I bring good tidings of great joy, which shall be to all people (A woman with packages stops to listen.) Bless you, Mary, the light is upon thy brow. (Roaring.) Now. Lord, I have loved the habitation of thy house.

And so forth and so on. He gets drunk to the glory of God.

Two Long Novels, Condensed

I. YOU CAN HAVE EVERYTHING

The land gathered momentum gracefully as it approached the small creek, and after that kept rolling to the small dry hills, then leaped into the larger rocky hills, and far away were the mountains which seemed to be made of blue rock. The Coast Ranges, they were called; on the other side, or rather in the other direction, the smooth valley land traveled in much the same manner to the mountains called the Sierra Nevadas. In between these two ranges, in the great valley, were the people—which is boring and was put down to be so—just to show you he, the writer, could do it. The only hitch, the writer knows, is the small creek. What's the small creek doing there? What's the creek got to do with anything?

The truth of the matter is the small creek has nothing to do with anything. It is just a small creek there in the valley. Water through land, over pebbles and rocks.

What's more, it was raining and the skies were black. When the writer says it was raining he means it was raining torrentially. The writer believes that's how writers put it. Nothing, however, ricocheted, the writer hopes. This rain continued to fall this way, that is, torrentially, for hours; for days; for weeks. During these weeks of rain it happened, although in another place. Up in San Francisco, as a matter of fact, two hundred miles from the storm. In December of that year.

He was a young sprout who knew deeply that you could have everything and was out to prove it, at the age of twenty-three, and did prove it, before the storm ended.

Do you want to know how he got everything? Of course you do.

He got it by dying. Then the storm ended and there was light in the big valley.

It's all a long novel, condensed.

II. YOUNG RED

This is one of those absurd, fantastic, unreal, super-real stories which sometimes occur to a writer but are never put down on paper—one of those delightful comedies that are real only to the imagination of a writer disgusted with the world.

What happens is that everybody in power is killed one day; the world is horrified, but in less than a month everything is back to normal, and new men are in control of the same power; everything seems to be all right again; the wars are resumed, the exploitation is resumed, and the way of the world appears to be the valid and only way once again. So far the comedy hasn't started. It really gets going when all these new men are killed. Once again the world is horrified, but not quite as horrified as a month before. About fifty percent of the people of the world are delighted, as a matter of fact. For about two months there is great confusion in important circles of the world, but after a while once again new men are in power and the world is well under control. About a week goes by and then the comedy begins to be hilarious: all the new men in power are killed. Every one of them: this includes everybody who in one way or another exploits people. Some of the exploiters seem to be relatively innocent and relatively good, but the power which is responsible for this destruction cannot be bothered. If they exploit they are killed, that's all.

Of course, following each wiping out of these powerful men there is violent partisanship all over the world. Nobody knows who is responsible for the strange events. It isn't Communism because the Communist executives have three times been killed, too. In fact it isn't any known form of control, or exploitation. Once again each region furnishes new men to carry on the old program. Once again they are all killed. This continues until new men have been furnished twelve times and have been twelve times destroyed.

And then nobody will accept the new higher positions and the chairs of power all over the world are empty. Exactly twenty-four thousand people have been killed, which is a great deal less than the number killed in one day of a medium-sized war. Not even a drop in the bucket, and yet the whole world has been changed.

There is no longer Capitalism, Communism, Fascism, or any other kind of unnatural order.

But as I say it's absurd and would never do. The twenty-four thousand would all be named instead of nameless. And after they were killed somebody else would have to be named instead of nameless.

It's ridiculous, and also a long novel, condensed.

Lauri

The most stupid Garoghlanian that ever lived, not counting a woman named Doudouk who died at the age of ninety-seven in 1884, was a giant of a man named Lauri. He was born in the family house ten years before the stupid woman died, and reached America in 1910 at the age of thirty-six. In spite of his stupidity—which was exalted—this man was not disliked by his relatives, and his shortcoming, or talent, was never dwelt upon by anyone. He knew nothing, and couldn't learn. In a conversation, all he could do was listen and not be impressed one way or another. He had an air of being continuously acquainted with everybody, a total

stranger every minute of the day, all his life. And yet he knew everyone—at least by sight, if not often by name. He didn't speak Armenian
very well.

When he was ten years old his grandmother spoke of him as being
poetic, and his grandfather said, He is shy—nothing more. He'll be as
noisy as any of the rest of us in twenty or thirty years. Everybody
accepted this theory and began to wait, while Lauri sat around eating
every meal and retiring early every evening. He was a very handsome
man, too. A picture of calm and strength. A stranger once asked of him,
Is he an Armenian? To which Lauri's grandmother replied, He is a poet.
He belongs to no nationality. He is his own nationality.

This irritated Lauri's grandfather, who said, He is not only an Armenian, he is a Garoghlanian. He is not only a Garoghlanian, he is a
handsome Garoghlanian, he is a strong one. Here, boy, break this chair.

Lauri was thirty-three at the time. He took the chair from his grandfather's hands and very peacefully broke it into eight or nine pieces, each
of which he returned, one at a time, to his waiting grandfather.

The stranger got up and thanked everybody for a delightful evening,
although he had just arrived. He didn't speak of the incident to anyone—not even his mother.

The rest of the evening the whole family went to work trying to repair
the chair which Lauri had not broken at the joints, but every which way.
The chair was never the same again and was silently regarded by
everyone as a monument to the love the family had for Lauri, and the
hatred it had for ignorant passersby who found him odd. Someone
would forget and sit in the chair, and hearing it creak, on the verge of
breaking to pieces, get to his feet quickly and say, That ridiculous
stranger, asking if Lauri is an Armenian.

As a matter of fact, Lauri did not look the least bit what Armenians
themselves come to believe Armenians look like, although he was
unmistakably a Garoghlanian, and, in fact, not greatly different in
features from his grandfather, who was himself less brilliant than proud
and less astute than easily irritated.

After two years, the broken chair was regarded by everyone as broken
by the stranger, who was utterly innocent and actually eager, if not
overeager, to be friendly. If someone happened to take hold of the chair,
some member of the immediate family would say, Don't take that
chair—it was broken one night by a crazy man. It's repaired again, but
the glue isn't dry yet.

When he reached New York Lauri was so stupid he didn't even seem
bewildered by the strange new city. He had an eleven-year-old nephew
with him of course, but as many as eight Garoghlanians arriving in New
York at one time, more than half of them full-grown, had been bewildered by the amazing and terrifying city.

Where is America? Lauri asked the boy.

This is America, the boy explained.

Where is the family? Lauri said.

Most of them are in California, the boy said.

What country is California? Lauri said.

It's the same country, the boy said. America. Only a different part of the country.

Well, Lauri said, let's walk quickly and see everybody again.

It's three thousand six hundred and seventy-two miles away, the boy said.

Do we have to take another boat? Lauri said.

No, the boy said. A train.

When Lauri was brought to California by his eleven-year-old nephew, all the Garoghlanians went to the Southern Pacific Depot in Fresno to welcome him to the new world and the new life. From the train he saw the family, and said, Those are Armenians, or some other people that has many children.

Those, the boy said, are all Garoghlanians—our family. They are here to welcome you.

The big man smiled and got down from the train. He went straight to a middle-aged Mexican who was standing half-asleep on the station platform.

My dear Uncle Vanik, he said in Armenain, it is so good to see you again.

The boy took him swiftly to his own people, while the Mexican hurried away, in confusion, for another drink.

Lauri, in all truth, a poet. Not only that, a philosopher.

Not only that, he believed in the brotherhood. That is to say, the brotherhood of all people to himself, Lauri. No exceptions. He was as great a stranger to his own family as to any man who might appear on Ventura Avenue and then disappear forever.

The family was delighted to see him. It is good for a family to be able to transplant itself from one world to another, traveling centuries and thousands of miles, and still have all or most of its people around and in good form. With the arrival of Lauri the family became more or less complete, and there was no telling what might happen.

When I speak of Lauri as being stupid, I am unfair to him, owing to the sorrowful limitations of the English language. Lauri was never exactly stupid. He seemed to be, but he wasn't really. What he really was, was immortal. He was born immortal. That is to say, the world was an alien place to him, and he never tried to change it to a familiar place. People were alien to him, and he never tried to become acquainted with them. Everything was alien to him, and he had no compelling impulse to understand the mystery, the way all the rest of us have. Lauri simply lived quietly and paid no attention to it. He simply breathed and stood by.

This is not the whole story of Lauri Garoghlanian. It is, however, all I have to say about him just now. I suppose some rainy day I shall find it impossible not to try to tell the whole story of his quiet, poetic life, which I am sure pleased God, although it irritated some people who had no imagination, and didn't know an immortal when they saw one.

The Boy from Kingsburg

He lived in a sort of two-room apartment on a mean street, and worked in a department store selling books. He was in love with a girl who worked in the same department store selling imitation jewelry. He was nineteen and away from home. He liked San Francisco all right, only he didn't know anybody. He knew everybody in Kingsburg. A year of living in Kingsburg was like nothing: the year went by and that was all there was to it: it just went by. But in San Francisco it was different. He had been in San Francisco a little over three months. It seemed like any number of years. It seemed like any number of long years.

It was because he didn't know anybody. He had met a lot of people and liked some of them and had had lunch and dinner with some of them. He had had lunch and dinner with the girl who sold imitation jewelry, and had talked with her and fallen in love with her.

The trouble was he didn't know her.

He wanted to know all about her. He was alone and a single day of twenty-four hours was like a year, because he couldn't get out of the city idea of time: the idea of passing time. Sometimes a single hour would seem like a whole year. In Kingsburg he had never known what it was to be aware of time going by. He had never known anything at all about time. There hadn't been any such thing. All he had done was eat and sleep and go to school and drive the roadster around and visit one or another of the many girls he had known many years.

Then the bottom fell out: all of a sudden he decided he wanted to leave home. He decided he didn't want to live in Kingsburg any more. There was something the matter with living in Kingsburg. There was something the matter with not feeling involved in something: the movement of the world-body, the world-man. He got this feeling now and then in books and it made him dislike Kingsburg. Finally he decided to leave the little town and go to San Francisco. After San Francisco he would go to New York, and after New York he would go to Europe, and before he died he would go to every important city of the world, every out-of-the-way place of the world where the living were living.

He would go about the world and try to find out.

His idea was to get a job on a newspaper, because having a job on a newspaper would mean getting close to *the thing*, the world-energy, the world-heart, and it would mean knowing about everything that happened everywhere. It would mean being in the midst of everything, which he wished put down on paper.

He decided to expose himself to the world and find out how it affected him and find out if he could put it down in what he believed would be a new kind of language. He didn't know many words and the words he did know, that he knew deeply, were words he didn't like and words he believed were unsatisfactory. He knew words like *nothing, crazy, lousy, phony*. He knew all the other words too, only they didn't mean anything. They were all right, only in his language they were nothing: truth, nothing; beauty, nothing; and so on. He couldn't understand words of that kind at all. If they meant by truth that two times two is four, he would know what they meant, but what about everything? What about all the people, all the places? What did it come to? And if they meant by beauty the shape of space in the sky on a clear day, he could understand that too, but what about everything again?

What he wanted to do was find out about the whole thing, all of it together. What was the force in living things that moved? What was the force in living things that did not move? What was the power of integration in things which did not live, but had shape and weight and reality? What was it that kept everything together? The body of man, every small part of the body. What kept everything together in the first place?

He had to have a job, so he decided to try to get a job on a newspaper. He tried very hard, but didn't get a job. They said he was too young to be a reporter and too old to be a copyboy. They got a big kick out of his seriousness and the way he talked.

Then he tried a lot of other places and one of the places was the department store. He showed up just in time. One of the clerks in the book department was sick, and another was quitting his job in several days. They asked him if he knew anything about selling books and he said he had read a lot of books but hadn't sold any. They didn't have much time, so they decided to give him a job temporarily. A week at the most. He himself said he didn't know if he would like selling books. That was a big laugh in the employment department of the store. They thought that was very funny.

Well, he liked selling books less than he liked doing anything else, but for some reason he sold a lot of them. He sold more books than any other clerk in the store. When the sick clerk got well and came back to his job, they didn't tell the boy from Kingsburg not to come to work the next day. He just kept his job. The manager of the book department couldn't make up his mind how this new clerk sold so many books because, by rights, he was the worst salesman in the whole department.

A lady would ask him if he had read a novel she was thinking of buying, and he would say he hadn't read it. He would say he had read the first page of the book and hadn't seen any reason why he should read the second. If the lady didn't buy the novel, she would buy six or seven other books, sometimes technical ones that ladies as a rule never care to read. The lady would usually buy the novel, though, because she wouldn't want to be influenced by such a young and naive person's obviously immature opinion.

He seemed bored most of the time, very unhappy and lonely in a way that was peculiarly his own. He was never enthusiastic about a book, a writer, or anything in a book, or anything anywhere. All the books put together were one of his words: *nothing*. On top of everything else, he never behaved as a clerk should behave. He was, in fact, rude.

He would be selling a book, for instance, and he would open it and a very distasteful expression would come into his face, and he would begin to read a paragraph somewhere and the distasteful expression would grow more distasteful, and he would forget all about the customer. Sometimes he would even back away into a corner, as if to get away from the customer, as if to get as far away as possible from everybody and everything, and then he would seem very much alone in the world. And yet a number of the wealthier customers found his personality so remarkable and so curious that they invited him into their homes.

He went, too, but never with enthusiasm. The manager of the book department sat in his chair and tried to figure the whole thing out. He couldn't do it, though, and was on the verge of firing the boy every day. He couldn't do that either.

The boy himself couldn't figure out anything, only unlike the manager of the book department and apparently unlike everybody else in the world he wanted to keep on trying to figure out everything.

He couldn't figure out the smell of his two-room apartment, and he couldn't figure out the mean street, but most of all he couldn't figure out the mean people of the mean street: the poor, sullen-faced, weary, dull-eyed, dreaming people of the street.

And he couldn't figure out the girl he loved, and he couldn't figure out love.

He could figure out the girl he loved as a girl, but he couldn't figure her out as something in the world, out of time, suddenly there, that he must want so desperately, and he couldn't figure out the wanting. All right, she was young, her face was good to see, her arms were lovely arms, her body was a good body, but why did there seem to be so much of mystery in her body, in the girl herself, seen and unseen, even after he had spoken to her, even after he had found out for himself that within her was no depth, no mystery? Why was that so?

He could figure out everything the easy way, but he couldn't figure out anything the hard way, and he didn't like figuring out everything the easy way and not being able to figure out anything the hard way.

Day was especially troublesome: when it was day the world-body wakened and began to move in the world, performing the wakeful half of the activity of living, and he couldn't figure out why the activity was invariably so petty, so pointless, so concerned with insignificant things, so harassed, so deeply troubled by a million kinds of fear.

Night was even more troublesome because then the time-body, the world-body, became the timeless-body, the worldless-body, the universe-body, and closed its eyes and slept and dreamed. And he couldn't figure out the dream.

He was lonely, but proudly so, and he couldn't figure out why the intensity of his loneliness increased when he was with the girl, and why, when he was with her, the depth of his question, which was all interrogation at once, why-who-what-when-where, grew with every instant of seeing her face and being in her presence until finally it reached chaos and nothingness, and he lighted a cigarette and smiled at her and said something any fool might say.

All this, within himself, was pretty much unknown and unsuspected by others, and most people, except for swift flashes, regarded him as a very naive and inexperienced and nice country boy.

He sometimes even laughed, but he knew, even though others did not, that he was laughing one or another of the words he knew deeply: *nothing, crazy, phony, pathetic.*

One night, four months after he had been in San Francisco, and two months after he had been in love with the girl, he could not sleep, even though he was very tired, even though it was very late. In the darkness of his room, he was awake. His eyes were open in the darkness, and his vision in the darkness was very clear. Although he could see only *nothing,* over and over again, he became very frightened. He was wide awake and greatly in need of sleep, and he began to be so fearfully afraid, not for him alone but for all who lived, that he had to get up out of bed, leaping suddenly, and turn on the light and put on his clothes.

It was very sad the way the darkness and nothingness remained with him after he had turned on the light, and it was very sad the way he busted out laughing because it was so sad, because everything the world-body had ever done was so pathetic, because everything everywhere was so pathetic.

He decided to put on fresh clothes, as far as possible, and it was very melancholy to look upon a brand new shirt, neatly pinned, and to remove the pins as if doing so were an activity of the profoundest importance, and to put on the shirt, and to put on new socks, and to tie a new tie, and to lace his shoes, and to put his hat on his head, and to light a cigarette and inhale.

There was no clock or watch in his apartment. When he went down to the street and glanced at the clock in the barber shop he saw that it was a quarter after twelve. The street was empty and it was very still and black in the world. He walked six blocks to a street where people were stirring and found a cab and got in. He told the driver to drive down the street, and after a while he gave the driver the girl's address and the driver turned the cab around and began to hurry in the opposite direction.

The house was dark. He walked three blocks to a drugstore and dialed the girl's telephone number. It wasn't her number. It was her father's number. The bell of the telephone rang four times before somebody lifted the receiver. It was the girl, wakened from sleep. He could tell she had been wakened from sleep by the way her tongue and lips articulated words.

What's the matter? she said.

I've got to see you right away, he said.

What's the matter? the girl said.

I'll tell you when I see you, he said. Put some clothes on and come right down. I'll be standing in front of the house.

What's the matter? the girl said.

I've got to see you, he said.

All right, the girl said. I'll put some clothes on and come right down. What time is it?

It's early, he said. It's as early as it ever will be. I'll be standing in front of the house.

All right, the girl said.

He walked out of the drugstore and went up the quiet street toward the girl's house. He was smiling foolishly, knowing now he would never know anything about anything, the same as everybody else in the world.

Old Country Stories, Part II

1. THE BALD-HEADED MAN, THE MAN WITH THE RUNNING NOSE, AND THE MAN WITH THE CROOKED LEG

These three were together one day, the bald man scratching his head, the man with the running nose rubbing away the water, and the man with the crooked leg straightening it out all the time, each to relieve his discomfort.

The bald man said, Let us see which of us shall be able to forget his discomfort longest.

It was agreed.

Flies lighted on the bald one's head and began to open the sores. The irritation increased until it was insufferable pain, so this one said, My friends, when I was a boy my father went to Constantinople and returned with a fez for me. It was an extraordinary fez. I would put it on top of my head this way and it would fall off; I would put it on over my left ear, in this manner, and again it would fall off; I would put it on over my right ear; again it would fall off; then I would put it on at the back of my head; then at the front; but no matter how or where I put it on, it would fall off.

Explaining in this manner about the fez, the bald-headed man drove away the flies, scratched his head all over, and relieved his discomfort.

The other two saw the cleverness of his performance. The man with the running nose said, How strange that when I was a boy my father should have gone to Constantinople too. He returned with a very fine rifle of German manufacture and used my nose for a target. One shot went this way; another this way; another this way; until the gun had been emptied.

In this manner the man with the running nose relieved his discomfort.

The man with the crooked leg was in great pain by this time and wondered what his father should fetch from Constantinople that would relieve his pain. The longer he thought, the more certain he became that nothing from Constantinople or anywhere else, when he was a boy or at any other time, could enable him to lift his crooked leg and kick it about.

He lifted his crooked leg and, kicking it about, said, If what you have said is the truth, let this crooked leg in this manner kick your fathers about through all hell, throughout all eternity.

2. THE KING AND THE BLIND MAN

A king was told that the blind of his realm were greedy and deceitful. How can that be? he said. They cannot see; how can they be greedy and deceitful? He was told to go to the blind and see for himself.

He went to this place of the blind and stood among them. When he had found one who seemed to have a saintly face he said, A kind man passing in this street gave me a gold coin.

The blind man said, My hand has never touched a gold coin. Please let me hold the coin.

The king said, It is like all other coins, except that it is larger and heavier.

I have never touched a gold coin, the blind man said. That is a thing I want to do before I die. Please let me hold the coin a moment. I will give it back to you.

The king handed the coin to the blind man. The blind man moved away silently and hid behind a rock. The king called out, Where are you, my friend? Please give me back my gold coin.

There was no answer.

The king called out again, but again there was no answer. He went close to the hiding blind man, lifted a rock, and said, Almighty God, let this rock find the head of the greedy, deceitful blind man who has stolen my coin of gold. He then bounced the rock off the head of the blind man. The blind man said to himself, That was accidental; pure bad luck for me, that's all.

The king picked up another rock and said, Almighty God, let this rock find the ankle of the blind thief. He then bounced the rock off the blind man's ankle.

The blind man said, His good luck is extraordinary.

The king picked up another rock and said, Almighty God, let this rock find the eyes of the blind thief.

Then the thief leaped to his feet and said, You keep Almighty God out of this; here's your lousy gold coin; you've got eyes and it ain't fair.

3. THE LION AND THE AMBITIOUS RABBIT

A lion wakened from sleep one afternoon and began to roar, waking all the sleeping animals for miles around. A rabbit wakened and saw all the other animals running away and hiding. The rabbit said, Why should the lion roar that way and make everybody run and hide? Why shouldn't I roar and drive them away too? So the rabbit began to roar. The rabbit roared with all its might. The roar was a squeak that a hungry fox heard. The fox came and pawed the rabbit's head, killing it, and said, You are a rabbit, not a lion; in the future remember your place.

4. THE DEAF VILLAGER, THE DEAF SHEPHERD, THE DEAF HUSBAND WHO HAS QUARRELED WITH HIS WIFE AND LEFT HIS HOME, AND THE DEAF JUDGE

Ramazan is the Mohammedan time of fasting. It endures about thirty days, when the time becomes the time of *beiram* and fasting again. *Ramazan* ends when three of the faithful go to the top of a hill, sight the new moon, return to the city, raise their hands, and swear that they have seen the new moon. Then guns are fired and it is *bieram.*

On the third day of *Ramazan* seventy or eighty years ago a deaf villager found two sheep in a street over which a half hour before a shepherd had passed with his flock. The villager said, I am a man famous for my honesty; I will return the two lost sheep to the shepherd.

He drove the sheep before him out of the village into the hills toward the shepherd. One of the sheep was lame in the right front leg.

A deaf husband quarreled with his wife and in a fury left the house, shouting that he would never return as long as he lived. He was through forever. To hell with her and her everlasting nagging. There was a limit to everything.

He began walking toward the hills.

The villager reached the deaf shepherd and said, My brother, my honesty is known throughout the width and breadth of the land. My name is Osman. Here are your sheep.

The deaf shepherd said, Son of Heaven, take this sheep with the lame leg for yourself.

The villager said, What is the meaning of this? I am good enough to return your lost sheep to you, and now you tell me I broke the creature's leg. What kind of a man are you anyway?

Please, said the shepherd. It was kind of you to return the sheep, but why should you insist on having a whole sheep instead of the crippled one? You are only going to slaughter and eat it. Why should you object to a broken leg?

The shepherd and the villager saw the angry husband stumbling about in the hills and called out to him, so that he might help them settle their argument.

I see, the husband said. They know of my quarrel and want me to go back to my wife. Well, they can mind their own business. No matter what they say, I'll not do it.

He joined the other two. The villager said, My name is Osman. My family is famous for its honesty these last seven generations. I found this man's lost sheep in the village and drove them before me three miles. I have returned the sheep to him and now he says I have broken one of the sheep's legs. That sheep, he shouted bitterly, was lame from the beginning.

Please listen to me, my friend, the shepherd said to the angry husband. All that I ask is that he take the lame sheep for himself instead of the whole one. I'm deeply grateful to him for his kindness in returning the sheep to me. I am rewarding him, but why should he demand a whole sheep? You be the judge. Am I right or not?

Speak all you like, the deaf husband said. I've quarreled with her for the last time. I'm through with her. No power in heaven or hell will get me to go back to that house. Talk to the end of time and still you won't get me to go back.

This discussion went on for a half hour, each man insisting that he was right. They came down from the hills to the village, to the court of the deaf Judge. One at a time, the villager, the shepherd, and the angry husband raised his hand and told his story. The deaf Judge listened to the end, then said, Three of the faithful have sworn that they have seen the new moon. Tell the villagers to fire the guns. *Ramazan* is ended. It is now *beiram*.

My Witness Witnesseth

A number of things have been asking to get on paper, but they have been asking at such unusual hours that by the time I have been ready to get them down on paper they have been forgotten.

They ask, for instance, at two in the morning when I want to sleep.

Naturally, I refuse to get up and go to work at that hour, so by way of compromise I turn over, go to sleep, and in the morning remember that I had an idea, but that now it is lost.

Some of these ideas are (if they could only be remembered) great; historical; important; likely to improve living for everybody; likely to change the whole behavior of man; and so on.

Last night, for instance. What an ocean of an idea: how smiling and kindly it was: how simple: how much a part of every man's heart: how miraculous and ordinary: how beautifully commonplace and, until last night, inexpressible.

An Englishman like H. G. Wells, even in his youth, even in his old age, would have gotten up in the middle of the night with a vision like that, taken it by the tail, and out of it written a book.

But what do I do? I turn over and go to sleep. I get up in the morning with wonder forgotten; prowl around in memory over coffee looking for the vision; prowl around after coffee; remember numerous forgotten fragments of no use now; little smiling pebbles of the great universe, little patches of shore, single waves of sea, and so on, but not the ray of light with the world in it which I knew half-asleep, which knew itself to be immortal, which knew it needed myself and a little language in order to be real for others, which asked for language, which I sought to remember, and by morning forgot.

Well, such is the life of the lazy writer. The fool puts sleep above revelation. He would rather dream the ordinary dream of the ordinary sleep (whether it be Freudian, Marxian, Christian, legendary, surrealist, antideath, or what, or how, or when, or whichever), and in the morning rise and seek to write the foolish story of the foolish waste of everything in the living, naming, for argument's sake, the world as the criminal, naming the wretched story "The Criminal World," itemizing the misdemeanors of the world, taking inventory of the mayhem of the world, the arson, the theft, the false witness, the murder, the rape, the sodomy of it, the confounded violation of article 632 of the Civil Statute of the State of California, or anything at all: telling a wretched story that gets nowhere, means nothing, except that the writer is a fool, that he ought to take a thousand years out of the next month and meditate long and piously on what the hell's going on and see if, by the Grace of God, he can't understand something and say something.

My witness witnesseth that at the age of twelve I was a better writer than I am now, a better writer than H. G. Wells ever was, a better writer in fact than almost any writer who ever lived ever was, except that I did not know how to write, and now, knowing how, I must openly say I have, I regret to say, lost the way, lost the vision, lost the world I knew must be made real, lost the realm of truth I knew was in myself, lost everything in fact except the few odd fragments of the commonplace world which so easily fit themselves into the so easily written words of the so easily sidetracked fool I have become.

You write of yourself, they say—the critics, relatives, good friends, and people who aren't friends at all, each with his own implication. That is what they all say, each with his feebleness implied. It all reads well enough. It is all entertaining enough. It is all quite interesting, but it is always about yourself. Why is that? My friends, it was I who was born into the body William Saroyan. It was not another. It was myself, and the spirit inhabiting this Armenian flesh is myself. If I wrote about somebody else, however artfully, it would still be about myself.

My witness witnesseth, however, as I've said, that I was a greater writer at twelve than I am at thirty.

It is indeed a small world; a world which reduces all to smallness; and not only that, also to ridiculousness. Nothing could be more ridiculous than myself, for instance, and H. G. Wells, and the countless others; writers or not writers. The way we carry on is most amazing if we could only stand back in time a moment and watch as if we were looking at it all for the very first time; it would be ridiculous, unbelievable, insane, heartbreaking and, simply, to say it again, unbelievable.

The way I write now instead of the way I should have written, from the beginning, is unbelievable. Out of three thousand words, for instance, sometimes no more than six come to life; the rest are all dead, like the billions of words in the millions of books, which were written by men at one time or another, which they sat down and deliberately wrote, which were printed and bound and for a time read, and which are all dead and meaningless, and in fact horrible and tragic.

It is all because, I suppose, they have all been cowards: afraid to do a thing as it might in all dignity at least be attempted; afraid to expose themselves by being out-and-out personal about everything; afraid to drop the cringing caution; holding in; holding out; bluffing; putting forth the strong shoulder, holding back the feeble heart; thrusting out the chin, holding the trembling mind; putting forth the powerful passion of the flesh, hiding the weeping feebleness of the heart's heart, the impotence even, the impossibility of ever having, that way, as much as it knows it should have, but in all truth can never have, a man becoming the father of another instead of the father of himself, a man unborn giving birth to another, knowing the falsity of it, the hollowness, the ridiculousness, and yet in despair or in shame or with deception accepting this fatherhood, putting on the garment of parenthood: fatherhood and parenthood of nothing, since the man himself is nothing, not yet born, nowhere, unknown to himself, unknown to God, the universe unknown to him, nothing of wonder gathered into him and made his own, nothing of his wonder brought forth and put upon and within other things, whether it is his child or his woman or what.

Most insistent has been a flash of vision containing, almost, the whole answer to the whole question, but a flash so difficult to translate into the feeble words they've given us, the feeble grammar, the feeble structure and prop of thought, that except a man go journeying after the truth the hard way, circling around it like a hawk around a dark cloud, waiting for the light to break through for a flash, and be shut off immediately, it is more than likely that nothing at all of it will be known, not even a hint— and what I'm trying now is only to hint.

I have no hope of ever being able to get it down in ordinary words, in the ordinary manner, with all the bluffing, all the fancy arrangement of words, the dead words, the dead arrangements; that's the kind of behavior I am regretting, in myself and in all the others who were impelled, for whatever reasons it may have been and which they alone know, to write, to send out the message, whatever it might be.

Nothing in the world is easier than to be a good writer if you know how to write; nothing is more convenient; nothing is more stupidly flattering to oneself than the realization that one is saying beautifully or powerfully—or rather seemingly beautifully, seemingly powerfully— that which is neither here nor there, but which at the same time is something which the other corpses of the world can, in their infinite ignorance, acknowledge, tabulate, accept, record, speak of, compare, praise, or any of the other things. Nothing is more pointless than to be another writer; anybody can be that; anybody at all. I can teach any man in the world to be that. That is a thing not worth teaching a fly, I might say. And anybody can blame me for the way I feel when the young men arrive and say with blushes or with firmness or with faith or with bitterness or with despair, I want to write; I know I can write; how is it done? I feel like an all-fired fool. That's how I feel. I feel stupider than if I were a jackrabbit being asked by a rock how to sing. Or something even more fantastic than that. I feel amazed at myself, at the foolish wisdom in myself, at the galloping idiocy of the others asking me how it's done.

I started out to be a writer once. Now I'm a dead fish. So they come and want to know from me—a dead fish, not a writer by a million years—how to write. I can't tell you how to write because all I did was the same thing H. G. Wells did. (Poor H. G. Wells. I'm not hounding him. I use that name because it is, after all, the name of one who has put a ton or two of new dead books on the shelves. When I speak of him, I speak of *all* the writers, big and small, in stature, in gross weight, themselves, in person, and their books. It is all the same, and I'm one of them, the good Lord forgive us and try to understand.)

Anybody can be a writer. There is no middle-class boy in England or America who cannot be an even worse great writer than H. G. That's no fantasy; that's the truth. All the boy would need to do is work; just work; just muddle through; and at the age of seventy or eighty he would be a cinch to be in command of a good prose style.

But why pick on poor H. G.? Why not forget the poor writers? Why not take up the others? What about poor Albert Einstein? What about what he's working on? It's all the same. They're all poor and burning, as the Armenian saying is. Poor and burning, and I might add for my own part, dead; born dead; and alive dead.

Of course it is all nonsense if you want to get down to it that way; and if you do, and you might as well if you feel that you must, then it is by all means all nonsense, all vast idiocy, all not worth troubling about—except for this: that calling it nonsense might be more complicating than trying hard to find out what it is in *addition* to being nonsense. That might make the waiting for death or liberation, earth to earth or heart to home, even more difficult; that might be the greater mistake of all the possible, and inevitable, mistakes. It is all no cinch. I myself am sure of one thing, but only for myself; not for you; not for H. G.; not for Albert; not for anybody, not even my brother; I am sure that for myself it is a thing—it is something—of the most unbelievably magnificent possibilities, and that nothing is known, nothing has even been suggested, it is all to come, or it is all to be lost, as these million years gone lost it, or it is all to be wasted, or it is all to arrive when our eyes open to glory; and something thoroughly fantastic happens to our ears; and something incredible to our nostrils and lungs; something to the pores all over us; something to everything of ourselves. But for myself, as I say, I have the faith that in my own lifetime I shall not go by without at least suspecting what it could be, and with luck, or faith, or something, I shall not go by without knowing a moment of it, as it could be.

If you belong to the It-Is-All-Nonsense School, then of course you won't care to bother about anything, except what is, as it appears to be in its most obvious dimension and relationship, but even so, you have some advantages and many chances for a casual kind of amusement and suffering—with what *is*, you have a good chance, depending upon your health and innocence, of getting something out of it, while you're around, and it is no matter—if you know you belong to that school, you're no fool as the others are, and in fact you're pretty bright; and you'll get yours; but you won't get more than you bargain for, and I'm with you, not against you. Soberly, apart from the witness witnessething, if I may, I belong to that school myself, and without qualm, I wish no man evil.

But the witness, he witnesseth, and I know better, and it asks to be gotten down on paper, and I wish to sleep, and by morningtime it is lost, or at best in such a miserable state as this is. You don't dare get into anything you can't get out of. You don't dare wish to say the message which is so confoundedly emphatic but also so confoundedly wordless. What the hell can you say? You just *know*. You're dead sure. It's a whole book, as the universe is a whole book; all the pages are there, all the meaning is there, all the poetry, all the wonder, but not any of it is in words, and it wants to get down on paper because it knows no other way, through YOU, to get anywhere at all. Notice that yelping "you." It's the truth. If that wisdom comes to a fox in the hunt, I don't know how the wisdom expects to get anywhere, but most likely it comes only to us; us suckers; us animals which are not animals; which are, in fact, counter-animal; which so sought to escape ANIMAL that to procreate ourselves physically we got all tangled up inside because the necessary contact and method of it seemed so ungodly to us, so animal and so like the method of so many things ugly to us.

We had to have an explorer of our troubled dreams tell us everything quietly, bringing everything out into light and air, and inviting us to look, to return to animal, to know if there would be more, it would have to be out of animal, otherwise there would only be more that was diseased, not more actually, not the real more, but an intensity of disease, but poor Freud is nothing more than the rag-bottle-sack man of the spirit; he's wonderful; we love him; we are grateful to him; he is a brave man; a hero; but he is not the bringer of beauty or light.

You ain't going to get any wonder into it by throwing the junk into the street. In other words, if there are other words, it's all got to get on the horse or the bicycle in one piece and it's all got to travel together. It can't get subdivided that way and mean anything; it's got to be all together. Or not at all. And not at all it has been for a long time, all the time of the poor books, all the time of each poor writer. What can anybody do when he only has so many years to live? And when the first twenty are the best and most difficult to know; when the rest are all off the track, off the record, in the world, out of it, compromise, forgetfulness, regret, and no sense? What can any writer born to write write when it's that way and there isn't time enough in the years after twenty and there isn't skill enough before? What the hell can the born writer say when he hasn't learned grammar, can't spell, hasn't found out what the limits are, how narrow they are, and all that?

If you get up in the middle of the night or morning and put it into words, the words usually number three or four, they're dead, and the vision is again lost because when you get up in the morning and look at them, they mean nothing; it's all lost; Freud got under the iceberg all right but he sure as hell didn't take a telephone with him; he sure as hell didn't take Victor from Camden, N.J., along to record the language there, and even Joyce didn't get anything but the surface of it—he got the sound; it was a nice idiot-laughing sound; but he didn't get the meaning. Not by a long shot. After Joyce, there's no telling. If he says something casually, maybe in a conversation sometime, it may be the word; it may be the message; most likely not, though; most likely it won't be; because Joyce went off into the dimension without all of it, with only a part of it, on the horse or on the bicycle: he rode well, but the rider had parts missing; many of them. He won't say it. James won't; H. G. won't; Albert won't; I forget Freud's first name, but he won't either; President Roosevelt certainly won't; old J. P. won't; the Rockefeller Institute won't; the Guggenheim Fellowship won't; the Pulitzer Prize won't; the Nobel Prize won't; but there they are, all going strong.

So what's to be, and *how's* what's to be to be? Most likely the same; as before; the same as ever. Because, I guess, even if you were born to write, even if you were born to look and see, listen and hear, feel and understand, sense and know, even then, by the time you're in command of the lousy language, they've got you off into the jungle they're all in, and you can write, but not really; you can write as they do and always have written; you can say everything that means nothing; you can do it expertly; you can make it a pleasure to read; and so on, but you won't carry them out into the living they want, you won't take them by the ear to life, you won't move the hour one second forward from where it was a million years ago because you will be the *same* as all the others; you won't say the word because you won't know it; you won't do anything but wait, dead, for death, the same as all the others—making the pathetic stab at living that all the others are making, but never even for a moment coming to life, arriving dead from the dead, out of death creating the new dead, putting them on their feet, putting them into the streets, turning them loose into the stupor and idiocy.

This is most certainly a sad transcript of the things which have been asking to get down on paper, but it is certainly the best I can do with the language they gave me, the culture I've inherited, the body I inhabit, the mind they tried to educate, the heart they threw in willy-nilly. This is most certainly not the word. I, Saroyan, am most certainly not the man to say the word. This is all most certainly about myself. It is all most certainly no better than the pathetic stuff written by the others; and most certainly no worse. It is all most certainly sincere. It is sincerely mine, and it is sincerely yours, as my witness witnesseth.

Old Country Stories, Part III

1. THE CITY SLICKER, THE OVERCONFIDENT KING, AND THE KING'S COUNSELOR

A king's counselor came to him and said, There is a fast talker in the city who is going about, getting honest men to give him money for nothing.

How is that? the king said.

He has a way, the counselor said. He catches your eye, talks to you quickly, and before you know what you've done you've given him money and he has disappeared. He has taken money from the wisest only.

I don't believe you, the king said.

It is true, the counselor said.

Go fetch him, the king said. I should like to see him fool *me*. If he fails to do so, you lose your head.

The counselor went to the slicker and said, The king challenges you to fool him, and you'd better be good.

I? the slicker said. Fool the king? God forbid.

If you don't, the counselor said, I lose my head and you lose yours with mine. Come along and don't forget to be good.

As you say, the slicker said.

The counselor took the slicker to the king.

The king said, I have been told that you fool the wisest of men, taking money from them. I take pride in my wisdom; fool *me*.

O Living King, the slicker said, I am sorry but that is impossible. I have placed all my tools in hock and without them I can fool no one, not even the most gullible of country bumpkins. I am at your mercy.

Go fetch your tools, the king said.

I have no money, the slicker said.

How much did you get on your tools? the king said.

Two hundred pieces of gold, the slicker said.

Counselor, the king said, give the young man two hundred pieces of gold and let him go fetch his tools. We shall see if he can fool me.

The counselor gave the slicker two hundred pieces of gold. The slicker modestly bowed his way out, promising to return in two hours. The king sat back to wait. The counselor smiled, ever so faintly.

What are you smiling about? the king said.

If you wait for him to return, the counselor said, you will wait in your children and their children. You have been fooled, O Living and Wise King. His tools are his tongue.

2. THE KING, THE SPY, THE ARMENIAN BARBER, AND THE ARMENIAN BUTCHER

A spy went to a king and said, We can learn nothing of the Armenians because they can speak to one another without speaking.

What are you talking about? the king said.

When they speak aloud we can learn a few simple and unimportant things about them, the spy said, but it is when they speak to one another and do not utter a single word that we cannot learn anything. They understand one another in a glance. It is then that we are helpless. Even when they speak aloud, what we understand is usually false because of their glancing at one another which changes the meaning of what they have said.

You are speaking of one or two exceptions among the whole people, the king said. That is nothing to bother me about.

I am speaking of all of them, the spy said. They *all* speak the unspoken language.

All right, the king said. We shall see. Bring me two of the humblest of them. A barber, let's say, and a butcher.

The spy went to Isro the barber and said, The king wants to see you.

The barber thought, Why would the king want to see me, a barber? He said nothing and went with the spy to the king.

The king looked at the barber, watching him. Is he speaking? the king wondered. The barber had said nothing. The king waited for the arrival of the butcher.

After a while the spy returned with Boghos the butcher, who also had wondered why the king would want to see him, a butcher. When the butcher saw the barber he knew the other was an Armenian. He glanced at the barber quickly as he moved toward the king. The barber glanced back quickly at the butcher.

The king said, Now that they are here, let them speak without saying anything.

They have already spoken, the spy said.

What have they said? the king said.

That is hard to say, the spy said. They have surely said one of a thousand and one things. From what I saw, the spy said, I would say that the butcher said, Countryman, what goes on? And the barber said, Countryman, I'm not sure, but it appears that these jackasses think they're going to get us to talk.

3. THE DEVIL AND THE NATIVE OF THE CITY OF BITLIS

The devil heard that the natives of the city of Bitlis were the cleverest people in the world and decided to visit the city and see if he could fool them. On his way to the city he became exceedingly weary from travel and was pleased to be overtaken by a young man moving forward at a furious stride.

My friend, the devil said, where are you going?

I am going to Bitlis, the other said.

I am going to Bitlis too, the devil said. Let us journey the rest of the way together.

That will be a pleasure, the other said.

How much farther have we to go? the devil said.

Ten miles, the young man said.

How long have you been walking? the devil said.

One night, two days, the young man said.

The devil had been walking only part of one day and was exhausted. It seemed very strange that the young man should be so vigorous after so much walking. In truth the young man had been walking two hours.

Are you going to the city of Bitlis for the first time? the devil said.

I went to the city of Bitlis for the first time, the young man said, when I was born.

I see, the devil said to himself, he is one of the clever ones. I shall fool him.

Since we are going to the same place, the devil said, let us make a bargain so that we will not exhaust ourselves. You have traveled a long way and so have I. You carry me on your back while I catch my breath and rest; then I will get down and carry you a distance on my back while you catch your breath and rest.

Good, the native of Bitlis said. How shall we decide on a just procedure, so that one of us shall not take advantage of another?

That will be simple, the devil said. The one who rides shall ride until he has finished singing a song.

That's fair, the other said. Will you ride first?

Thank you, the devil said. He got on the back of the young man and began to sing. He sang the song of the Armenian alphabet, "The Morning's Light," which takes each of the 36 letters of the alphabet for a verse. Sung slowly, as the devil sang it, the song will end only after a half hour or so. The devil was quite refreshed with his rest and quite pleased with the bargain he had made. He got down and the native of Bitlis got on his back and began to sing.

He began to sing a chant of the Armenian church which endures as long as the chanter chooses: *dai ni, nai ni, nai ni, ni; don ni, non ni, no.* Over and over again. If necessary the song can continue into infinity.

What kind of a song do you call that? the devil said.

It is a simple song of a simple people, the young native of Bitlis said.

How many verses are there? the devil said.

One and a million, the young man said.

Surely it begins and ends, the devil said.

No more than the world or Almighty God, the young man said, and continued to sing, *dai ni, nai ni, nai ni, ni; don ni, non ni, non ni, no.*

The devil carried the young man all the way out of the hills into Bitlis.

He had been shamefully fooled and wanted to fool the one who had fooled him.

My friend, he said, what is your labor?

I work with the earth, the young man said.

Let us be partners, the devil said.

Good, the young man said.

They planted a field of onions and the day came to harvest.

What will you have, the devil said, the tops or the bottoms?

Either will please me, the young man said.

No, the devil said. Make a choice.

Very well, the young man said. I'll take the tops.

The devil had been fooled once; he had no intention of being fooled twice.

If you please, he said, I will take the tops; you take the bottoms.

The devil cut off the tops of the onions and tried to sell them. The young man dug out the fine onions and sold them all.

The devil had been fooled twice. He had been humiliated twice and was more than ever eager to fool the native of Bitlis.

Let us be partners again, he said.

Good, said the other.

What shall we plant this time? the devil said.

Wheat?

So it was wheat. The day of harvest came and the devil said, What will it be this time, the tops or the bottoms?

Well, the native of Bitlis said, I'll take the bottoms again.

No, the devil said. This time you take the tops and let *me* take the bottoms.

So again the devil was fooled. In the evening he quietly went away from the city and to this day has never returned, except incognito and for the pleasure of admiring the natives.

A Word to Scoffers

From Reno to Salt Lake City all you get to see from a bus or any other kind of conveyance is desert, and in August all you feel is dry heat. Desert is sand spread out evenly in every direction, different kinds of cactus, and the sun. Sometimes the sand looks white, sometimes brown, and around sundown the color of the sand changes from white or brown to yellow, and then black. Then it is night, and that is when the desert is best of all. When the desert and night join one another you get what amounts to silence.

This is a thing you remember and remember.

The remembrance is full of the hush and mystery of the world.

I know all this because I rode in a bus from Reno to Salt Lake City once, on my way to New York.

My uncle Gyko told me to get out of town and go to New York. He said, Don't stay in these little town. Go to Nor York. I tell you, Aram, eat ease insanity.

That's how it happened that I rode in the bus from Reno to Salt Lake City.

That was country I had never seen, or imagined. Wide dry wasteland, full of nothing. I kept my eyes open night and day watching that country. I didn't want to pass through country like that without finding out all I could about it.

The bus left Reno a little after midnight. Reno is one of those American towns that lives on nothing but the disease of people. The only thing there is gambling and whoring.

Consequently, the city lights are bright.

I remember going into a gambling joint and seeing clearly all the way from the rail to the poker game in the corner of the room the three black hairs growing out of the dealer's nose. It was that light.

Then the bus rolled out of Reno into the desert. That was a mighty remarkable difference to dwell upon: first the bright lights of the gambling joints of Reno, and then the desert at night. I dwelt on those bright lights and the desert from midnight till morning, and even then I didn't find out enough for one small sentence of three words.

All I did in the morning was yawn. When the bus stopped, I got out and had a good look. Well, all it was was dirt and sky, and the sun coming up. I couldn't think of three little words with which to clarify the situation. It was nothing. That's all. Nothing at all. No streets, no buildings, no corners, no doorways, no doors, no windows, no signs, nothing.

My uncle Gyko told me not to stay in a small town like the small town I was born in, and now I couldn't wait to get out of the desert into a big town and be able to understand something again. I began to figure it wouldn't do my uncle Gyko any harm to get out of our small town and pass through the desert himself. I figured he might not be so sure about everything if he got himself all surrounded by the desert, day and night, and felt that sullen silence. My uncle Gyko hadn't read as many smart books as I had read because he read slower and with greater difficulty, but he had read everything he had read very carefully and memorized whole pages of the works of writers who had lived in Europe as long as two hundred years ago. In his own broken-English way he used to cut loose with a lot of derivative invective. He used to call people sheep, and claim that he himself wasn't a sheep. I myself was just as wise as my uncle Gyko only I didn't speak with an accent. My uncle Gyko said, Get out of these town and go to Nor York.

I figured my uncle Gyko ought to visit the desert himself and see how *he* felt. I figured I couldn't figure out anything in a place so empty as all that. I didn't feel like feeling smart at all. I felt lonely too. That's why I tried to start a conversation with the only girl on the bus, inexperienced as I was in the art of polite conversation.

What's the name of this place? I said to the girl.

She was at least thirty-five and very ugly.

What place? said the girl.

All this land around here, I said.

I don't know, said the girl.

That was as far as the conversation went until late the next afternoon when the girl asked me what time it was and I said I didn't know.

I didn't even know what day it was. I was beginning to find out that all I knew was that I didn't know anything and wanted to get to Salt Lake City as soon as possible so I could see streets and places again and people walking around, and maybe get back my tremendous book learning that was so useless in the desert.

Just let me get to a city again, I said, and I'll be as smart as the next fellow. Maybe smarter. Just get me out of this desolation and I'll start throwing wise cracks all over the place.

Well, I was wrong. When I got to Salt Lake City I felt more confused than ever. I couldn't find a room for fifty cents, or a restaurant where I could get a big dinner for fifteen cents. I felt tired and hungry and sleepy and sore at the people in the streets, and the buildings there, and I wished to Christ I hadn't left my home town.

I paid a dollar for a little room in an old hotel. The room turned out to be haunted. It was the toughest room I ever tried to stay in, but I used to be very stubborn in those days and I stayed in the room until I could see every kind of evil form that never in the history of the world reached material substance, and could hear every kind of awful sound that science insisted didn't exist. I was scared stiff. In two hours I didn't move from the rocking chair in the middle of the room because I was sure something would grab hold of me and strangle me before I could get to the door or window. The room was full of evil things. I don't know how I got out of it alive, but I got out all right.

I walked through the streets of Salt Lake City and found a restaurant where you could get a hamburger dinner for a quarter.

After dinner, I went back to that little room in that little hotel and got in the bed without taking off any of my clothes, not even my shoes or my hat. I wanted to be ready to sprint in case of riot, fire, earthquake, flood, pestilence, or any other kind of emergency. Before turning out the light I practiced getting out of the bed and getting to the door. I was making it in record-breaking time, one jump to the door, and maybe three or four seconds to the street. I left the room only three times during the course of the night, but awoke in the morning refreshed and cheerful.

I got up at five in the morning because I didn't want to miss the bus that was leaving town at half past nine.

At a quarter past nine I was standing in front of the bus depot, smoking a five-cent cigar, trying to get back my young irreligious poise so that I could be happy again when a very tall and melancholy-looking man of fifty in overalls handed me a little pamphlet and said, Son, are you saved?

I had never before seen such a melancholy-looking man. Six feet two or three, no more than a hundred and twenty pounds, unshaved, and full of religion. I figured he was going to ask me for a dime because he looked more like a hungry tramp than a holy man, but all he did was hand me that religious pamphlet and ask if I was saved. The title of the little story on the pamphlet was "A Word to Scoffers," and the missionary had found his man all right. I didn't know. I couldn't tell at the time. I was all mixed up.

I took a sophisticated puff on the nickel cigar and said, No, I don't think I'm saved, but I'm sympathetic.

Brother, said the religious man, I can save you through the gospel of Brigham Young.

I'm leaving town in fifteen minutes, I said.

That's all right, said the religious man. I once saved a man in four minutes.

That's fast work, I said. What do I have to do to get saved?

Son, said the religious man, you don't have to do anything. You have no idea how close to being saved every man alive is. Any man you can think of. I used to be something of a rounder myself, snappy clothes, strong drink, panatela cigars, cards, dice, horses, sporting girls. Everything. Changed overnight.

Why, I said.

Lost my luck and couldn't sleep, said the religious man. Fell to thinking and found out I never was intended to be an enemy of the truth.

What truth? I said.

God's holy truth, said the missionary. No man is ever much of an enemy of the truth. All them crazy things people do is because they don't know what they're after.

Well, what *are* they after? I said.

Truth, he said. Every man who cheats at cards, carries on with women, holds up a bank, gets drunk, or travels, is looking for truth. I guess you're going somewhere, son. Where you going?

I'm on my way to New York, I said.

Well, he said, you won't find any truth there. I been there six times in the last thirty years. You can go hopping around all over the world and never find out anything because that ain't the way you find out anything. All you got to do is change your attitude.

That ought to be easy, I said.

Easiest thing in the world, he said.

I'm game, I said. I've got nothing to lose. How do I change my attitude?

Well, said the religious man, you stop trying to figure things out and you *believe*.

Believe, I said. Believe *what*?

Why, everything, he said. Everything you can think of, left, right, north, east, south, west, upstairs, downstairs and all around, inside, out, visible, invisible, good and bad and neither and both. That's the little secret. Took me forty years to find out.

Is that all I have to do? I said.

That's all, son, said the missionary.

O.K., I said. *I believe.*

Son, said the religious man, you're saved. You can go to New York now or anywhere else, and everything will be smooth and easy.

I hope you're right, I said.

You'll find out, said the religious man.

The big bus got to the curb and I got in. The lanky man of God came to the window, smiling proudly.

You're the fifty-seventh man I've saved, he said.

Well, so long, I said. Many thanks for the little secret.

Glad to do it, he said. Only don't forget. Just believe.

I won't forget, I said. I'll believe.

Anything, he said.

The motor of the bus started.

Any old thing at all, I said.

The bus belched smoke and slowly rolled away.

I thought I was kidding the old padre of Salt Lake City, getting back my vast book learning and antireligious poise, but I was sadly mistaken, because unwittingly I *had* been saved. In less than ten minutes after the bus left Salt Lake City I was believing everything, left and right, as the missionary had said, and it's been that way with me ever since.

The Small Trouble That Starts at Home

I was leaning up against the bar drinking a Scotch and soda, talking to Sam. We were discussing trouble.

You're a writer, Sam said. What's the reason for all this stuff going on everywhere?

I told him I didn't know. Which is the truth.

Maybe, I said, it's on account of all the energy going to waste.

What energy? Sam said.

Well, I said, the stuff that's brought me here, after sweating all day, to drink and talk to you. *That* energy.

What about it? Sam said.

Nothing, I said. Only maybe it's the reason for all this stuff going on everywhere. You mean the war in Europe, don't you?

No, Sam said.

What *do* you mean? Weren't we talking about wars?

Sure we were, Sam said, but them things are what happens afterwards. The trouble I mean is the *small* trouble that starts at home and works out in every man until it's big enough to be a war or a riot or something crazier.

What small troubles you talking about? I said.

For a writer, Sam said, you're pretty dumb. I suppose you've been through college too. What small troubles do I mean? I mean like when you go home and nothing's the matter, everything's fine, you're working, you're out of debt, you're in good health, your wife's in good health, she's got supper on the table, you've been saving money, everything's wonderful, and instead of feeling swell you feel lousy, that's what I mean.

Oh, I said.

Oh, Sam said. I mean having all the things which when you didn't have them you thought would make you feel wonderful when you got them and then after you got them you feel worse than you felt when you didn't have them.

Oh that, I said. You're getting into mighty dangerous territory there, Sam. I wouldn't wander into that awful region if I were you. Many a man's gone in there in all innocence and never returned alive.

Take yesterday, for instance, Sam said.

O.K., I said. Yesterday. What happened?

I don't know, he said.

He sounded awfully tragic for a man who mixed drinks. I couldn't figure out a guy like that being like that.

The way I feel now, he said, I'm disgusted.

What you disgusted with?

Myself, he said. But it ain't that. It's not *me*. It's everybody.

All right, I said, you're disgusted with everybody. What happened yesterday?

It's like I said. I went home and everything was swell, everything was great, but instead of feeling fine I felt lousy.

All right, I said, you felt lousy.

Lousy ain't the word for it, he said. You think this is funny. It ain't funny. I got into one of those crazy arguments with my wife. Over nothing. Tomato soup out of a can. I mean, it doesn't make any difference what it was. I like tomato soup out of a can. It would have been something else if it hadn't been tomato soup. The only thing I know is they're never going to be able to do anything for people. It's hopeless.

Get me another, I said.

He did.

Go ahead, I said. Tell me everything.

What I mean is, I hurt her feelings.

That happens all the time, I said. Nothing to feel bad about there.

I mean at first. Then I felt so bad about hurting her feelings I went to work without knowing what I was doing and the first thing I knew she was crying. So instead of eating supper, there she was crying and there I was hating her for crying and hating myself for making her cry. Don't think I didn't try to get out of it before it got too late. I tried my best. I wanted to straighten everything out, but I couldn't.

So far nothing much had happened, he said. I should have been able to straighten the whole thing out by getting out of the bad mood I was in. I wanted to do it. That's what I'm asking about. Why couldn't I do it? Why did I have to let it go on? There was time to get out.

Sam, I said, I hope you haven't gone to work and killed your wife.

You think this is a joke, he said. Well, maybe it is. Maybe it's funny. If it is, then everything else is too. Everything everybody does. It's all goofy, just like this. It wasn't enough to make her cry. It wasn't enough to hurt her feelings. I had to hit her too.

Sam was disgusted with himself.

You shouldn't have done that, Sam, I said.

She said something that made me know how much of a heel I was. I couldn't help it. I didn't mean to do it. That's the first time in my life I've ever done a thing like that. It made me sick to my stomach.

You're pretty sensitive, I said.

Sensitive my eye, Sam said. I've been knocked out cold and it's never made me feel the way I felt last night.

I think everything'll straighten out by itself, I said.

Sam shook his head.

No, he said. It won't straighten out by itself. We're just kidding ourselves when we think these things will take care of themselves.

Nobody's to blame. It's just the way we are. We're no good. We'll always have all kinds of trouble. It won't stop when everybody gets the things they want. It'll never stop.

Well, I said, I guess maybe it won't at that.

Nothing's happened, he said. I mean I know she'll be home tonight. I know supper will be ready. I know she'll be all right and I know I'll be sorry, but there's no hope. We're just naturally no good, that's all.

Maybe you'd eaten something that didn't agree with you, I said.

That's a lot of hooey, Sam said.

All right, I said. Maybe in addition to having eaten something that didn't agree with you the weather was bad. Maybe it was sultry. Maybe the air was depressing.

That's a lot of hooey. Don't be trying to apologize for people that way. You can't explain all this crazy stuff going on everywhere that way. We're no good, that's all.

We ain't so bad, I said. I've never known a man to feel more nobly guilty than you feel this evening over practically nothing at all.

Practically *nothing*? Sam said. If you think what I'm talking about is practically nothing you're dumber than any writer has a right to be. Don't you understand what I'm talking about?

I was all right at this time. Kind of pleasantly drunk.

If I ain't badly mistaken, Sam, I said, you're talking about that profound inward discontent which since the beginning of time has irritated, strengthened, destroyed, and resurrected the human spirit.

What? he said.

Just what I said, and I ain't going to say it again.

No, he said. What did you say?

He got all ready to listen very carefully this time.

I can't remember, I said.

What was that about destroying and resurrecting?

Well, I said, whatever it was, it was what happened to you yesterday and today. All them things. They all happened. Without what's happening to you now all of us would be no good. It's on account of what is happening to you now that we aren't no good. We lose everything and then we get it back. You've gone through the whole historical comedy in one night and a day. Unless, of course, I'm sadly mistaken. If I ain't sadly mistaken, Sam, you've got as good a chance as anybody in the world to be a great guy for at least four or five days. After that anything's liable to happen, but when it does just remember that you'll be healed again and while it's happening try to be good-humored about it because more often than not it's as comical as it is sad. Fix me another.

The Man Who Was Born Under the Sign of Scorpio

Any man who knows fine whiskey, Sam, is a man worth knowing.

I know fine whiskey. I know all about it. I got a way with a bottle. I don't say a word, but on account of this way I got with a bottle people get reckless and ask for the glasses and the bottles.

What does *that* mean? What does it mean, Sammy?

It means money.

It means money in the old iron box.

Sam, you need a man who knows whiskey around here. No offense, brother, this place is dying, and you're either going to turn it over to the undertaker or you're going to turn it over to old Doctor Floyd, old Doc Floyd Smith, butcher, barber, baker, soldier, friend and brother.

I ain't got no card.

I never saw you before but, brother, my name is Floyd Smith and boy when I say Smith I mean Smith, what I mean.

Smith, Sammy. That's me, old Doctor Floyd from Philadelphia.

I wasn't born in Philadelphia, friend, I was brought up there. I had as nice a bringing up as any man in the world. That's me. Floyd Smith from down Philadelphia way and any man who shakes my hand as you have shaken my hand is my friend. My friend, my friend. Year after year and hour after hour. Day in and day out. My friend to the end.

What I know about whiskey and every other kind of bottled stuff nobody else in the world knows or will ever learn, including what happens when the bottled stuff in the bottles gets out of the bottles into people. I know all about that too. I'm a specialist on that brand of the science. I've made a lifelong study of insects, worms, reptiles, lizards, fish, dwarfs, mammals, and birds. Birds bigger than the average man.

I got a way with a bottle that nobody else has. A gentle and wicked way that is irresistible. The average bartender has a maudlin way with a bottle. The poor ignorant average bartender is ignorant. Watch me sometime when I grab hold of a bottle. Make a study of my stance. It will be a sight for sore eyes.

Boy, when I take hold of a bottle containing bottled goods, well, a man with sore eyes sees something he'll never be able to forget to his dying day. It's stark raving beautiful the way I fetch a glass and let the stuff gurgle out.

I got no sentimental prejudices against any political affiliation. I knew a Republican once. Why, by God, I didn't hate the man. We got along fine. Not a cross word in three hours.

You ain't got the temperament of the saloonkeeper. You don't look like a drinker. You don't talk like one. You don't act like one. You look like a tailor. You talk like a choirboy. You ain't cut out to be a man behind a bar.

I was born to the bar.

It's my God-given gift and what God gives, let no man seek to take away.

What God gives, my friend, let no man, beast, insect, worm, reptile, lizard, fish, or midget seek to take away. That's the holy handwriting on the wall. When the big finger wrote the word in letters of fire across the pitch-black sky, when the big finger wrote the word that was my name, Floyd Smith, brother, he wrote *bartender* behind it.

I was born under the sign of Scorpio the bug.

That doesn't mean much to the average ignorant man, but there's a mob of meaning in that coincidence. Scorpio. Floyd Smith. What does it mean? Smack: *bartender.*

There ain't no power in heaven or earth that can keep me away from a dark corner in a big city where glasses and bottles are around. It's my fate. Year after year and day after day. I guess you ain't been noticing the way I been putting away this whiskey. I guess you ain't been admiring me from a safe distance. I can take my little finger and lay low the average ignorant man just like that. Flick and zowie. What's happened to him? He's out. He's floored. Flick. Boom. He's fainted. And if I double my first and wind up, what happens? He dies. I ain't got no use for them bums.

I been here three hours steady, and you ain't had one solitary customer. What you need in this little dump of yours is me. Under the sign of Scorpio, overhead, in heaven. I was born under that sign. It was a long time ago, but the date is written down in a book somewhere and there ain't nothing phony about it. I'll flick my little finger at the first average man who so much as intimates there's anything phony about that. Scorpio. And I can do you a lot of good. I can floor any man in the world with the littlest flick of my littlest finger, and I'm going to get right behind that bar and take my stance. I ain't going to walk around the way the poor average man would do. I'm going to elevate my legs easily and comfortably and rise up and land right behind the bar and take my stance.

I was born under the sign of Scorpio, my friend. Watch carefully now. I'm coming over to be bartender here for the rest of my life.

Old Country Stories, Part IV

1. THE SCOUNDREL FROM ODESSA AND THE BOY OF BITLIS

A dishonest man came from Odessa to Bitlis because he was too well known in Odessa. In Bitlis he saw a boy of eight who wore on his finger a ring with a priceless jewel in it.

My child, he said to the boy, if you will give me that toy on your finger I will give you three pieces of gold and you can buy a hundred of them.

If you will get down on your hands and knees, the boy said, and walk up this street, braying like a donkey, I will do so.

The dishonest man was unknown in the new city, so he got down on his hands and knees and began to walk up the street, braying like a donkey. At length he got up and said, All right, my child, give me the ring.

Go back from wherever you came, the boy said. With your donkey's brains do you think you know the value of this ring, and I with my man's brains do not?

2. THE SIMPLE HUSBAND, THE UNFAITHFUL WIFE, THE LOVER, AND THE GOOSE

A simple husband one morning took his wife a goose and said, Cook this bird for me; when I come home in the evening I shall eat it.

The wife plucked the bird, cleaned it, and cooked it. In the afternoon her lover came. Before going away he asked what food he could take with him to his friends. He looked into the oven and saw the roasted goose.

That is for my husband, the wife said.

I want it, the lover said. If you do not let me take it, I shall never love you again.

The lover went off with the goose.

In the evening the husband sat at the table and said, Bring me the goose.

What goose? the wife said.

The goose I brought you this morning, the husband said. Bring it to me.

Are you serious? the wife said. You brought me no goose. Perhaps you dreamed it.

Bring me the goose, the husband shouted.

The wife began to scream, saying, My poor husband has lost his mind. My poor husband is crazy. What he has dreamed he imagines has happened.

The neighbors came and believed the wife, so the husband said nothing and went hungry, except for bread and cheese and water.

The following morning the husband brought his wife another goose and said, Is this a goose?

Yes, the wife said.

Are you dreaming?—No.

Is this the goose's head?—Yes.

Wings?—Yes.

Feathers?—Yes.

All right, the husband said, cook it. When I come home tonight I'll eat it.

The wife cooked the goose. The lover came.

His friends had praised him highly for taking them such delicious food, he said. He was the most popular member of the whole group.

There is another goose today, he said. I can smell it.

You cannot take it, the wife said. I had a terrible scene with my husband last night, and again this morning. It is too much. I love you, but you cannot have the goose.

Either you love me or you don't love me, the lover said. Either I take the goose or not.

So he took the goose.

Bring the goose, the husband said.

My poor husband, the wife screamed. He's stark raving mad. Goose, goose, goose. What goose? There is no goose. My poor, poor husband.

The neighbors came and again believed the wife.

The husband went hungry.

The following morning he bought another goose in the city. He hired a tall man to carry the goose on a platter on his head. He hired an orchestra of six pieces, and with the musicians in a circle around the tall man carrying the goose, he walked with them through the streets to his house, calling to his neighbors.

When he reached his house there were many people following him.

He turned to the people and said, Mohammedans, neighbors, the world, heaven above, fish in the sea, soldiers, and all others, a goose.

He lifted the bird off the platter.

A goose, he cried.

He handed the bird to his wife.

Now cook the God damned thing, he said, and when I come home in the evening I will eat it.

The wife cleaned the bird and cooked it. The lover came. There was a tender scene, tears, ksses, running, wrestling, more tears, more kisses, and the lover went off with the goose.

In the city the husband saw an old friend and said, Come out to the house with me tonight; the wife's roasting a goose; we'll take a couple of bottles of *rakki* and have a hell of a time.

So the husband and his friend went out to the house and the husband said, Have you cooked the goose?

Yes, the wife said. It's in the oven.

Good, the husband said. You were never really a bad wife. First, my friend and I will have a few drinks; then we will eat the goose.

The husband and his friend had four or five drinks and then the husband said, All right, bring the goose.

The wife said, There is no bread; go to your cousin's for bread; goose is no good without bread.

All right, the husband said.

He left the house.

The wife said to the husband's friend, My husband is crazy. There is no goose. He has brought you here to kill you with this enormous carving knife and this fork. You had better go.

The man went. The husband came home and asked about his friend and the goose.

Your "friend" has run off with the goose, the wife said. What kind of a friend do you call that, after I slave all day to cook you a decent meal?

The husband took the carving knife and the fork and began running down the street. At length in the distance he saw his friend running and he called out, Just a leg, my friend, that's all.

My God, the other said, he is truly crazy.

The friend began to run faster than ever. Soon the husband could run no more. He returned wearily to his home and wife. Once again he ate bread and cheese. After this plain food he began to drink *rakki* again.

As he drank, the truth began to come to him little by little, as it does through alcohol.

When he was very drunk he knew all about everything. He got up and quietly whacked his wife across the room.

If your lover's got to have a goose every day, he said, you could have told me. Tomorrow I will bring *two* of them. I get hungry once in a while myself, you know.

How It Is to Be

When George Gershwin died, I believed I ought to have an X-ray picture of *my* head taken, but the doctor told me it wouldn't be necessary.

It's something we don't know anything about, he said. All we know is that there are two kinds of growths, benign and malignant. We don't know why there is either. That's the part *you're* supposed to find out about.

Me? I said. What do you mean, me?

I mean, he said, your guess is as good as anybody's, maybe better.

Thanks, I said, but how about these pains in my head every once in a while?

Well, he said, how about the pains in *my* head every once in a while: Get the idea? It's nothing, or at any rate nothing that isn't a natural or at least an inevitable part of living.

That's different, I said. Just so everybody has them. Just so it's not because I'm a writer.

It's not because you're a writer, he said. It's because you're dying, so forget it, because everybody's dying.

My God, I said, is that true?

You know it is, he said. You know better than I do that it's true. None of us are more than two hours from death at any time. You know that. Absence of oxygen and hydrogen, as when a man is drowning, can carry us out in practically no time at all. Loss of relationship, equilibrium, or position, as when a man is falling, can do it in two or three seconds. Collision, as when a man is carried swiftly to an object composed of firmer substance than himself, can do it instantaneously. These are the accidental and more violent passages, but even normally none of us is more than a day from death.

So I decided to ignore the pains in my head.

Even so, that was the saddest news I'd heard in years because one night In New York I'd met him and talked to him and he'd played the piano for a couple of hours. He was only a kid. Nobody wants anybody like that to die at the age of thirty-five or thirty-six. Nobody wants anybody who can hear music to die while he's still a kid. I talked to Sibelius once. That's how we want it to be. Sibelius was close to seventy.

I was in my hometown when I heard about it. One of my cousins told me about it. He came over to my grandmother's in his Chevrolet roadster and we started driving out to Kingsburg. When we got out on the highway near Malaga he turned on the radio. There was an orchestra swinging around, and all of a sudden my cousin remembered.

Gershwin's dead, he said.

Well, all he had to do was say it and I knew it was true, so I wasn't surprised. If my cousin said it, it was true. I couldn't believe it, but I believed it without a question. Remembering Gershwin in New York I believed my cousin when he said Gershwin was dead. By God, it was true. There it was. He was dead. I started looking at the grapevines in the beautiful light, the lovely trees, the roads, and the whole valley.

Did you know him? my cousin said.

I met him one night in New York, I said. It was a big party and there were a lot of people and everybody was drinking and talking.

We went out to the vineyard in Kingsburg and saw the vines and the grapes on them.

Then we went back to my grandmother's and had lunch: grape leaves wrapped around lamb and rice, Armenian bread, and cold watermelon. Then we drove out to the park and I kept looking at everything. I kept wondering how it is to *be*. How it is. How incredible and splendid it is. How strange and mournful and fine: having all the quiet things that were painted by great men who painted when they wanted to know how it is: the still lifes, the forms of the lovely quiet things, the pear, the peach, the cluster of grapes, the fish on the plate, the loaf of bread, the

real things, in light. How magnificent and good and mysterious the
living things are that all men have loved.

At two in the morning that night I took the train for Frisco and went on
looking at everything: the darkness of the landscape and the sky,
waiting for the coming of light, the wan arrival of morning, the coming
up of the sun, lighting up the world we have made, the ugly lovely
world we have put on the earth, the railroads and industrial buildings,
and the quiet sorrowing dwellings of poor people. I dreamed all night of
how it is.

I'll try to tell you how it is. If I can remember, I'll go to all the places I
have gone to by train or ship, and if I can remember what happened, I'll
tell you, because if the pains in my head aren't because I'm a writer what
it is to me is what it is to you, and what it is to you is what it is to all the
others who are still alive, who have not yet traveled, in wars or accidents
or disease, the two hours or two minutes, to the other side. If I can keep
from trying to say everything at once, I'll tell you how it is, or at least
give you an idea.

I'll go back to the beginning, if I can. That's got to be, otherwise it
won't be whole. The beginning is when *you* begin, and that isn't when
you're born, except in a matter-of-fact statistical way. When you're born
is the beginning all right, but not the one I'm thinking about. The
beginning I mean is the one when you yourself look and for the first time
see.

The beginning I mean is when you come out of the dream being
dreamed by the universe and feel the lonely, fierce glory of being, of
being out of emptiness, of possessing shaped matter, of being charged
with energy, of being related to, and a part of, the great source of energy,
of having warmth and animation, of being an entity, whole and perisha-
ble, benign and malignant.

The beginning I mean is when you know the difference between what
men pretend to be and what they are: not anything but visitors of the
world, borrowers of time, coming and going. Not possessors of anything
but the privilege of inhabiting substance and enduring time. Men are
miraculously living things, never more than a day from death, never far
from glory, and as long as they live they are children, because living is in
its infancy. Men who travel the last moment to death at the age of
seventy, or eighty, or ninety, travel as children. They go as they came,
helplessly.

Let them have been great in the eyes of their fellows, or small, or
unknown, or in the eyes of God let them have been noble and good and
true, men, when they travel that last moment, travel as men *coming* here
travel that *first* moment. Those moments, that of coming to this place
and that of leaving it, are the moments of mystery and miracle, benign
and, if we choose to put it that way, malignant, although coming is no

more benign than going is malignant, although each is simultaneously malignant and benign.

Each is *together*, except for climate, and light, and the fragments of time each man knows that are of glory, the vision of the peach, the sense of animated substance in warmth and light that is one's own. The delight of reaching destination in opposite of one's kind. Benign and malignant are one in the living, in all things, except for these moments when the moving of time is halted by the infinite rise of heart, the immeasurable lift of spirit, the momentarily unending expansion of dynamic in substance seeking destination, and finding it.

This is a suggestion of how it is, a suggestion of how *some* of it is. The parts are so numerous and so variable that no man may say how *all* of it is. Even for himself no man, no child here, great or small, or in the eyes of God noble and true, may know how all of it is, or even how all of *may* be. It may be for now, as the ballad goes, or it may be forever. But for now or forever, no man may know.

The evening of that day, in my hometown, my cousin and I rode around the Sunday streets and suddenly saw one of the opposite of our kind, born in that place, walking through the evening, as lovely as a cluster of grapes, and my cousin roared. He drove the roadster up and down the street, keeping the girl in sight, roaring with delight and adoration, slapping the side of his head with sorrow, groaning in Armenian, and in English saying, Oh my God.

The girl was no more than sixteen or seventeen, or maybe no more than fourteen or fifteen, but as lovely as all young things of our earth are, as charged with grace and proportion as all things coming into this life are: the coming of day, fruit to the bough, sea to the shore, humor to the heart. And with my cousin, I was smitten with that grief which comes from delight and adoration of substance so lovely it is holy, though it be possessed by the daughter of a drunkard or an idiot or any man, great or small. My cousin and I saw mortal loveliness, and when it disappeared into a hovel on a desolate street by a railroad track, my cousin, still groaning, looked about furiously and said, Let's go get a root beer.

We drove to a place on Ventura and had two of them. Then we drove out to his house. A dozen of us, all from the same sources, sat around and talked. The older ones remembered the old country and the ones who had died; the early days in this country, and how beautiful everything had been, and how beautiful and different, and the same. The hard times and the times when one of us still alive was on his way to the last moment and the others prayed and swore and finally the one who was journeying turned and came back to us and at last all the others fell down and slept and in the morning the journeyer slept peacefully and a week later or two or three, was back with us again, still one of us, talking with us, aged three or twenty, or forty, and laughed with us, and we were together still and there would be tables together still, food and drink together, seasons together still, and light in the world still. We talked of the dead as if they were not dead, as if the years had not gone by, as if Dikran was among us still, brilliant and swift and full of comedy, roaring with laughter, hugging the children of his sisters, bringing them gifts. We talked of Hovagim and his old rattletrap Buick and his ferocious anger when somebody was unkind or a liar, his fury one day when a neighbor lied to him, and how he lifted the neighbor's Ford and tipped it over on its side and shouted, There! Now lie some more. And all of us roared with laughter.

Later that night my cousin and I drove to town again and went to a bar.

Do you remember the men they were talking about?

A few of them I remember, I said. Some were before my time, but I remember Hovagim. He took me and my brother out to his vineyeard once in his rattletrap Buick, and he took us hunting and played Armenian records on his old phonograph, and he used to bring us grapes and peaches and watermelons. I remember this man, but I don't remember Dikran. I remember *hearing* about him from his sister, my mother, and from his mother, my grandmother. I like him. He seems to have been a solemn man, even though he was always comical.

We went to the Basque saloon on Tulare Street. There was a nickel-in-the-slot phonograph there and for two hours we sat around drinking Scotch and listening to Spanish tangos and love songs. It was a good place. It was one of the best places of drinking I ever drank in, and I kept thinking of the night in New York when I met George Gershwin and he was still with us and told me about how it was with him when he composed.

Drinking, I knew how it is, but I couldn't say. It's the way nobody knows. He had journeyed past the last moment, but he was with us still because while he possessed substance he journeyed back and forth, into the darkness and back to the light, looking and listening, going into the region just beyond all of us, and coming back. I knew it was *that* way, and but for the grace of God any of us is to be dead before we have come or gone, before we have begun, before we have reached any moment to remember, we are earth again, or rock, or nothing.

On the train going home I was a sad Armenian, as they say of Indians. It wasn't because Brahms died, or Bach, or any of the others, Cézanne, or Goya, or Dostoyevsky, or Dickens, or Robert Burns, or Byron, or Daniel Boone, or Andrew Jackson, or Mark Twain, or any of the others we love. It was because that's how it is, malignant and benign and by the grace of God.

I probably haven't told it at all because it's one that isn't easy to tell. It will take me five years to know if I've even suggested it. What it is, though, is everything, with the benign always shot through it, through the ugly and malign and deathly and cruel and wrong. It's all to us somehow nothing, the great and the small, the unknown and those who in the eyes of God are good and true, all of us nothing and somehow everything, halting the malignant for a moment, the vision of the good things of the earth for a moment, the taste of fruit, all things with form and grace for a moment, all dying things kept alive for a moment by the grace of God.

A Couple of Miscellaneous Prophecies, More or Less Guaranteed to Come True

Ever since my eighth year I have enjoyed considerable fame as a man who can predict things. For years now my brother has been asking me such questions as, Who do you think is going to be elected President—Roosevelt or Landon? and I have looked deeply into the can of condensed milk on the table which I use for a crystal and have discovered the truth.

Roosevelt, I have replied, and Roosevelt it has come to be.

Or my brother has said, Do you think it's going to rain tomorrow? and I have looked out the window at the sky which I use for a crystal, and again I have discovered the truth.

Yes, I have said, and the next day there has been rain all day.

I don't claim to possess supernatural powers or anything foolish like that. It's simply that I can use so many different things for a crystal in which to gaze and discover the truth.

Gazing into the newspapers which I use for a crystal I find that many astounding truths are revealed to me, which I feel obliged to give to the people of the world, for what they may be worth to them.

One thing I see continuously in the newspaper crystal is death. I hereby predict that Benito Mussolini, Adolf Hitler, Josef Stalin, and an eighty-eight-year-old farmer in Czechoslovakia named Gropka are going to die. I further predict that when each of these men dies he shall stop breathing and begin to decay. I predict also that at the very moment when each of these men dies at least one child shall be born into the world. I predict still further that when each of these men dies the world will not know the difference, the sun will rise in the morning and descend in the evening; rivers will go on flowing; the four seasons will come and go as they always have; seeds will grow out of the earth and bring forth their produce; and all living things will go on living.

Gazing still deeper into the crystal I discover that *during* the War all these things I have just mentioned will go on happening; also *after* the

War. The number of living people in the world will always be somewhere in the vicinity of two thousand million—minus, during the War, anywhere from half a million to maybe five million. During the War I predict increased manufacture of firearms; the firing of them; and the arrival of heavy projectiles among immovable objects, such as buildings, and among movable objects, such as people. I predict the flying of army bombers, the roaming about in the seas of submarines, the rambling over the earth of tanks, the roaring of big guns, the fogging of the sky with smoke, and befouling the land with gas.

October 19, 1938

Another Day, Another Dream

Tuesday, October 5, 1937.

5:22 A.M.

I have been up since four this morning, awake since three. I went to bed at eight last night. My sleep was the eager, smiling sleep of boyhood. It was not so much a sleep of remembrance as it was boyhood itself. Waking at three used to be a common occurrence. In the stillness before morning I used to dream while I was awake, feeling great delight in the strangeness, confusion, and mystery of life.

In the mornings of boyhood, I kept saying to my enemies, whose identity I did not even know, I'll show you. I'll show you. Then smile and dream, moving down some street, going somewhere at an hour of night or day when no one else was aboard, and as likely as not grow fabulously wealthy, waken again for half a minute, remember my worldly poverty, tabulate my wealth: health, humor, energy, intelligence, and that not completely understood or realized element in myself which I knew was more valuable than wealth of any kind. This element is, I should say, benevolent force, or impulse. It is one's relation to the great dynamo of the universe, one's kinship to it, one's awareness of being inexhaustibly driven by earth, sun, moon, sea, sky, and time. Of being, though eleven years of age, a man of importance in the world, one who, on one way or another, must function notably.

If it was summertime and there would be early sunlight I would get up and put on my clothes and leave the house and walk to town. I have always moved toward town, toward the world, the center of the community, and merely by walking through town, looking at everything, loving everything, the smallness, the shabbiness the pretense, the absurdity, the bravery, the childish courage, I would feel that, at least in the eyes of God, I had behaved notably, and admired where admiration was in order. If it was wintertime and there might not be sunlight all day, or if there was rain, I would get up and put on my clothes and go into the kitchen and start a fire in the stove and move around, talking to myself.

This morning, in the first days of my thirtieth year, I am once again in that youthful time and mood of living, still with no worldly wealth to speak of other than a few books, three suits, a dozen shirts, two pairs of shoes, one old and one new hat, a radio-photograph, two hundred records, and a signed photograph of Jan Sibelius. Of money I have nineteen cents, one dime, one nickel, and four pennies. One penny has a hole in it and cannot be spent. My debts are not many this year. I do not owe a penny more than five hundred dollars. From a small magazine I shall soon receive a check for twenty-five dollars. Coffee is cheap and inasmuch as morning is the most important time of every twenty-four hours to me, I am pleased about everything, except viciousness. I have also this typewriter.

6:20 A.M.

It is now daylight. The sun is brightening the sky in the east. I shall now walk to St. Anne's. If I think of anything interesting while I'm gone, or If I remember anything, or if anything happens, I'll speak of it.

7:07 A.M.

Just as I turned the hill on Parnassus the sun hit me smack in the back, and the 6 car went by, containing one intern on his way to the U.C. Hospital. Two nurses were playing singles on the hospital courts. One wore a brown woollen skirt, and the other shorts. The one in shorts had a nice serve. Her arms and legs were red. Five nurses in blue uniforms came out of their home as I passed. Another, in a white uniform, came up the street, shivering. It was a fine morning.

I walked to St. Anne's but didn't even think of going in. I used to go in for the view, the spaciousness, and the light coming in from the big colored windows. A lot of people don't think so, but I am very much in favor of the church. Religion misunderstood is better than none at all. Faith and ignorance are better than ignorance alone. There was a little dog abroad near St. Anne's. He was part terrier, no collar. There is a quietness about street dogs, a mortal loneliness in them that sometimes amuses and sometimes saddens me. The quietness in this dog amused me because he wasn't a sad dog. He was as gay a dog as any. We greeted one another. I scratched the dog's head. Then he went his way and I went mine. Otherwise the walk was uneventful. I didn't find a penny. I still look for money whenever I go for a walk.

7:27 A.M.

No worldly wealth to speak of, I say, and yet no poverty of any kind either. I have never squawked about anything, personally, any impression to the contrary notwithstanding, as I have learned to say. I have forgotten something out of everything, good and bad. When I put my typewriter in hock so I could eat in a restaurant, and when I put it in hock so I could gamble, and when I wrote about doing so, I didn't squawk. That was a false impression. All I meant to say was what I said. My enemies are negligible. I don't mean critics. As for the world, it is my friend. A crummy friend at best, and yet at times, at best, as gracious a friend as any. The world is no worse than you, or I. Economics are at the bottom of a lot of the trouble, but economics are neither at the top or bottom of a lot more. Christianity, even to one who isn't a Christian, is as fine a formula for the good life as any.

In a way I've gotten by with murder. Somebody ought to, though. At least in a way. On the other hand, I've taken no advantages. In the clinches I haven't fouled anybody. Next to the enormous and intricate and lovely pattern of the universe, the order of life, I love music because in music one man at a time has saved mortality. Letters are mischievous. Writers are mischief-makers. There is health in mischief, however. I've made my share.

7:45 A.M.
So another day is here.

Liberty, 5¢

Once upon a time, I worked for the *Saturday Evening Post* of Philadelphia, the City of Brotherly Love, I understand. That was years ago. I must have been about ten. *Geboren* 1908, as the Germans say. In Kalifornien, I believe is the way they put it. Ten years from 1908 comes to 1918, eleven to 1919, twelve to 1920. I know it was one of those years. I've changed a good deal since that time, I imagine. For one thing, I'm not as spontaneous a comedian as I used to be, and as for my sense of the tragic, it's changed, too. I mean, I often find it impossible to decide if an event is comic or tragic. That comes, I believe, from what is known as experience.

The following event, I am afraid, is neither, but something in it impels me to make a record of it.

Ten years after I was *geboren* in Kalifornien I went to work for the people of Philadelphia I have just mentioned. The job was to fill a white sack that hung over my shoulder with fresh copies of the *Saturday Evening Post* each week, go around town and try to interest clerks, mechanics and office workers in literature, or belles lettres. I used to hustle the *Saturday Evening Post,* in addition to hustling the *San Francisco Examiner,* sometimes the *San Francisco Chronicle,* and without fail every afternoon the *Fresno Evening Herald.* Fresno. That's my home town, where I was *geboren* in 1908, on Eye Street, across the street from the Southern Pacific Railroad tracks, three blocks down from the depot. Art? I should say.

Now, for the boy who was born in San Francisco in 1928; and yesterday, 1938, was on Market Street, selling *Liberty*, five cents.

He was myself, don't you know, not yet wise, and so forth and so on. I was walking up Market Street with the five-o'clock mob going home after work, and there all of a sudden I was on the corner, aged ten, red-headed, wild-eyed, eager, and out to make my way in the world, selling *Liberty*, profit per copy two cents. Saroyan went by, not quite responsible, not quite aware of the history involved. The boy of 1918 or 1919 or 1920 came in the opposite direction and said,

Remember?

Remember? I said.

There you are. He's hustling for all he's worth, and what are you doing? What is everybody doing? You're ignoring him. Everybody's ignoring him.

So I came to a swift halt.

What am I doing? is what I wanted to know of myself. There he is, and here I am going by as if he weren't there, or as if he didn't matter. What's come over me, anyway? So I turned against the tide and pushed through to the boy.

He was hustling like a house afire, as the saying is. *Liberty*, he was saying. *Liberty*, five cents.

Give me one of them things, I said.

I made it dramatic, so he'd know he wasn't wasting the first years of his life.

He was dramatic himself. He handed me a copy of the little magazine, I moved on, and he put new life into his hustling.

What's *Liberty*? It's an American magazine, not bad, not good. But what about the boy who sells *Liberty*? The boy all over the country? What about him? I threw the magazine in the gutter, pulled down the brim of my hat, turned against the tide again, and went back and asked to have five cents' worth of it. And once again we made the deal.

I threw that one in the gutter, too. It was the same magazine. I went back once more and this time my coat collar was up.

I went back fourteen times because that's how many of them he had. I went back until they were all gone.

I imagine the boy got twenty-eight cents out of it. I can't tell you what I got out of it. All I know is that I drive a hard bargain.

I'm Right. The World's Wrong

I was never cut out to be a man of the world, but at the age of thirty I am still trying to give the impression that I am nothing if not urban. The absurd impulse to appear worldly has been overpowering in me from my earliest years, and to this day, in spite of the fact that I know better, nothing pleases me more than the belief that I have made a delightful impression on people who do not know me. If I couldn't see through myself, this behavior would be tragic. As it is, my behavior has come to be a source of amusement to me, a childishness within myself which I am pleased to tolerate and forgive because there is nothing else to do about it.

I am like the peasant in the old country who stole a watermelon, cut it open, and ate only the heart, saying, I, traveler along this road, will see what I have left of the watermelon, eat it, and say to himself, A lordly man has had a bite of watermelon, may God bless his generous heart. After a few moments, however, the peasant grew hungry again and began to eat more of the watermelon, saying, The traveler will say the lordly man fed his servant. He is truly a noble man. Still later the peasant grew hungry once again, and this time ate all of the watermelon, including the skin. It's quite all right, he told himself. The traveler will simply say, The lordly man not only fed his servant, he also fed his horse.

All my life I have wanted to be unreasonably generous, kindly, sympathetic; and reckless with money, but never in my life have I had money enough to enable this wish to become a reality. It is true that I have been reckless with money on many occasions, but I have always known that I was behaving like a fool and that very soon I would be penniless again, which nullifies the purity of such behavior.

Impressing people with the way one spends money is not, however, the kind of impressing I have in mind when I say I have always wanted to leave people with a delightful impression of me. The manner in which one spends money of course is part of it, but the least part of it. The greater part of it is the manner in which you give away the other things you have. Your energy, your good humor, your wit, your intelligence, and anything else you may happen to have at the time. Sometimes it may be the opposites of these things. Instead of energy, ennui; instead of good humor, bitterness; and so on. In any case, it has to do with giving away whatever it is you happen to have at the time, good or bad, and the generosity with which you do it. You give away of course because you know you get back only in proportion to what you give away.

In spite of all this, I am one whose basic values have little or nothing to do with money. My delight in living has never been delight in the possession of material things. The greatest material poverty has never reduced me to poverty of any other character, so that when there was very little of material things, there was not so very little of immaterial things, but on the contrary such an abundance of them that the material poverty was not poverty at all, with one exception: if then the true poverty, material and immaterial, became humiliating. The necessity to offer to sell my time has always offended my spirit and made me despise the world and the few who happened to inherit it and the multitude which meekly accepted it. At work or not at work, I have never accepted the world. I have always disbelieved in its reality and rejected its rules, which I know to be stupid. Nothing has ever seemed more impertinent to me than the barefaced assumption of the world that I must sell time out of my years for the privilege of staying alive from one day to another. That is a bargain I have never made with the world, because I have always known that my time is *my* time and too valuable to be traded for a security essentially degrading.

If a man labors at the labor which does not delight his heart, he is a slave; if he labors at a labor which does delight his heart, then no matter how difficult that labor is, it is not labor at all, but play. I say that as long as men labor, they are slaves. As long as they are willing to trade, they will be swindled. Until their activities please their hearts, they are fools. For my part, I will have no part of the bargaining with the world. My bargaining will be direct with God.

I am certain of one thing, which no power of the world will ever make me disbelieve:

I am right. The world is wrong.

August 9, 1938

My Financial Embarrassment

All my life I have waged a losing war against money.

Nevertheless, the first short story I ever wrote was called "How I Earned My First Dollar." The title wasn't mine. It was my third-grade teacher's. Her name was Miss Eulalia Pinkerton Washoe. She was the first person on the Northern American continent daring enough to point out fearlessly that I was a writer.

I turned in a good workmanlike contribution to English letters, which for a writer only eight years old, and only the preceding summer only seven, was probably a small triumph of its kind, or, as book critics sometimes say of the works of forty-three-year-old children, a work of rare charm. A work, in short, which doubtless showed great promise, which after all these years I am glad I have at least fulfilled for Miss

Washoe, whom (in case she didn't know it in those days). I secretly loved all during the weeks of the latter part of May and the whole of June that year, and for whom the messages of adoration in the corner of the blackboard were intended. No signature of course. Just the good old melancholia. *I love you.*

I am glad I have made good for this old sweetheart of mine.

Although my first story showed promise and was about how I earned my first dollar, knowing all about earning a dollar at that tender age didn't, as you might suppose it might, help me to become a financial tycoon, or even to learn the value of a penny, as my grandmother is always trying to get me to do. I am always bewildered by her desire, and ask her what the value of a penny is? She, in turn, becomes irritated and says, Shall I say something? I say, Yes. Well, she says, you will never be a great man. You are a fool.

All this in Armenian, mind you.

It is true, however, that at the age of seventeen I tried my best to become a financial tycoon and founded with my brother The Paramount Distributing Company, which lasted seven days and lost a grand total of $327.48. At least that's what it came to after my brother, who was expert at figures, deducted large sums of money for all manner of things, such as stationery, tips, food, recreation, games, candy, and experience. The firm failed in seven days, however, and I, with my brother, retired to the more philosophic and quiet type of living which seemed more in our line. My brother abandoned this type of life six or seven days later and now after about twenty years, he owes no man in the world a penny, as he says, and can look everybody straight in the eye, unless of course, as he says, the man's cross-eyed. Few people, fortunately, are, so it cannot be said that my brother hasn't made the grade financially.

I, on the other hand, practically haven't.

So far, in spite of years of strenuous effort, I find that financially nothing I have ever done has paid. Everything has seemed to be a losing proposition before I have even started to do it, and after I have done it, it has *remained* a losing proposition. As I see it, there is no way of beating the game. It is a wonder anybody anywhere is able to so much as live from hand to mouth, from day to day, because obviously there isn't enough money for everybody, and unless somebody very brilliant figures out some clever scheme real soon all of us will be not only broke but in debt up to our necks.

The only scheme I myself can suggest is double-jointed. That is to say, either money must be immediately prohibited by law or every man must be permitted to design and manufacture his own money according to his needs. Being a capitalist at heart, and perhaps by instinct, I am in favor of the second plan. I am in favor of letting every man who wishes to be a millionaire to go to work and make his million, but when I say make, I mean *make*. I mean to go to work and manufacture the coins or the paper itself. Any man with any dignity will see that his picture, his name, the date of his birth, his coat of arms, if he has one, or a reasonably good replica of his Sunday coat, appears in a neat design on his paper money, and as much of these things as space will permit, on his pennies, nickels, dimes, quarters, half-dollars, and dollars.

From the very beginning my financial embarrassment has been a ferocious thing, and unless some such benevolent change as the one I have suggested is established in the world, it seems likely that I shall continue to be embarrassed, blushing every day until I die.

1937

The Wonderful World of Geniuses

The most interesting thing about the world is its fantastic and unpsychoanalyzed character—its wretched and gallant personality—its horrible idiocy and its magnificent intelligence, its unbelievable cruelty, its equally unbelievable kindliness, its gorilla stupor, its canary cheerfulness, its thundering divinity, and its whimpering comnmonness.

Another interesting thing about the world is its population, counting everybody. Two years ago I didn't know what the population was. When I heard, more I was amazed. I've been amazed ever since. This is so because I believe with the early philosophers that no man in the world is not a genius. From the little I know of myself, I'm sure two thousand million geniuses is several too many.

Fifty cents a day for the two thousand million geniuses of the world is hardly too much to ask. That's one thousand million dollars a day, and we all know there just isn't that much money—not even if we saved. For a year the figure would be 365 thousand million dollars.

The need for this tremendous sum of money day after day is one of the basic causes for the trouble in the world. Another, I have been told, is the need these geniuses have for love. In a religious era the geniuses would have loved God, which is inexpensive. In our era they seek to love one another, which costs a little something: glass beads, colored feathers, coconuts, orchids, champagne, jewels, fur coats, rent, or one or another of many other things.

A complication of this order is not easy to get out of, without poetry and imagination. If the truth is known we've never gotten out of it; and probably never will. Every genius unquestionably gets out of it—personally at least—when he dies. This was doubtless a poetic and imaginative invention of the poetic and imaginative Omnipotence, and a solution I myself regard, after years of constant and profound meditation, as probably the most reasonable of all possible solutions. It is certainly the most democratic solution, and the only one that has a chance of ever making brothers of all men.

In the meantime there is the delightful, delirious, demented, death-defying disorder of life, and the world. How to go about enduring this inevitable disorder pleasantly is by far the most fascinating problem to be faced, and if possible solved—by every genius.

Each genius can speak only for himself of course, although an exceptionally bright genius, such as myself, can, with some effort, say something that may be valid for other, perhaps less bright, geniuses. Or geniuses too busy with other things to have time to say anything at all.

As I see it, there are two fundamental ways of enduring time and disorder: the hurried way and the unhurried way. Each way has its virtues and its defects. The wise genius will exploit the virtues of each way and reject the defects, and try to keep to pretty good physical shape all the time, inasmuch as a strong body has a better chance of getting along with a weak mind than a weak body has; and inasmuch as a strong mind has an excellent chance for many varieties of comedy if it is wedded to a strong body. The genius with an extremely strong mind and an extremely strong body will do wisely to endure time hurriedly, if only for the sake of his sanity. He will do wisely also to be somewhere where the chances for amusement are great.

The whole world should be such a place, but unfortunately isn't. As a matter of fact, good places for amusement are becoming fewer and fewer every year, owing in part to the sorrowfully diseased spending of energy of a number of the more notorious geniuses. Most of Europe, including France and England, is no good at all any more for amusement, even if the genius has all the necessary equipment, including money. Even most places of America, at least in certain seasons, are no good—and especially no good for the genius without a great deal of money. In the winter, for instance, almost all of America, excepting the Pacific Coast, is no good at all for amusement.

What is needed is a new world.

December 8, 1938

How They Got Rid of the Unwelcome and Greedy Visitor

A man visited a family and began eating them out of house and home, as the saying is. There was no getting rid of him. In February he began talking of what fun all of them would have on Easter, so the wife and husband began trying to get him to go back to his own city; first they stopped giving him their best food; instead they gave him cold sour milk, mixed with three parts of water; he said that the other food had been too rich and that this food was healthier for him; then they took away his quilts and put him to sleep in the barn with the cows, on straw; he said that all his life he had slept on straw and that beds and quilts made him uncomfortable and spoiled his sleep; nothing seemed to have effect on him, and his talk of the fun in the future continued, so the husband went to the priest and told his story.

The priest said he would get rid of the man and asked the husband to bring the man to church the following Sunday; the priest asked the husband to get a piece of string and measure the height of the man, which the husband did, taking the string to the priest. On Sunday, as one of his announcements, the priest said that a murder had been committed and that the government has asked him to help find the criminal; he was so tall; from one end of the piece of string to the other; the people were asked to pass before the priest so that he could measure them; the man who wouldn't go home was the exact height; the priest said, Whether you have committed the murder or not, they will take you and perhaps hang you, so in the morning you had better escape; get into a grain sack and be placed on a donkey and if anyone asks your friend what he is carrying, he will say, I am carrying grain, and you will escape.

This was done.

The priest came upon the husband, the donkey with the two sacks, one of which contained the greedy man, and said, My friend, what are you carrying?

Wheat, the husband replied.

Then let me bless the wheat, the priest said, so that it will grow abundantly.

The priest came to the sack in which the greedy man was hiding, struck the top of the sack with his whip, and said, May the good Lord bless this spring wheat; he struck again and said, May the good Lord bless this summer rye; again, May the good Lord bless the fall oats; again, May the good Lord bless the spring barley; in the meantime, the greedy man was suffering terrible pain.

The priest went his way and after a moment the greedy man whispered, My friend, has that priest gone?

Yes, the husband said.

Then hurry along before he comes back, the greedy man said. He forgot the fall radishes, thank God.

The Parachute Jump

When Miss Wheeler came into The Tavern on McAllister Street near Buchanan, Ike Levy, who lived around the corner with his married brother Irwin, was on the verge of beating the marble game entitled "Parachute Jump," in which the more men you got to jump out of the airplane the better your score was. If you got thirty-two of them to jump, you got two free games. If you got thirty-six of them to jump, you got four free games. And if you got forty-two of them to jump, you got *ten* free games, and in all probability the highest medal of honor of the French or British governments. Ike had twenty-nine parachute jumpers out of the airplane, and still had another ball.

It looked like a cinch.

He felt the way a young man who hasn't had a job in two years and is looked down upon by all his friends and relatives feels when, at last, it appears as if he has gone to work and asserted himself. Accomplished something.

O.K., Ike hollered to Harry the old bartender, there's twenty-nine of 'em out of the airplane, and I've still got ball number five.

So what? Harry said. So you've got twenty-nine out. So what?

So *what?* Ike said, bringing ball number five into the chute. You won't catch me throwing away good money on a crazy marble game. I'll let you know in a minute how much you got to pay.

Ike was all set to send the last ball into the game when Miss Wheeler came into the saloon.

She was a well-dressed American girl whose body was a good deal more attractive than her face.

A Scotch and soda, please, she said.

Instead of keeping his eyes on the game, Ike turned to see who it was. The ball rolled out, dropped one jumper out of the airplane, and that was all. Ike didn't see what happened. He heard. He knew he had lost, so he didn't look back at the score.

Harry broke out with a cackle of innocent delight. So how much do I have to pay you, Mr. Levy? he said.

You keep out of this, Ike said.

He turned to Miss Wheeler.

Get out, he said.

One moment, if you don't mind, Harry said to Ike. You are not yet the owner of this establishment, and unless you improve on the parachute game I don't think you are going to be the owner for a year or two at least.

I told you to stay out of this, Ike said.

There was a beer bottle on the bar. He took the bottle by the neck and held it in his hand.

Are you crazy? Harry said. What's the matter with you?

Get out, Ike said to Miss Wheeler. Get out before I murder you.

Miss Wheeler finished her drink, turned and walked out, moving slowly, and not seeming the least amazed at the peculiarity of the situation.

Ike threw the bottle against the wall near the door.

He went over to the swinging door and pushed the left half of the door open, looking toward Miss Wheeler. Then he walked to the marble game. Without looking at the score, he brought his fist down on the glass and broke it. Then he pushed the table over and broke a leg off and began breaking the rest of the contraption.

Ike, Harry said.

Ike sat down at one of the small tables and, looking straight ahead, began to cry. The bartender wanted to do something about a fellow like Ike, but he didn't know what to do. He didn't care anymore about the broken bottle, and the broken marble game. He'd sweep the glass up in a minute, and he'd tell the marble game people some friends of his got a little tight and broke the machine. He would pay for the repairs. It would cost ten dollars maybe. He didn't care how much it cost. He took the broom and swept up the broken glass. Then he took the broken marble game and put it in the back room. He didn't say anything to Ike. Ike was crying without tears and almost no sound. If somebody came in for a drink, he might not even notice anything wrong.

After a while Ike began to talk out loud, but not to Harry.

Ike, Harry said. Go home.

Go to hell, Ike said. I'll never go to Jews again. I am leaving Jews. I am through with them. I have never been a Jew. I have never loved Jews. Go to hell.

Ike, Harry said patiently. Go home and go to sleep.

Sleep yourself, Ike said. Two years they look at me and say everything except what I know they mean. You are a Jew. That's what they mean. So I come here and fight with a marble game that dumps parachute jumpers out of an airplane. I come here to be in a dark place, so I won't get too hungry walking. I come here and waste the lunch money my brother gives me every day. Twenty-five cents. I don't eat. I don't want to eat. If I eat, I feel guilty. To spend that money for food makes me feel guilty. I can't swallow. I am through with Jews. I am through with my brother. I am through with Ike Levy, too. To hell with Ike Levy. He is a Jew. I am not a Jew.

Ike, Harry said. Have a beer.

Have a beer yourself, Ike said.

I'll trust you, Harry said. You can pay me anytime. You'll get a job one of these days and you can pay me when you've got your own money. You can drink all you like.

No, Ike said. I won't get a job. I won't ever have any money of my own. I am a Jew. Jews steal. They cheat. They kill for money. They never have any money of their own. You don't know what it is to be a Jew.

He got up from the table and began to walk out.

Go home, Harry said.

To hell with home, Ike said. I've got no home. To hell with Jews.

He walked out of the saloon. The bartender stood behind the bar and wondered what would happen to a Jew like Ike Levy, twenty-two years old, out of work, no money, and no home. He thought about Ike a long time. Then he drew a beer and began to drink it. What the hell could he do about Ike?

A Survivor of the Influenza Epidemic of 1918

Jim is a waiter. He is a good-natured Greek of forty-four or forty-five who seems younger. He is a little under medium size, but not quite small enough to be a small man. He is well built, and waits table with efficiency and style. He knows how to be helpful without being obtrusive, and his manners are naturally refined.

Like all people who have always worked for a living, he is a gambler and feels that someday he is going to make a killing and have all the money he wants. He follows the horses every day, sits down to a game of stud now and then, and sells Irish Sweepstake tickets whenever they're on sale. So far his luck hasn't been the best in the world, but every six or seven days one of his long shots comes in and keeps his faith from going sour.

Like all people who have always been busy making a living, he is also full of stories about himself.

Of the three stories he has told me about himself, I like best the one about the time he nearly died of influenza, in Chester, Pennsylvania, in 1918.

I was sick, he said. When I got up in the morning I felt funny, but I put on my clothes, to go to work. When I was putting on my pants I fell down, but I got up quick. When I was walking to the door I fell down again. I didn't know what it was. I couldn't stand up. The rule was if you was working for the government and you didn't show up for work, they sent somebody to ask what's the matter. I tried to get up but I was too weak and I couldn't get up. After a minute I crawled back to the bed and fell on it and the next day the nurse came and said, What's the matter?

I don't know, I said. I'll come to work tomorrow.

She gave me an examination and said I must go to the hospital. I got up from the bed and said, No, I will go to work now. But I fell down, so the nurse helped me and said, Well, stay in bed here anyway.

In the afternoon, the landlady came and said, My boy, how are you?

Mother, I said, I do not know.

There was a Greek doctor from Smyrna, so I said, Mother, tell the doctor to come and look at me.

When the doctor from Smyrna came, the government doctor with the nurse was already telling the landlady I must go to the hospital, but I said, Let my countryman see me.

So the Greek doctor looked at me. He told me to go to the hospital. So. If I am sick, I got to go to the hospital, but I said, No. I will stay here.

They all went away. About an hour later came the police patrol and the doctor and two policemen and the nurse in the room and said, Get up.

What for? I said. I work for the government.

We know, they said. We got orders. We must take you to the hospital.

No, I said. I want to go back to work.

So I got up again, but I couldn't walk. So. If I am sick, I got to go to the hospital.

Take me in a boat to the best hospital in Philadelphia, I said.

All the hospitals in Philadelphia are full, the doctor said. We'll take care of you.

So they took me in the police patrol to the hospital. But what is the hospital?

Stable. One big room, with an aisle down the middle and beds on both sides. They put me in a bed and I began to wait. For three days they gave me nothing to eat and no water to drink. Only smashed ice. You put it in your mouth and suck it like an all-day sucker. One night I see the nurses bringing us food, but what is it? It's fishes' tails. Fried. The nurse put down the dish and I looked at the fishes' tail.

What is this? I said.

Food for you, the nurse said.

Food? I said. Please, I said. Take it away. Get me a glass of milk.

I began to look around and think about it. What kind of a place is this? I said. What's the fishes' tails for?

There was a dark nurse there who looked like a Greek, so I called her over.

Are you Greek? I said. I talked to her very quietly. I didn't know what kind of a place it was. I didn't feel good.

I am Serbian, the nurse said.

I don't like this place, I said. Do they want to kill us?

She told me in this place they pushed them out. They were all too sick. All the hospitals were full, and everybody was dying. But this place was the worst. If I'm going to die, I'm going to die at home, not in a slaughterhouse.

I am Greek, I said to the nurse. I want to go home. Tonight you bring my clothes and I get dressed and go home.

If I lose my job, the nurse said, I will do it. You're very sick. Do you think you will be able to walk?

I'll walk, I told her. Please bring my clothes, so I can go home.

So. In the night-time she brought my clothes and helped me put them on because I was so weak. When I tried to stand up I began to fall, so she helped me. Everybody was sick, but they knew what I was doing. Jim, they said, Where you going?

I'm going home, I said. If I'm going to die, I'm going to die at home.

I tried to walk but I couldn't do it, and the girl began to cry.

Please try to walk, she said. I will hold you till you get a little fresh air.

She walked with me to the door. Outside it was all snow, below zero. In front of my eyes I couldn't see, but she stayed by me until I got a little fresh air. Then I could see, but what could I see?

All snow.

How will you get home? the girl said.

I'll get home, I said.

She closed the door and went back, but I couldn't walk. I sat down on the top step and my eyes began to close. I began to dream about the days in Greece when I used to run in the hills and eat berries and drink water from the rivers. Then somebody put his hand on my shoulder. It was an officer in the army.

What's the matter? he said.

I'm going home, I said.

Do you belong in this hospital? he said.

This is not a hospital, I said. This is a slaughterhouse.

Come to my office, he said.

In the office he said, Sit down. He telephoned and told them when the bus left for Chester to come and get me, and when the driver came into the office he said, Take this man home. Walk with him to his door. See that he is taken care of.

The bus was full of different—different workers going home. In the bus I fainted on the lap of an Italian fellow. I was out, but I could hear. The Italian said, That's all right, my friend.

When the driver woke me up the bus was empty. He walked with me to the door. The Greek doctor from Smyrna told the Greeks I was going to die, so a Greek fellow told the landlady I was dead. When she opened the door she didn't know if it was me, or my spirit. You know Lazar? I was like Lazar. My face was long beard and bones. He told her I was dead. You know that little fellow? he said. I buried him yesterday with my own hands. Do not wait for him. She was very scared. So.

Do not be scared, Mother, I said. It is me. I am not dead.

My boy, she said, how are you?

I am sick, Mother.

She took me to my room and put me in my bed. My eyes closed, but I could hear. My boy, she said, what can I do for you?

Mother, I said, please go downstairs and get me some chicken broth.

So she went downstairs and got me a bowl of chicken broth. I finished the broth and closed my eyes. In the night something began to come up inside of me, very cold.

In the morning I couldn't open my eyes, but all night I didn't sleep. I didn't want to sleep. I wanted to stay awake all the time. The landlady came and said, My boy, tell me what I can do for you.

Mother, I said, please go downstairs and get me some chicken broth.

So she got me some chicken broth and I waited. About an hour later she came again and said, My boy, what can I do for you? If there is anything in the world you want, please let me know.

She was crying. So.

Mother, I said, don't cry for me. If I am going to die, I'm going to die. We came into this world to live one life. Please get me some chicken broth.

In the night the Greek doctor and the government doctor came to look at me again. My eyes were closed, so they thought I couldn't hear. They said I was going to be dead by nine o'clock in the morning. Well, I said to myself, I don't know. Maybe the doctors know. I don't know. When they went away the landlady came to me and began to cry.

My boy, she said.

Mother, I said, it's all right. Don't cry for me.

She went away and after an hour she came back again. I could hear her walking around in the house.

My boy, she said, can I do anything for you?

It's all right, Mother, I said. You go to sleep.

So this time she went to sleep. Inside my body the cold kept coming up. I didn't know anything like that. I didn't know what it was. Then my nose began to bleed. At first I didn't know it was bleeding, but when I put my hand to my face my hand was warm and I could smell the blood. It was coming fast. Under the bed I bent down for the pot and the blood dropped into the pot for a long time. All the time it was falling I began to feel better and better. Everything went away. Everything came out of my nose with the blood. The room was dark but I knew I could see again. The cold was gone from the inside too, so I began to laugh. I was very hungry but it was nighttime, so I sat up in bed and waited for morning. In the morning I could hear the landlady walking past my door. She walked past many times, and then once she stopped, so I said, It's all right, Mother. I am not dead. You can come in.

So she came in, but she was very scared. I showed her the blood. I was ashamed and I said, Please forgive me, Mother. I couldn't help it.

My boy, she said. How are you? Are you all right?

I am very hungry, Mother.

She went downstairs and brought me some chicken broth. She went upstairs and downstairs all morning bringing me chicken broth. When the doctors came I was sitting up in bed. They expected to see a dead body.

What's this? they said.

I told them everything. They looked at me again. I was all right now.

I didn't like them and they didn't like me.

The government doctor wrote down in his book and went away. The doctor from Smyrna walked around in the room. Then he said, I am going to ask you one question. Please tell me the truth.

What is it? I said.

How old were you when you left the old country?

Seventeen, I said.

All right, he said. This is the question. How old were you when you began to wear shoes?

My father bought me shoes when I was three years old, I said. But I threw them in the closet and ran into the hills in my bare feet.

That's the reason, the doctor said.

Then he went away.

You see, the waiter said. From the earth to my feet came the strength of the old country. If I had worn shoes in the old country I would be dead now, not alive.

The Friends of the Monkeys

The oldest one is the one who feeds the monkeys grapes; he throws them to the animals out of a bag, talking to them and delighting in their recognition of him, and the way they obey; at least Henry, a baboon that turns flips for this man. The smaller ones, who are more nervous, apparently can't be taught tricks, even by one who loves them as much as this man does. They just hurry over affectionately when they see him and wait for him to throw grapes into the cage.

The other one, who is younger and bigger and a lot less impressive, bright, subtle, or profound, feeds the young gorilla called Mary; and also the two older gorillas in the next cage. He feeds them pieces of flat chocolate broken off a bar. His favorite seems to be Mary, and he loves to tease her. He does this by showing her the candy and then going like a dog and giving it to the two big gorillas in the next cage. When this happens Mary jumps and screams and is terribly unhappy. The whole thing is a minor romance. The people at the Zoo love it, but it scares a lot of the kids. Maybe that's because they would behave the same way; or would if they were Mary and had to live in a little cage that stank and looked so sad.

The chocolate-candy feeder is a worker at the Zoo, and nothing more than a show-off. He is an actor in a little drama, and like all actors is terribly flattered by the applause of the people. It is all a performance with him. He is a man of six feet two or three and should be more interested in the nobler animals: the tigers, lions, and panthers, not the miserable, wretched, neurotic monkeys. He should pick on something his size.

The man of the grapes is a worker on the WPA Project nearby: the new Zoo they're building. It's against the rules to feed the animals, but not for him, apparently. Apparently he has been given permission to feed them grapes during his lunch hour. Apparently the people who know what's good for the monkeys have been generous to him, in view of his fine affection and regard for the monkeys, and granted him permission to feed them grapes. The grapes probably balance the diets of the monkeys. He is a man of fifty-five or so, with most of his teeth gone, and a shuffling way of walking. He's no show-off, has no desires to entertain the people, and ignores every timid person who timidly asks him a question about the monkeys. He ignores all the people, the timid as well as the bold. His friends are the monkeys, not the people.

He comes down the walk, speaking to them loudly. Henry, he calls. How is my Henry? How are you, Henry? Here, Turn over. That's right. Again, now. Again, Henry. That's right. Then he throws the baboon a handful of grapes. He moves down to the next cage, the cage with the half dozen little monkeys in it. How are you, gangsters? Here. Here's something sweet for you again; and he tosses the little monkeys three handfuls.

As far as he's concerned anybody can have people for friends, but it takes somebody like *him* to have monkeys for friends. Henry, and the little gangsters, and all the others.

Does it stack up to anything? Nothing much. Some people are eager to win friends: uncaged and not nervous and neurotic the way monkeys are. Others, on the other hand, scoff at such impure ambitions, and, tossing grapes, win friends, and influence monkeys.

It is all history. It is all art, somehow or other.

October 24, 1938

Notes of Days Gone By

THE EYES AND EARS OF THE WORLD

One day in November, in 1935, the sky over San Francisco in the morning was black, and there was no light in the city. The streetlights were out and in the morning, with the city full of people, it was night, without any of the freedom and calm of night. It was a time for rest because the morning and the night were together as one, and still the people were in the city, going to work, the same as on any other day.

November 23, 1935

AFTER THE LAST WAR AND BEFORE THE NEXT

People interested in prose and poetry and painting and sculpture and music and many other things, after the War, seemed to do very little in the way of making these things, but seemed to get a great deal of enjoyment out of talking about these things and making this talk the important thing of their lives.

Peace is probably impossible or at any rate undesirable, so perhaps they dislike the *kind* of conflict, not the idea of conflict itself, and they dislike the weapons, which these days are much too enormous or efficient or accurate in every particular, and the pain or damage they do much too abstract and pointless, making victory aesthetically impossible. They dislike military war, and they dislike the economic war, but they need and want war all right. They want the other kind.

May 24, 1936

I THANK YOU

The function of literature is to increase in men the capacity to endure nicely, and perhaps to enjoy, presence on earth, but this happens also to be the function of everything else people do, which if they didn't do would make thieves or murderers of them on the one hand, or bores and neurotics on the other. The function, for instance, of heroism is certainly to increase in men the capacity to enjoy mortality, as is the function of banking, or being janitor. Service is the motto: we aim to please. If you like our place, tell others. If you don't like our place, tell us.

I thank you.

August 24, 1936

MEMOIRS OF A FRIEND OF MY FATHER

Somehow other, he said, when I was coming from old country to Nor York was said by frands there is much *para** for honest man, but after I am standing off Alice Island on Broadvay I see no *para,** only *galabalakh*.†

No *para*, only *galabalakh*? I said.

No moaney, he said. Only *galabalakh*. You know. *Shamata*.‡ You speak Haiyeren, *cheh*?

Sure, I said. I am an Armenian, why shouldn't I speak Armenian?

June 11, 1937

A LIFE

The New Hat which was blown Off the Head of the Young Man Who was Bald and did not Catch Up with it for Four City Blocks—His Biography, Philosophy, and a Brief Commentary on the World.

June 13, 1937

MOSCOW IN TEARS

The day after I reached Moscow from Sevastopol, in July 1935, it rained and I wrote a short story called "Moscow in Tears" which the Russians stole from me and, to this day have not returned to me.

Unless the story is returned, it is lost, because I do not type carbon copies of my stuff. I don't believe in carbon copies. I trust everybody.

June 24, 1937

AHF WIEN

What I remember of Vienna is a cripple on a motorcycle, a railway station porter who lived in New York at one time and spoke typical foreign-American language and was a Communist, the roof garden restaurant with the view of the city, the beautiful young girl who was quarreling with her lover at the next table, her hands, and the way she smoked cigarettes, the policemen with rifles and bayonets.

July 1, 1937

EVERY LAST ONE OF THEM WAS A FOOL: A SHORT STORY

Of course propriety is against anything worth anything and nobody can ever do anything except something that doesn't amount to much,

*The Turkish word for money.
†Hullabaloo.
‡Noise, din, bustle.

like writing a nice story about people and leaving out everything that is the part that makes them important or at least human, like the dirt and the inner sorrow mingling with the inner mischievousness and eight or nine other things, and like the pity on every hand, all the strange kindly compassion which nobody ever speaks of, like all the things nobody ever speaks of.

October 11, 1937

THE YOUNG MAN WITH THE BRILLIANT IMAGINATION

A young man with a brilliant imagination was planting a tree in the old country one day two or three hundred years ago when his imagination began to move forward by what might best be described as leaps and bounds. This tree, the young man said, although small now, is certain to grow, and, as I see it, myself, in a year or two, am bound to meet a very beautiful girl, marry her, and shortly afterward become the father of a fine boy who of course is bound to be lively, like myself. He is bound to climb this tree and if I am not badly mistaken he is bound to fall and break his neck and be killed.

The thought of this tragedy grieved the young man so much, he did not plant the tree.

November 26, 1937

My Grandmother Lucy Tells a Story Without a Beginning, a Middle or an End

On this twenty-sixth day of December 1941, the day after Christmas, perhaps the most anticlimactic of all days of the year, my grandmother Lucy, visiting here in San Francisco, has just told me another story which I shall of course write. But as I do so I must wonder if Lucy is not losing her memory. I refuse to believe it is her memory that is going, consequently it must be that, like myself, she is becoming impatient with plot and formula and wants to tell a story for nothing more than the fun or sorrow of it.

We were sitting at the table, drinking afternoon coffee, listening to a rebroadcast of Churchill's speech to the American Senate and House of Representatives, and remembering cups of coffee of long ago, particularly the morning I drank eight cups in a row, while my uncle Melik had only half a cup and got up from the table to remark, You are now nine years old—in twenty years if you are not famous I shall not speak of this event again. If you are famous, I shall know the reason. Eight cups of coffee. Will you pass water now or a little later?

Here Lucy began her story.

A man packed up and went to other countries. Before departing he was asked what city it was he wished to reach. The city without worries he replied. He was told, When you get there, please see if you can do anything about *my* worries—my wife and children. My wife wants me to be a success, and my children refuse to believe that I am poor—they want things whch I cannot give them.

On the way, my grandmother said, the journeyer noticed an apple tree, beside which sat an old man. As other journeyers came to this tree they plucked apples from its boughs, took one bite and threw them aside. The journeyer went to the old man and said, Why do they take one bite only and then throw them away?

Beneath this tree, the old man replied, is gold.

The journeyer began to dig under the tree. He uncovered a great deal of gold.

Here my grandmother stopped speaking. I waited patiently a full minute, while Mr. Churchill emphasized various points and lifted his voice. At last I decided to urge my grandmother on.

Yes? I said.

Yes *what*? she said.

The story, I said. Please tell it all.

That is all, my grandmother said. And then, as an afterthought, she added, The point is that there is often great wisdom in old men.

Is that the whole story? I said.

Yes, Lucy said. Why do you ask?

Well, I said, the man started out by wanting to get to the city without worries. What happened to that part of the story?

Nothing, my grandmother said. People want to go away now and then and when asked where it is they wish to go, they make a remark of one sort or another. This man said that he wished to get to the city without worries.

I thought he might reach the city, I said.

This explanation seemed unsatisfactory and mysterious, therefore I brought up the matter of the man who asked the man where he was going and after he had been told asked the man to investigate his worries which involved his wife and children.

What about the man whose worries were his wife and children? I asked.

A fool or a wit, my grandmother said. It is no matter. There is no man in the world without some sort of a worry. This man's worry was of the commonest variety.

Then perhaps, I said, you have left something out of the story regarding the gold. Why was there gold under the apple tree?

My grandmother did not seem to regard this question as one worthy of an answer.

What is this man saying? she asked of Mr. Churchill.

He is talking about the war, I said.

What about it? Lucy said.

He has come from England, I said, to talk to the members of the American government. He is talking to them now. He made this speech this morning. It is being rebroadcast this afternoon for those who missed this morning's broadcast, and it will be rebroadcast several times again tonight for those who miss *this* rebroadcast. What about the gold under the tree? Haven't you forgotten some of the story?

My grandmother Lucy considered the story a moment and then said, That is the whole story, exactly as I have always told it.

It sounds like one of *my* stories. I said.

It is quite complete, my grandmother said. Today is the day after Christmas. It is good enough.

Isn't there something to say about the apples being bitter? I suggested.

No, Lucy said, the apples were very sweet. Large, red and sweet.

Then why did the journeyers take one bite and throw them away? I asked.

They did not like apples, my grandmother said.

This did not seem convincing.

I believe you have forgotten the story, I said.

I forget nothing, my grandmother said. Shall I tell you about your father as a small boy of three? How he looked and the way of his speech?

I am sure you could tell me about my father as a child, I said, but I still have a feeling that this fable of the journeyer and the apple tree is not quite complete.

A nest of birds perhaps in the tree? my grandmother suggested.

Perhaps, I said. But that would only make the story longer and more involved. What would the birds do?

They would do nothing, Lucy said. Or sing.

I have never before heard you tell a story such as this, I said. I shall have some trouble writing it, and I may even have to invent a beginning, a middle and an end.

A beginning, a middle and an end? my grandmother said. What in the world for? If it's names you want, call the journeyer Markos, the old man beside the tree Harkos, and one of the others Zarkos.

That I will do, I said, but I am afraid the story will have little point.

Here the Senators and members of the House of Representatives cheered the conclusion of Mr. Churchill's speech. An announcer took over to comment on the event. No one must imagine that there is some connection between this incomplete fable of my grandmother's and Mr. Churchill's day-after-Christmas speech, for there is absolutely no connection between them. I have put down the background for no reason other than its verity—I wanted to hear Churchill's speech and I wanted to hear Lucy's story. I heard both at the same time. This fable has absolutely no political or cultural implications. Although I do not like to think of this, my grandmother may be dead in another ten or twenty years. Last year my other grandmother, my father's mother, died and left us all a little lonelier than before. We speak of her often, and every time I go to Fresno I look at her wonderful old house as if it were a thing which had, itself, perished and crumbled into the earth of fables. Lucy will one day be dead, and there will be no more of her stories to write. This may be one of the last. I myself may be dead, although I doubt it, or if not dead, I may be traveling. I can always invent stories for my grandmother to tell me of course, but they will never be like the ones she herself tells, I'm sure. No one else in the world could begin a story with this simple remark: A man packed up and went to other countries.

I feel a terrible loneliness for Lucy already, although she is upstairs in the kitchen, no doubt wondering what I meant by all the foolish questions I asked her, or wondering if she is not losing her memory. She remembers my father as a boy of three, and he was born in 1874. Things are changing in the world, there is no doubt about that.

The Man Who Knew My Father As a Boy in Bitlis

Sarkis Janian was born on the last day of the year 1874, which is also the year of my father's birth and to me therefore one of the years of particular interest. I have always felt a closeness to this year, to these four figures, 1874, and each time I have seen them in print I have said to myself, That is the year my father was born; and of the year 1911 I have always said, And that is the year my father died, at the age of thirty-seven.

Sarkis Janian knew my father in Bitlis, and then again he knew him in Paterson, New Jersey. And now after all these years he lives in San Francisco, not far from where I live. Now and then he and his wife come and visit us. Every time he steps into the house, he turns to me suddenly and says, I knew your father.

Tell me about him, I say.

Well, he says, your father and I were friends. We went swimming together.

Sarkis Janian is a most remarkable man. He is open-spirited, straightforward, earnest, full of fun, and very much alive. He is what is known as a reading man too, and lately he has become a writing one. He has written a poem about me, beginning each line with the letters of my name: W-i-l-l-i-e S-a-r-o-y-a-n. In Armenian of course. The poem was read to me by my mother and seemed to be quite fine—in fact, I was amazed, and concluded that all Armenians are essentially writers, or poets, or at least unusually expressive.

There is probably no Armenian in the world, I told my mother, who cannot write.

I regard my mother's letters to her sisters as the most beautiful writing I have ever heard.

My beloved sister, these letters begin.

I do not believe any other language can be so pure and intimate and dignified as our language. Armenian is a language in which insincerity is impossible. It is a language, in fact, evolved solely to hold its people together as a family. If there could be contemporary saints their letters would be written in Armenian, and if the world were to write for itself a new Bible it would be written in Armenian. The other languages are for the advancement of science or culture, but the Armenian language was made for the extension and improvement of human relations, and for the ennobling of the human spirit.

(I have just been called upstairs by Sarkis Janian. There is something I forgot, he said. Do you know the priest who passed away? He gave me this snuffbox. My grandmother used to say that snuff is good for the eyes, for the ears, and that it takes away headaches. Besides, it brings good luck. Here he took a pinch and snuffed it into his left nostril, then into his right. That is what I wanted to tell you, he said. Now, this box is from the old country, with old country decorations.)

I studied the box which was most beautiful.

Now I am back at my table to tell the little story.

As I was saying before I was called upstairs to behold the old country snuffbox, the Armenian language is one of the great languages, and Sarkis Janian writes poems in Armenian.

One day I asked him how he had happened to take up the writing of poems.

Well, he said, I read a poem in one of the Fresno papers, and I was surprised to discover that it was written by a man I used to know, a Vanetsi, a man from Van. I thought to myself, Well, let me see about this. If *he* can write a poem, maybe I can write a poem, too. So I thought about it all day and that night I wrote a poem. I sent it to the paper and they printed it. Now I write poems all the time, taking a name, and beginning each line with the letters of the name—which is not easy to do. Everybody cannot do that, he said. They can write, but they cannot write poems taking the letters of the name that way. It is the same as the people who write stories. They can write stories all right, but not like *your* stories. Not with the same taste and smell.

Sarkis Janian has a sort of carpenter shop on Ninth Avenue. He is a cabinetmaker, and in the winter the stove in his shop sends out a warmth which draws me into the shop whenever I am down that way. It is a pleasant atmosphere with a fine smell of wood, varnish, glue, shavings and fire heat. Sometimes the man who knew my father in Bitlis is at work, working along easily, never overworking, never breaking his neck or anything foolish like that, always calm and boyish about the whole thing, absorbed in his work much as a child is absorbed in his silent, solitary games; or if he is not at his work, he is in the rocking chair by the stove, reading an Armenian newspaper, magazine or book.

Oh, he says, I am glad you have come here. I was just thinking about your father and myself in the old country. I was thinking of the wonderful walks we used to take.

Where did you walk? I would say.

Oh, he would say with a wonderful sigh and a wonderful smile on his happy youthful face, everywhere—everywhere. We would walk through the city—through Bitlis itself. We would walk out into the country, sometimes to Gultik. We would walk into the hills for grass for the cows. Or we would go to the fountain Tsaperrgore. Oh, yes, I knew your father. We walked together many, many times.

We would talk for a while. I would ask a dozen foolish questions, and then I would say goodbye and go. I would ask him about what he was making, and then I would ask him about my father's voice; and then I would ask him how things were going with him, and then I would ask him if he ever heard my father laugh; and then I would ask him if people were coming into his shop and buying his tables and chairs, and then I would ask him to tell me something my father told him in the old country—a few of his words, the *exact* words.

What did my father say that you remember? I would say.

Many things, the carpenter would say. Oh, he said many things. I cannot tell you what he said, but he said many things.

It is very likely that my father scarcely spoke, but it seemed to his friend that he had said many things, and of course in a way he had, although he hadn't spoken.

Tonight when Sarkis Janian came to this house, I was at the kitchen table after supper, reading about the War. When I heard his voice I went out into the hall to welcome him. He took my hand and would not let go of it. I knew what he was up to, so I pretended to protest, to amuse my mother and my sister and Sarkis Janian and his wife. The old men like to kiss the foreheads of the young, but as this is an old country custom, I pretended that it was old-fashioned and not for me—not for the likes of me—and purposely made a fuss of drawing away from him in a sort of tug-of-war which made everyone roar with laughter. But Sarkis Janian would not let go. No, he said earnestly. No, you must let me kiss your forehead. I knew your father.

All right, I said, and he kissed my forehead.

After we were seated he said, People who have read my poems come to me and say, What is this—are you a poet? And I tell them yes. One word: Yes. Poet? Yes. Today a letter came to me from New York, but it was not a letter. It was a form with questions. It is sent to distinguished Armenians. I filled it out and sent it back. It said Name, Address, Date of Birth, Place of Birth, and so on and so forth. It said, What universities have you gone to?

And what did you answer to that one? I asked.

None, said Sarkis Janian. I went to no universities. To every question regarding schools I replied, None. For I have gone to no schools. And then it asked, Have you done any teaching? Six months, I said—for I taught in Bitlis once for six months when I was eighteen. And then the form asked if I was a lawyer or a doctor or a priest—and at last it asked if I was a poet, and there I wrote in one word: Yes.

My father's boyhood friend, Sarkis Janian. I have rushed into this portrait, so that I might not forget to do it, doing other work. This is not enough—not nearly enough—to say about my father's friend, but by rights I am supposed to be doing other work, and I have taken an hour out to make these few notes. The important thing about my father's friend is that he is so truly an Armenian, so truly earnest and serious, and at the same time so full of fun; and so proud of the important things. They come and ask me, What is this—are you a poet? And I tell them yes. And Sarkis Janian is truly a poet. He is a true poet. His whole life is poetry.

Tonight I told him that I would like to write about him.

Yes, he said, put me in somewhere, as a hero. There is room for everybody, put me in somewhere, too.

I will, I said, I will, and now I have done so, and may therefore return to my regular if less pleasant work.

One Hello and One Goodbye

A lot of friends of mine are what I call hello-and-goodbye writers. Everybody they write about is always saying hello and goodbye.

It's not a bad idea, though.

My boy came home from Catholic School in Beverly Hills about two and a half years ago and he said, Goodbye, Sister Rita Bernadette.

I'll explain why he said that.

One Friday, I took him and his sister in my car to San Francisco for a weekend visit, so of course they missed school that Friday. Well, Sister Rita Bernadette told the principal of the school that my boy's father was always taking him out of school on Fridays. My boy told her that his father had done that only once. Sister Rita Bernadette told him not to speak, and again she told the principal that I was always doing that.

She's a liar.

I did it once.

That's the reason my boy came home from school that day and said, "Goodbye, Sister Rita Bernadette."

He waited a moment and then he said, "I didn't pass, Pop. She didn't pass me."

And there he was almost eight years old, trying very hard not to show how bad he felt about it.

"You don't *have* to pass," I said, "and you're not going back to that school, either. You don't *have* to go back. That school happened to be near where you live, so your mother and I thought we'd let you and your sister go there, but you're not going to go there anymore. And when you go to the new school you're going to go into the grade you would have been in if Sister Rita Bernadette had passed you. You're not going to stay back."

And that's how it happened too. Sister Rita Bernadette didn't like him, that's all. And the odd part about it is that he was not unfond of the dogmatic stuff, although the catechism was too long. It took me some time to explain about hell and everlasting punishment. I put it this way, "It's not for you or anybody like you, to begin with. And then it's not for anybody at all, because it just *isn't*, in any case, not the way they've been telling you. The nice things are all nice and I'm all for them, but they don't have to put you to thinking you're some kind of bad human being, because you're not, that's all. If you want to say the nice prayer or a couple of Hail Marys now and then that's O.K., but don't think you'll burn in hell if you don't. You won't."

That's the goodbye.

Here's the hello.

I'm in touch with the Internal Revenue because I haven't been able to pay my taxes, and they've put a lien on my life.

I want to reach the tax man on the phone, but every time I get the girl at the tax office and ask for the man she gives me a runaround, so I write to him and get no answer; then one day the operator at the tax office is giving me the usual runaround, and I'm sure I'll be told in a moment that the man I want to talk to is out of town until next Tuesday, but instead the man I want to talk to—the man I've been trying to talk to for five months—comes on the line. His voice is warm, friendly, excited, as he calls out with enthusiasm and pleasure, "Hello, George!"

It's half past twelve and I figure the tax man and George are old pals and will be going to lunch any moment. I feel almost guilty about not being George, whoever he is, but I have got to come clean, so I tell the tax man as simply and directly and earnestly as I can who I am.

His voice changes, the joy goes out of it, he's received six letters from me in which I've explained everything, in which I keep asking for an appointment to meet him so that he and I and the U.S. Government can reach an agreement whereby I may be permitted to meet my personal obligations and try to work, and make money, so I can catch up with my back taxes, but he's never answered any of my letters, and I've tried to reach him on the phone, and he has always been out, and his secretary has said he will call me at such and such a time, and he has never called, so of course now that it is actually me on the line, and not that devil-may-care fellow George, that lunch-eating pal, the tax man's voice changes, he forgets how to pronounce small familiar words, but he manages, with my help, with the help of the operator, with the help of his secretary, to set up an appointment for me, a week later, in his office, which is thirty-five miles from where I live.

"Hello, George!" the tax man shouted, and I shouted it to my boy a few days later. and told him the story of it, and after that every time I saw my boy he would try to say it the way the tax man had said it and then he would say, "*You* say it, Pop. That's the funniest thing I ever heard. 'Hello, George!' What did you tell him, Pop?"

"I said, 'This is William Saroyan speaking.' " My boy jumped up and roared with laughter, and he said, "Ah, Pop, say it again, will you. 'This is William Saroyan speaking.' It's not George, it's not your old pal, but a crazy mixed-up guy who owes taxes for ten or twenty years."

"Three," I said, and my boy jumped and roared with laughter again.

"Just three," he said, "that's all. Just fifty or sixty thousand dollars, that's all. Hello, George! Who's George? Maybe he's a thief." My boy said all the things he'd ever heard me say about the episode, and he roared with laughter.

That's the one hello and the one goodbye.

There are a lot more of them, but one hello and one goodbye will do for just now, I think.

A Moment of Freedom and Fun

I had promised my son and my daughter a summer holiday drive to anywhere they might like to go.

We were up at half past three in the morning because children about to go on a motoring trip want to get started. Not to mention writers. We started at Malibu, where I have a house on the beach. It is a small house on piling, on the sand, and high tide brings the sea under the house. Half the people in the world would like to drive to Malibu for a holiday, I suppose, but we closed the front door, turned our backs on the sea, and began to drive away.

Sure enough, there were many cars on the highway coming in the opposite direction, some of them on their way to Malibu, no doubt.

"We're going to San Francisco," my son said. "Where are *they* going?"

"Malibu," I said.

"Where's Malibu?" my daughter asked.

They were both wide awake and excited, but at the same time more asleep than awake, too.

"Well," I said, "Malibu is where our house is, to begin with."

"Where else is it?" the boy said.

"It's along this highway, for twenty-five miles."

"Where's the *town*?" the girl said.

"There isn't a town," I said. "Along the highway now and then is a store or a group of stores, but nowhere in Malibu can you walk around the block."

"Why not?" the boy said.

"There's no block to walk around."

"In Beverly Hills," the girl said, "you can walk around many blocks."

"Beverly Hills isn't along the highway. Malibu probably isn't a town at all."

"If it's not a town," the boy said, "what is it?"

"Twenty-five miles of highway beside the sea, people in houses built on sand—if you want to sleep, why don't you stretch out on the back seat?"

"Sleep?" they both protested. "Who wants to sleep?"

Still, in five minutes they were fast asleep, the girl using my leg for a pillow, the boy stretched out on the back seat.

When they woke up it was almost daybreak and we were on the outskirts of Ventura on Highway 101.

"How long did we sleep?" they asked.

"Oh, about an hour."

"Did we miss anything?"

"A few little things, I suppose, but I missed a few, too."

"What did *you* miss?" the girl said.

"What you saw in your sleep."

"Can two people dream the same dream?" the boy wanted to know.

"Everybody dreams the same dream."

"What do they dream?"

"They dream of freedom and fun, and here we are free, in the midst of the best fun of all, in our own car scrambling up the highway at daybreak with not a care in the world."

We broke into song. After half an hour of it they were hungry and went to work on the stuff I had thrown together for breakfast or lunch or any time we felt like eating: milk, hard-boiled eggs, cheese, rolls, apples, bananas, raisins, cookies, licorice, chewing gum. They wondered what to start with. They voted for licorice, but I vetoed it in favor of rolls, cheese, and milk.

"You said *fun*," the girl said. "Well, licorice is fun."

"So is bread and cheese."

"Licorice is more."

"First things first, less fun before more fun. Plenty of time for licorice."

The car rolled along quietly, swiftly, easily, and on the first day of July we drove straight up Highway 101 to San Francisco.

Motoring is a time of great book-length conversations, and we had several of these during the ten-hour trip. Travel makes you talk. That's one of the reasons travel is so popular.

The boy said, "You're broke, Pop. How did you ever get this fine new Ford?"

"I made a deal with the Ford people."

"What kind of a deal?"

"I traded some writing for this car."

"Boy!" the boy said. "I'm going to be a writer someday."

"Don't ever do it," I said.

"What did you say?" the boy said.

"I said it's the best profession in the world."

"Where's *Malibu* now?" the girl said.

"Where it has always been."

"What was Malibu before?"

"Before what?"

"Before you moved there," the girl said.

"No," the boy said, "not before *you* moved there, before *anybody* moved there."

"In those days," I said, "Malibu was a secret."

"What do you mean, Pop?" the boy said.

"Can I have some licorice?" the girl said.

On and on the car rolled, and along the way, from Malibu to San Francisco, we saw many towns, streets, and people, and we thought many things, said many, and left many more unsaid because you just can't put into words every wonderful thing that occurs to you. You just can't. You keep it. You put it with the whole great assortment of secrets, like the secret of Malibu itself before anybody moved there, or the secret of the real joy of getting in your car and taking off, after months of hard work.

Hayastan and Charentz

Two things sent me to Hayastan in the spring of 1935 when I was twenty-six years old: a writer's restlessness, and a son's need to see his father's birthplace.

I took off, however, for a much simpler reason: I could afford to do so. By writing, by the sweat of my brow, I had at last earned both money enough to pay my way and the right to move about as I might see fit.

I had always found too many things wrong in the world, and too much of man's nature mean, and too much of his life meaningless, not to be restless.

And I had always been unimpressed by anybody I had ever met, although I had found many people amusing or kindly. The kindly man was generally a weak man, though, and the amusing man was almost invariably clever, or crooked, or both.

In a way I suppose it was just as well that my father was dead, for it is not unlikely that I would have found fault with him, too; but since he was dead, I dwelt in thought on his good qualities, and paid no attention to his bad ones; his inability to prosper in the world, to get along among commonplace men on their own terms, to take the world with a grain of salt, and to make a joke of it.

In my boyhood and early manhood my father was simply a good man, dead at the age of thirty-seven.

Nobody ever had a critical word to say of him, so that I myself in asking questions about his life and work tried to provoke criticism. In this I was unsuccessful. The worst that anybody was willing to say of my father was that he was too good for this world. I accepted this theory with simultaneous admiration and disbelief, but I made up my mind to go back where he had come from as soon as possible.

My chance came at last after my first book had been published.

I took a train from San Francisco to New York, and a ship from New York to Europe.

I was not unaware that in reaching Soviet Armenia I would not be reaching my father's Armenia, or his city, Bitlis. It was enough at that time to reach the general vicinity of my father's birthplace, and to be in a nation named Armenia, inhabited by Armenians.

On my way south from Kiev to Kharkhov to Rostov to Ordzonekidze to Tiflis to Erivan a great expectancy filled my heart, as well as a great sorrow, as if I were on my way to the place where all of my family, and my father, had tried very hard and had failed; his failure driving him to America at last, where, if anything, he became more homeless than ever.

As the train moved south, more and more Armenians came aboard. Just seeing and hearing them gave me great pleasure, but the greatest pleasure of all was in sitting with a family, or with three or four young men, with more arriving to join the talk and laughter.

Only one Armenian on the train was a political man. He was a very old and famous economic philosopher who had taught at various universities and had written books, but even this quiet-spoken man was not zealous about the political theories he had studied. He was a man of culture, wit, and an air of worldliness which seemed to suggest that while it was expedient for him to investigate economic theories, it would be a mistake to believe that he cared more for one order of them than for another. He neither criticized nor praised the economic and political systems of Russia or of America.

I had to wait for a boy of eleven in the lobby of the New Erivan Hotel to point out to me the terrible flaws of the American economic and political system. I have frequently wondered about this boy. By now it is not unlikely that he is one of the great men of Soviet Armenia, or perhaps even of Soviet Russia. I did not find him at all offensive, although as a general rule excessively bright boys tend to annoy and irritate me. As a joke I asked him if he could play the violin and was delighted when he told me he had no time for such frivolity. My laughter did not move him to so much as a smile. He simply remarked that Americans were forever laughing because of the contradictory nature of their economic and political system, and their own ignorance of proper procedure. I finally told him quite warmly to go away.

Several hours after I reached Erivan I took a chauffeur-driven car to Etchmiadzin where I met an old man who carried an old musket. He said he was the guard of the ruins of the nearby church called, I believe, Zvartnotz Vank. We walked among the ruins and came to an apricot tree which the old man shook, whereupon half a dozen small apricots fell to the grass beneath the tree. We picked these up and ate them, and he remarked that the apricots were small this year. Last year, he said, they were small, too, but not as small as they were this year. When we came to the open plains beyond the ruins I said suddenly, "Where is Bitlis?"

The old man looked at me, and I saw laughter come into his eyes.

"Your family is from Bitlis? Is that it?" he said.

"Yes," I said.

To the right was Ararat. The old man turned a little to the left and looked far out on the golden grass of the rolling plains. He stiffened his right arm at his side, then lifted it slowly as if it were a mechanical device designed specifically for the purpose of indicating the way to Bitlis. Now, he leveled his vision along the length of his arm, as if his arm were a rifle.

"Bitlis," he said. "Straight ahead is Bitlis. If you walk six days and six nights you will reach Bitlis. Walk, then."

I burst into laughter, for he had performed for my amusement as well as for his own, and he himself chuckled softly.

One frequently hears of somebody or other that he is a character out of a book. I will not say such a thing of the old man, however. He was a man out of the earth and life of Armenia, an unschooled peasant whose whole life had been difficult, but the first thing he did was to shake the apricot tree in order to share with me, a stranger, the little that he had.

I stayed in Erivan six or seven days, and then it was time to continue my travels: to Tiflis, to Batoum, by ship to Sevastopol on the Black Sea, and from there by train to Moscow.

A day or two after my arrival in Moscow I was taken by a young woman guide of the Intourist to pay my respects to Charentz, who occupied a suite of rooms with a balcony at the best hotel in town. My own hotel, the New Moscow, was a little west of Red Square, past St. Basil's and the Moscow River. East of Red Square, in the heart of town, was the hotel where Charentz was living at that time. The guide took me up in the elevator to the third or fourth floor and together we walked down a corridor and stopped at an open door. From somewhere inside Charentz appeared quickly, smiling, and he and I shook hands and spoke in Armenian. He then spoke in Russian to the young woman, and she went off, saying in English that she would leave us alone and return in an hour or so.

It was late afternoon of a day in June in 1935, and ever since Charentz has been in my thoughts. I have wanted to write about him, but I have not done so for several reasons. First, because my writing might be misunderstood and thereby bring him embarrassment, anxiety, personal difficulty, or even misfortune. I could not have such a possibility on my conscience. I could only pray from year to year that, wherever he happened to be, his fate and fortune might not be too much for him. I felt deeply grateful that I had met him at all, and while he himself never urged me not to write about him, or about Soviet Armenia or Soviet Russia, I felt that it was personal courage and pride which prohibited him from doing so, and I sensed that his straightforward, warm, and gallant manner toward me was the consequence of an implicit trust in my discretion. Second, I did not write about him because he is a poet whose poetry I do not know, since he writes in Armenian which I do not read. And finally, because I saw him only three or four times.

A few things, however, I believe I may say about Charentz. To begin with, I am afraid I was unable not to notice instantly that he was a very small man in stature and a very ugly one in appearance. I am sure Charentz must have noticed my awareness of his size and appearance, but if he did, he did not permit me to notice his awareness of my awareness. In surely less than half a minute he was no longer a small man. His size was entirely irrelevant. And instead of being an ugly man, he was one of the handsomest. His voice had warmth, and his eyes were direct, swift and intelligent. Charentz was not a small body with a large rather grotesque head and a huge hooked nose. He was a living personality, whose place of residence, the body, was by accident what it was. I found it impossible not to feel proud to be in his presence, and he in turn made me feel he was proud to have me in his presence. But I do not mean that our conversation was routine in its cordiality, or that all we did was compliment one another. Quite the contrary. Having met as countrymen and fellow writers such routine courtesy was soon put aside, and we spoke as if we had always been friends but simply had not met before.

In short, I liked Charentz straight off, but more important than this was the feeling I had that he was a truly great man. Human greatness is a rather difficult thing to account for, and more often than not one is mistaken in one's hunches about somebody one has met. Charentz seemed great to me, I think, because he was made of a mixture of astonishing virtues and amusing flaws. On the one hand, his independence of spirit was balanced by a humorous worldliness, his acute intelligence by a curiosity that frequently made him seen naive, his profoundly gentle manners by a kind of mocking mischievousness which might easily be mistaken for rudeness. But he was never rude, he was witty, and the purpose of his wit was to keep himself from the terrible condition of pomposity. He was swift, and there was a quality in him of both passion and violence—the violence of a creative man whose passion for truth has been tricked and troubled by unavoidable forces. These forces seemed to have compelled a wise but nevertheless uncomfortable moral expediency. Now I had found a number of eminent Armenians whom I had met in Armenia and Russia quite guarded in their conversations with me. I might, for instance, ask what seemed to me a most innocent question about the life of Armenians in a certain town, and I might hear a reply full of caution, indefiniteness, and even suspicion. This was a new experience for me, but I was able soon enough to understand the necessity for such caution. Charentz, however, simply could not be bothered about such caution. He said precisely what he wanted to say at any given point of a conversation, and his speech was full of that order of contradiction which is the mark of the spirit which is still free and still eager not to forfeit its freedom. At the same time, however, he might suddenly say something preposterous and unacceptable, but whenever this happened I noticed that he chuckled or said something under his breath, as if to himself. I did not find his Armenian nor his speed of speech difficult to follow, for he spoke with great simplicity. Nor did he find my Armenian at all confusing to him. As a matter of fact, I never found it necessary to repeat any remark, or to put it another way.

Charentz said, "You write in English, but you are an Armenian writer just the same." I agreed and remarked that while I did not know his writing, it seemed to me that although he wrote in Armenian, he was essentially a world writer. Charentz said, "Perhaps, or let us hope so, although it would be quite enough to be an Armenian writer." Now, there is no need to expect that I have remembered the precise words that Charentz and I exchanged almost twenty years ago, for I haven't. The greater part of the meaning of what we said I have not forgotten and will not ever forget, but the actual words have long since lost their precise context. For instance, Charentz informed me that he had repudiated his earliest writing, and I told him that it didn't matter that he had done so because the writing had its own life and he himself could no more end that life than I could. Charentz looked at me and smiled quickly. "Yes," he said, "that is quite true."

Now, when he said that he had repudiated his earliest writing I got the feeling that he expected me to believe him, but when I remarked that *I didn't* believe him, I got the feeling that he was quite glad that I hadn't. And that is an example of how all of our conversations moved along. The better part of the value of the conversations was not so much in what was actually said as in the true meaning of what was said, based upon the reason behind the remark, and upon that which was simultaneously communicated without the use of words, by a pause, a glance, an inflection.

I found Charentz bursting with energy and ideas, with intensity and health, but a moment later I was not at all surprised to find that he was also quite profoundly troubled in spirit and ill in body. He asked suddenly to be excused a moment while he administered medical treatment to himself. There was no explanation or awkwardness on his part. I stepped out on the balcony and watched the people in the streets a moment or two. He came out on the balcony and we continued our conversation as if there had been no interruption. But after that I had to wonder about his life—his *whole* life, from childhood to boyhood to early manhood—and I knew it had been laden over from the beginning with pain, sorrow, frustration, anger, bitterness, hatred, and all of the other things which will kill one man and carry another to greatness. His laughter on the balcony was heartier than ever, but in it now I heard great and almost unbearable sorrow and anguish.

In Erivan I had met many young and old Armenians, and I had felt that they were all members of my family, including even those I disliked. But it was not until I had reached Moscow that I came upon an Armenian who seemed to me both the most challenging of all as a person, and by all odds the most evolved, civilized, worthwhile, intelligent, troubled, unhappy, and yet somehow right as the symbol of the indestructible spirit of Armenian life and culture—anywhere in the world. I wished Charentz could come to America for a visit, or even to live. He smiled at the idea and shook his head almost imperceptibly. "I am here," he said. "You are there. Someone else is somewhere else. So let it be."

I thought of Charentz as a brother, and I still do. I have met many writers in many countries, but I have met none who impressed me more than Charentz, and I still do not know his writing, and very little about his life. This slight memoir of him is entirely without politics. I liked him.

I admired him. I was proud to be a countryman of his, and a fellow writer. I am devoted to his memory.

The Gambled Coat

"This is my brother's coat," he said. "I'll want to buy it back before you close tonight. What time do you close?"

"Six sharp," the man said. "You sold it, you didn't hock it, but as a special favor I'll let you have it back for five dollars."

"O.K."

He hurried from Sixth to Third, to The Kentucky, and sat down in the quarter game. In less than an hour the three dollars were four eighty-five. As soon as he got hold of six, he'd run to Sixth, get the coat, run back, get back in the game, and see about running the dollar up to ten. With ten he'd hurry back to Turk and get into the game there. With luck he'd run the ten up to fifty, and tomorrow take the train to Fresno and if he picked a couple of good horses from there he'd go anywhere he felt like going.

He gambled with the three dollars until two in the morning, then walked four miles home in the heavy drizzle.

His brother was waiting at the head of the stairs.

"What have you done with my coat?"

"I sold it," he said. "I lost the money gambling. Three dollars."

They fought in the hall and down the steps, knocking each other against the walls. His brother got him in the eye, and then in the mouth.

And then he had his brother bouncing head over heels down the stairs.

His brother picked himself up, looked at him, and left the house.

"I didn't fight until he made me," he said, and he went down the steps too. When he got back his brother had gone to bed, but he knew he wasn't asleep. He went to bed, and after an hour he said, "I'll make it up to you someday. Don't you think I knew you were right? But what's a man going to do? Just because I'm trying to write doesn't mean I don't need money the same as anybody else. You know I didn't want to fight, but I know that you had to. I'll make it up sometime."

He was at the place the next day at nine in the morning and the man said, "Look, today's Saturday, I'm very busy. You sold the coat. If you want to buy it, O.K. But I'm not *holding* it. It's for sale."

"I want to buy it," he said. "How much is it?"

"I'm asking seven-fifty for it," the man said, "but if you want it right now, O.K., give me six and take it."

"I can't buy it now," he said. "If I get six dollars by six o'clock will you let me have it for six?"

"If I don't sell it in the meantime," the man said. "Saturdays I stay open until nine."

He walked to The Kentucky and sat down, not a penny in his pocket. If he lost and was unable to pay he would be disgraced. He almost lost the first, then almost won the second, then won the third, and the danger was almost over—the terrible danger of humiliation, of having them know he had sat down in a game without any money in his pocket. He won another game several games later, and finally after three hours he had more than a dollar's worth of checks, but what good was a dollar?

He went across the street to the bookie and bet a half a dollar on Panther Rock and it ran second. He then bet his last half dollar on Earl of Warwick and it won but only paid six to two, so he had a dollar and a half now, but he was scared. He was scared because his luck was good but not good enough, and he knew how quickly it could go bad. He wanted to get his brother's coat back. He didn't want to tell anybody about it. He just wanted it to be hanging in the closet the next time his brother looked. It was his brother's only overcoat.

At a quarter to six that night he had a little over five dollars. At a quarter to nine he had six dollars. A little before midnight and at one in the morning he had six again. He had to get hold of seven-fifty, for then he would be able to get home and hang onto the money and get the coat on Monday—if the man hadn't sold it for seven-fifty.

He got home at five in the morning, broke again at last. "Open another window," he said. "You smell like a saloon."

"I'll make it up to you," he said. "Don't think I don't know how right you are."

In the morning when he got up nobody wanted to talk to him. He walked to the Presbyterian Church and sat through the whole thing. When the collection plate reached him he noticed that there were around seven dollars in it, and passed it along. He needed the money in his pocket—thirty-five cents. He needed it more than the Presbyterians did. He would make it up to the Presbyterians, too.

He went home and his married sister was there visiting.

"Listen," she said, "what you did wasn't right. For God's sake, try to do the right thing. Here's a dollar." He took the dollar and looked at it. Then he handed it back.

"I've got money," he said. "You've got a family. I can't take money from you."

"Take it," she said. "Get a job tomorrow. Forget this silly writing. You can't be a writer. Get a job. Find a nice girl. Get married. Be happy. What's the use living like this?"

He got a job the next day and worked a week, but spent his lunch hour at The Kentucky every day. At the end of the week he had eleven dollars. He went to the man on Sixth Street, but the man had sold the coat. In fact, he had forgotten it, but after a while he remembered, and said he had sold it long ago.

He went to the Emporium the following Monday and found a coat something like the one his brother had had, but it was twenty dollars.

He went down to The Kentucky and gambled until midnight, losing three dollars, not counting the whiskey he paid for and drank.

One day his brother came home wearing a new coat.

"I'll make it up to you," he said to his brother, but his brother wouldn't talk about it. He would talk about other things, but not about that.

Once his brother said, "What did you write today?"

"Nothing," he said.

"If you're going to write," his brother said, "you'd better do it."

"I know," he said. "And don't forget, someday I'll get your money back."

"Never mind the coat," his brother said. "Just write. If you're a writer, write, that's all."

"Thanks," he said. "I'll never forget this."

A Note on Contemporary Poetry

By cablegram you should know
Queen Liloukalani sang aloha oe
(Farewell to thee).

I sing to Queen Liloukalani,
And no farewell, to thee,
Or to the Queen.

You should also know
King Kamehameha conquered the Island.
(With ukelele, I believe.)

I continue to sing
Aloha oe which means
Until we meet.

What say?

The Theological Student

I began to meet the theological student about a quarter of a century ago in the plays of certain Russian writers. Tolstoy, Dostoyevsky, Chekov, Andreyev and Gorki seldom wrote a play in which the theological student did not appear. The theological student seemed to be the playwright himself looking back at his youth with an amused but admiring eye. He was certainly a good man to have around—young; nervous; pale; often pimply; not the least bit handsome; ridiculous and pathetic; ill-clothed; ill-fed; eager for tea; full of the lore of heaven, hell and earth; and yet for all that a man who could be counted on to liven matters up considerably, for he was a devil at heart.

He was certainly always in the midst of a desperate struggle with sin, which appeared to be an overwhelming longing to kiss the girls, a longing that never failed to startle him and bewilder them. Some of the girls were women with children older than himself. These rather liked him, for he was clumsy, inexperienced, inept, and therefore amusing to them. More in charity than in passion they permitted him to breathe heavily in their arms, only to discover later in the afternoon that he was thinking of killing himself. His habit of coughing nervously in their faces made them cry out, "Oh, Alexander Alexandrovich!"—which he took for an expression of love. He disgraced himself in company by his ill-timed remarks and by his uncontrollable desire to escape being good.

He was useful to each playwright, however, in that it seemed perfectly natural for him to explain why humanity was unhappy.

In the plays of Tolstoy the theological student blamed man's unhappiness on women, and sometimes went so far as to mention certain physical parts of them to which men were so powerfully attracted that they could not give their undivided attention to God or farming; and then, in another play, Tolstoy would have the theological student blaming something else.

Once, I believe it was the railroads, tempting men to run away. (From women of course, although the playwright mentioned only crying children and members of the local government who were forever greeting people in a most insincere manner.)

Another time the theological student, having had no stronger stimulant than a cup of tea, shouted that man is a beast because of his stomach; and went on to ask if anyone had recently noticed how frequently men sit down to eat, how much precious time is wasted in eating or in planning to do so, and what mischief attends the circumstance of a stomach full of meat, wheat, greens, cheese, wine and water.

Dostoyevsky's theological student claimed that man was unhappy because his very birth had been a nervous disorder.

Gorki's theological student was the best of the lot, though, for he hated everything which made life miserable, and everything made life miserable. The theological student proceeded quite logically to find fault with God, whereupon another side of Gorki, embodied in another character in the play—a notorious waster of sixty who had recently read a book from cover to cover—came forward with an attack on the government, blaming it for his present age and ill health, and remarking profoundly that he had once been thirty—no, even less than that— twenty! But now what? A ridiculous thing in a ridiculous black cloak! (Looking meaningful across the room at Tatanian Lvovna, age eighteen, and detecting in her the faintest trace of admiration.)

Having met the theological student and having found him an odd sort of fish—in no particular greatly different from anyone else I had met in the Russian plays—I began to wonder what it was that he was supposed to be studying. Whatever it was, did he study full-time or part-time? Or was he called a theological student simply because he was young? None of the playwrights was very clear about any of this, other than to hint that what the theological student *wanted* was perfection.

At length I decided for myself that he studied theology books, and I decided to do so also.

A whole small mezzanine balcony with a floor of thick glass was devoted to books of theology at the Public Library in Fresno. Climbing the steep narrow stairway to this section of the library was like climbing upward on a small cramped ship. Once there, the feeling of sailing was very great, and the faces of the other readers seemed flushed by a mild fever, as if they were all a little seasick and were trying their best not to throw up. They were certainly dizzy from the height, the hot air, and the narrowness of the aisles between the shelves of books. I joined them and began to examine every book on the theology shelves.

Every book seemed depressing, but I was fearful of putting one of them back in its place until I was reasonably sure it was absurd and did not have hidden away in it somewhere what I was looking for.

What *was* I looking for? It did not occur to me at the time—nothing much occurs to anybody at the time and we might just as well come right out and admit it—but whether I knew it in so many words or not I was very definitely looking for a theology which I myself might have written, or might one day write. That is to say, I was looking for what I believed was the only true theology. Robert Burns had already summed it up with Scotch economy, but one frequently forgets the remarks of poets. "A man's a man for all that" was right enough, and the implication of laughing about it was the remark, but I imagined there would be a fuller recitation on the theme.

There wasn't, however.

The millions of words in the hundreds of books were little more than nonsense. Even so, I took home with me after each visit two or three of the theology books which I felt might not prove to be altogether senseless, and read around in them until I was convinced that the author was as ridiculous as any theological student in my Russian play.

No writer is more pathetic than the one whose passion is to complicate, and theology appeared to be a matter of complicating. If it was a matter of believing, why not believe and be done with it? Swedenborg sweated like a horse and wrote a couple of million words that must have had the effect of making it impossible for any reader ever again to smile, itself a kind of theological act, although uncomplicated and surely no more meaningless than Swedenborg's two million words.

All of which brings me to the plot of this story.

One evening on my way home from the public library I was met in the Santa Fe freight yards by a man who was profoundly complicated and desperately theological.

"Do you know," he called out from a distance of twenty yards, "that the world is going to end tonight?"

"What time?" I called back.

"Don't know the exact hour," the man said, "but it will be sometime tonight."

From his shoulders the man brushed dirt which had gotten there when he had leaped from a freight train and fallen.

"Did you just get to town?" I said.

"Yes, but I was born here twenty-seven years ago," the man said.

"Are you ready for the end of the world?" he went on, as he took to brushing dust from his pants.

"As ready as I am for anything else," I said. "Are *you* ready?"

"That's the trouble," the man said. "I'm not. I'm not at all."

Suddenly, the man fell down.

"Do you know where the Emergency Hospital is?" I said. "It's at the back of the Police Station on Broadway, across from the Public Library, but if you don't want to go there, you can go to the County Hospital. It's across Ventura Boulevard at the Fair Grounds, but I suppose you know where these places are. I live on the way to the County Hospital and I'll go with you as far as my house. Maybe you can pick up a ride."

The man leaned on me and we stumbled in silence past Inderrieden's Dried Fruit Packing House. Crossing Ventura he fell again, and an automobile stopped. The driver of the automobile got out and came to the man and said, "What's the matter?"

"I am," the man said softly.

"He ought to get to a doctor," I said. "He's hurt."

The driver of the automobile helped me get the man into the car. On the way to the County Hospital the injured man took one of the three books I had borrowed from the Public Library and opened it.

"*Either-Or*," he read. "By Soren Kierkegaard. Who's he?"

"I don't know," I said.

"A man ought to know who these people are," the man said.

He began to read the book. When we reached the hospital his grip was so tight on the book that I felt sure it would be damaged and the girl at the desk in the Public Library would examine the damage, and then me, and wonder how it had happened, but not say anything.

The driver of the car—a man who had remarked on the way to the hospital that his name was August Bockbell, a name I have never forgotten, perhaps because the driver—sensing that the other man was dying—gave an account of his *own* life, which included almost killing his elder brother over the ownership of a pocketknife—helped the injured man into the reception room, and then went off, apologizing that it was necessary for him to do so.

I did not go with him because the injured man was still reading the book I had borrowed from the Public Library, and it seemed to me that it would have been rude under the circumstances to ask him to return it. He was reading the book with incredible swiftness. When it was necessary for the injured man to go off with a nurse and a young man in a white coat who did not seem to be much of a doctor, I followed them down a hall to swinging doors, partly from anxiety about the man himself and partly from anxiety about the library book. At the swinging doors this nurse told me to return to the reception room. I wanted to ask her to please get my book for me, but instead I said, "He's going to be all right, isn't he?" The nurse gestured severely, as if to say, "No difficult questions at this difficult time, please."

I returned to the reception room and sat down.

When I examined the two remaining library books, I discovered that my library card with my name and address on it was in the book by Kierkegaard which the injured man had taken. My library card was as important to me as a passport is to a traveler. I had thought of waiting only ten or fifteen minutes for the book, when I discovered that my library card was in it, I decided to wait two hours if necessary.

It was necessary to wait longer than that, however, during which time I grew very hungry—half-sick from it, in fact—and very angry, too. At first I was angry at the nurse who entered the reception room every ten or fifteen minutes in a state of confusion and excitement and refused to listen to what I had to tell her or to tell me about the condition of the injured man. After a while I became angry about the man himself, whether he was to live or die—for he had most rudely taken off with a book I was charged on my honor to return to the Public Library in the same condition in which I had found it. Finally, I became angry about Kierkegaard, a man concerning whom I knew absolutely nothing except that he had written a book with the strange title of *Either-Or*.

After having waited more than three hours for the return of my book, the nurse came up to me in the reception room in a manner which revealed unmistakably that she meant to speak, and began by announcing a hopelessly garbled version of *my* name.

"Yes?" I said.

"He's dead," she went on. "Dr. Humpkit (at least that's what I *thought* she said) did everything possible for him, but it was just no use."

"I'm sorry. The thing I wanted to tell you was to please let me have my book."

"What book?"

"The book by Kierkegaard."

"He said it was *his* book. *His* library card with his *name* and *address* on it is in the book, at any rate."

"The card in the book is *my* card," I said. "Why do you get everything wrong? I was walking home from the Public Library with three books when I met the man in the Santa Fe freight yards. He had just jumped off a train and had hurt himself, so I helped him to Ventura Avenue where he fell down and a motorist stopped and brought him here. In the automobile he took one of the three books I had borrowed from the Public Library and kept it. Now he's dead, and just because my library card happened to be in the book, you've given *him* my name. Well, I'm sorry he's dead whoever he is, but I'd like to have my book back anyway."

"He himself told us his name," the nurse said. "I am entering it in the hospital records. We shall return the book to the Public Library for him."

"You've been to school," I said, because I was so angry and hungry, and then left the hospital and began walking home.

When I got there I found the street full of automobiles. The house was full of uncles and aunts and cousins from all over the city.

My uncle Khosrove was the first to see me, for he was sitting alone on the steps of the back porch smoking a cigarette.

He got up and shouted at the top of his voice into the house, "I told you it was a mistake. Here he is now, the same as ever, but very much in need of food."

Everybody inside the house came tumbling out, and then, after having seen me, they all hurried back in to set the table.

After I had had all the food I could get into my belly, my mother asked very sweetly, "Why did they come in an ambulance and say that you had died?"

"If I had known they were going to come in an ambulance," I said, "I would have come with them instead of walking three miles on an empty stomach at ten o'clock at night. They didn't tell me they were going to come in an ambulance."

"We've been terribly worried about you," my uncle Zorab said.

This was too much for my uncle Khosrove.

"We've been terribly worried about you!" he mocked. "When the man from the County Hospital told us you were dead, it worried us terribly, for fear you would not recuperate."

He turned to my uncle Zorab.

"Why do you talk nonsense?" he said. "Is it possible to worry about someone who is dead?"

My uncle Zorab cleared his throat nervously as he said, "Well, all I can say is, we worried, and here he is alive!"

"Man," my uncle Khosrove shouted, "will you never understand that very simplest sort of thing? He never died. He never came anywhere near dying. There has been a mistake, as I said. Your worrying did not bring a dead man back to life. The boy's been involved in some sort of typical American complication. Unless you understand this now, there is no telling what terrible distortions will come into the telling of this family episode in years to come. Now that the boy has had his supper, let him tell us the whole story, and then one by one let us return to our own homes and our own lives. Whoever it was that died, we shall all join him soon enough, and it is quite all right." He turned to me. "Now tell us what it was that happened which the people of the hospital reported to us as having been your death at the age of twenty-seven. I tried to tell these people that it was not you who had died, for you are not twenty-seven years old, but they replied that perhaps you had given twenty-seven as your age in a last attempt to be impressive. How old are you, and then tell us the story."

"I'm fourteen," I said.

And then I told the whole story, accurately, point by point.

My aunt Khatoon took to weeping softly for the young man who had died, claiming that he had died for *me*, so that I might go on living, a theory which made my mother angry; but my grandfather twisted his moustaches and said, "All very well and good, but who the devil is this man Kierkegaard to make such an ungodly fuss in this desolate and faraway village which is trying to pass for a city?"

"He is the man who wrote one of the three books I borrowed from the Public Library this afternoon," I said, "but that's all I know about him."

"Well," my grandfather said, "that's fine. Now, all of you—get out of here. Go home where you belong. If it's for him you've been crying, there he is trying to get meat from between his teeth, so go home."

Everybody embraced lightly by way of celebrating my survival; there was kindly whispering among the women; the small boys took to wrestling in the living room; and then at last everybody was gone excepting the Old Man and my uncle Khosrove. These two exchanged quarrelsome glances and then my uncle Khosrove said, "I know what you are going to ask him. Well, I'll give you the answer, to save him the trouble. You are going to ask him what he means by getting into complications of all sorts every other Friday, and I will answer for him that he doesn't mean anything at all by it. Some people come into this world asleep and go out of it asleep, and that is very thoughtful of them. A few others—like myself and this boy, my nephew Aram Garoghlanian—come into this world asleep, and then one fair Friday wake up and look around and see ourselves as we are."

"What are we?" the Old Man asked politely.

"Armenians," my uncle Khosrove said quickly. "Could anything be more ridiculous? The Englishman has an empire to govern. The Frenchman has art to guide and measure. The German has an army to train and test. The Russian has a revolution to start. The Swiss have hotels to manage, the Mexicans mandolins to play, the Spaniards bulls to fight, the Austrians waltzes to dance to, and so on and so forth, but what have *we*?"

"Loud mouths to shut up?" the Old Man suggested.

"And the Irish," my uncle Khosrove went on. "The Irish have a whole island in which to be poverty-stricken; the Arabs a thousand tribes to bring together in the desert; the Jews child prodigies to send on concert tours; the Gypsies wagons and fortune-telling cards; the Americans chronic nervousness which they call freedom, but what have the Armenians?"

"Since you insist, tell me," said the Old Man. "What have the Armenians?"

"Manners," my uncle Khosrove said.

"Are you mad?" the Old Man said. "Nothing is so unnatural as a polite Armenian."

"I did not say *good* manners," my uncle Khosrove said. "I said manners. The good or bad of it I leave to others. Manners is what we have, and very little of anything else. You are going to ask this boy what he means by getting into complications of all sorts every other Friday. Your asking is manners. Well, go ahead and ask him. I'm going to the Arax Coffee House for a couple of hours of *tavli*. My going is more manners."

"Before you go," the Old Man said, "I think you ought to know I wished to ask the boy to report to me about the book by Kierkegaard, if he ever reads it. Now, I will go to the Coffee House *with* you."

The Old Man got up and yawned enormously. He yawned in three movements, after the fashion of symphonies, very slowly, wildly, and finally slowly and wildly by turns.

He went out of the house by the front door while my uncle Khosrove took the back. The screen doors slammed one-two, and I went looking for half a watermelon to eat, for I was very thirsty.

The following day I went out to the County Hospital and after a great deal of effort identified myself, retrieved my book, and brought it back to read. The injured man had reached page 99, for he had folded the edge of the page over, so that he might easily find his place when next he took it up. After reading an hour and three-quarters I too reached page 99, and decided that I did not wish to read any further. I took the book back to the Public Library and as I had expected the girl at the desk noticed the damage, examined it, examined me as I whistled softly, but did not say anything. I climbed the steep stairway to the mezzanine and continued my search for the book of theology that I hoped to find.

That evening I reported to my grandfather that Kierkegaard appeared to have been a Dane who had been born in 1813 and had died in 1855 after having spent the greater part of his time struggling with the devil, the church, and the complications of theology.

"Died at the age of forty-two," the Old Man said. "Struggling with the devil is most destructive, I see, but perhaps had he *not* struggled he would have lived only twenty-two years and left behind him not even the book he wrote. Have you read the book?"

"He wrote more than one book," I said. "I read the first ninety-nine pages of one of them, and then I got tired of it."

"What did he say in the first ninety-nine pages?"

"I'm not sure, but he *seemed* to say that everything is not enough."

"That is how it is with these fellows who are forever struggling with the devil," the Old Man said. "And the unfortunate man you met yesterday in the Santa Fe freight yards, what about him?"

"He died. Yesterday was the end of the world for him all right, just as he said."

"His real name?"

"Well," I said, "I have a name written down here from the book at the County Hospital which is *supposed* to be his name, but I am sure it is only another mistake. It's no mistake that he's dead, though. I suppose he might have lived had he not fallen into the hands of people so sure of themselves, and so quick to get things accurately wrong. I'm sure he didn't expect to die, for he turned down a page of the book, so that he might go on reading it. Here's the name I got from the Hospital book. Abo Mogabgab."

"How can that be?" the Old Man said. "Abo Mogabgab is the man from whom I buy my clothing, the Syrian with the shop on Mariposa Street, a man older than myself. Here, look into the lining of this coat at the label and read to me what is said there."

I looked at the label inside the coat and read aloud, "Abo Mogabgab."

"A magnificent example of American efficiency and theological accuracy," the Old Man said. "A man has been killed and a coat label has been given the majesty of death. And yet, here we are, all of us who are *still* alive, none the worse for the terrible efficiency or the fierce accuracy. Thank you for reporting to me on the gospel of Kierkegaard. I am still eager to learn, but I find that the farmer's gospel is still the best we have. Now, the vine is planted thus; and thus it is intended; and thus protected from rabbits; and thus are the grapes harvested; and thus are they made into wine; and thus dried by the sun into raisins; and in the winter thus it is that the branches of the vines are pruned; and in the spring thus it is that the vines are watered. What other gospel is half so pleasant, since it is all out in the weather? To hell with these stifling chambers in which poor men sit and confuse themselves. When they are all through for the day don't they get up and go home and eat a bowl of stewed raisins with a piece of black bread, or drink a glass of wine with a lamb chop, or eat a bunch of grapes with cheese and crackers?"

"I guess so," I said and went home.

When I got there I spent three hours in the backyard, working. My uncle Khosrove sat on the steps of the back porch and watched.

At last he got up and said, "For the love of God, what is it now? Why are you pestering the life out of that poor old Malaga vine? You have cleaned and repaired it until it looks like the ghost of a wretched old man, and only a moment ago it resembled a handsome, dreaming youth. Matter is beautiful only in its imperfections. Only blockheads seek perfection, which is death. Let perfection seek you. You needn't seek it. Now, go inside the house and sit down and eat half a cold watermelon. You are not perfect, the vine is not perfect, but you can eat watermelon and pass water, so do so."

"What nonsense," I thought, but as I ate the watermelon I wondered if my uncle Khosrove was not just about the best theological student of them all.

The Foreigner

Hawk Harrap, whose father came from somewhere in Asia Minor and used to sell vegetables and fruit from a wagon drawn by a horse, was of my time in Fresno, so I remember the days when he was a kid in overalls hustling *The Evening Herald* or sneaking into the fights at the Civic Auditorium or playing hooky from Emerson School to sell soda pop at the County Fair and make a lot of money.

His father was Syrian but seldom spoke the language, as he had married a woman who was Scotch-Irish. Harrap was his name on all the school records, although his father's name was something that only *sounded a little* like Harrap. He was given the name Hawk by myself for being as swift as that bird or as swift as I imagined that bird was. By the time we were at Longfellow Junior High School together, the nickname was on the school records, too. Actually, his mother had named him Hugh after a dead brother.

The day I first met Hawk at Emerson School, in 1916, he took me to a boy named Roy Coulpa and insulted him by saying, "Roy, you're an *Italian!*" It did not seem to matter at all that Roy Coulpa *was* Italian. It was Hawk's tone of voice that was insulting. After making this painful and preposterous remark, Hawk shoved me into Roy with such force that we fell and began to wrestle. Roy was surprised and angry, and strong enough to make me exert myself. The school playground was Fresno dirt, so a lot of dust got kicked up as each of us broke free of all kinds of holds. The match stopped when the recess bell rang, and Roy and I got up and had a look at one another. We looked around for Hawk, too. We were not permitted to move until we heard the second bell, at which time we fell in at the entrance of the school. When a third bell rang we marched to our classrooms. Hawk was standing among the two dozen spectators. When I caught his eye he winked, and I wondered what the hell he meant.

After school he and Roy and I walked to California Playground, and there the three of us wrestled for the fun of it.

The point is, it was impossible to dislike him.

Hawk lived on O Street, so he and I walked home together when Roy set out for his house across the S. P. tracks on G Street, beyond Rosenberg's Packing House.

"What are you, anyway?" Hawk said as we walked home. "Even the teacher can't pronounce your name."

"I'm American," I said.

"The hell you are," Hawk said. "Roy's Italian, I'm Syrian, and I guess you're Armenian."

"Sure," I said. "I'm Armenian all right, but I'm American, too. I speak better English than I do Armenian."

"I can't talk Syrian at all," Hawk bragged, "but that's what I am. If anybody asks you what you are, for God's sake don't tell them you're American. Tell them you're Armenian."

"What's the difference?"

"What do you mean what's the difference? If you're Armenian and you say you're American everybody'll laugh at you. The teacher knows what you are. Everybody knows what you are."

"Aren't *you* American?"

"Don't make me laugh," Hawk said. "I'm a foreigner. My father sells vegetables from a wagon."

"Weren't you born in America?"

"I was born in Fresno. I was born in the house on O Street. What's that got to do with it?"

"Well, I'm American," I said. "And so are you."

"You must be loony," Hawk said. "But don't worry, you'll find out what you are soon enough."

One day months later, after lunch, Miss Clapping, our teacher, suddenly stopped teaching and said, "You Armenian boys who go home for lunch have got to stop eating things full of garlic. The smell is more than I can stand and I'm not going to put up with it any longer."

Hawk turned to see how I was taking the insult.

As a matter of fact lunch for me that day had been dried eggplant, okra and string beans made into a stew with chunks of shoulder of lamb, in which garlic was absolutely necessary.

The day wasn't so cold, however, that the windows of the room could not be opened or the radiator turned off. The classroom was airtight and overhot.

"Open the window," I said to Miss Clapping.

Hawk gave a hoot of amazement and Miss Clapping looked at me as if she had no intention not to finish my life immediately. The rest of the class stirred in their seats and waited for developments. I decided to kill Miss Clapping and be done with it, but when I got to thinking how I might do it, the scheme seemed impractical. Miss Clapping went to her desk and studied her class book.

"Yes," she said at last. "Here is your name. I'm sure you know how to pronounce it. The Lord knows I don't."

Another insult!

She closed the book and looked at me again.

"Now," she said, "what did you say when I said you Armenian boys will have to stop eating garlic?"

"I said open the window."

"Perhaps I don't understand," Miss Clapping said, her lips beginning to tremble a little.

She put down the book she was holding and picked up a twelve-inch ruler. She stepped away from her desk and stood at the foot of the row in which my desk was the last one.

"Now, tell me," she said, "just *what* do you mean?"

"I mean," I said, "it would be stuffy in this room no matter what anybody ate for lunch. This room needs fresh air. It's easier to open the window than to ask people to cook stuff without garlic."

Hawk hooted again, and without any further discussion Miss Clapping moved down the row to my desk.

"Put out your right hand," she said.

"What for?"

"For being impertinent."

It happened that I had recently learned the meaning of that word.

"I haven't been impertinent," I said.

"You're being impertinent now," the teacher said. "Put out your right hand or I shall send you to the principal, who will give you a thrashing."

"No, he won't," I said.

"Oh he won't, won't he?" the teacher said. "We'll see about that. You're not going to make a fool out of me in *this* class. Put out your right hand."

Miss Clapping waited a full minute for me to put out my hand. So many things happened to her face, to her eyes and mouth, that I almost felt sorry for her. I certainly felt disgusted with myself, although I knew she was being ridiculous.

Finally she returned to her desk and with a shaking hand scribbled a note which she folded and handed to a little girl named Elvira Koot who took the note and left the room. The class sat in silence and the teacher tried to occupy herself looking into her book, and I wished I lived in a more civilized part of the country. At last the little girl returned to the room and handed the teacher a note which the teacher read. I was sure the principal had considered the situation and had urged her to open the window; I was ready to apologize for having made so much trouble; but when I saw the evil smile on the teacher's face I went back to planning to kill her, for I knew I was headed for hard times.

"Report to the principal in his office at once," Miss Clapping said.

I got up and left the room. In the hall I decided to kill the principal too. I had seen him from a distance, the usual tall man around public schools; and I had heard about him; but I hadn't believed what I had heard. The report was that he was quite a rooster among the old hens who taught school and that he wouldn't think of giving you a chance to tell your side of a story. If one of the old hens said you deserved to be punished the rooster punished you.

Instead of reporting to his office immediately, I left the school building and walked home.

My mother was in the kitchen cutting up half a dozen cabbages for sour cabbage soup.

"What are you doing here?" she said.

"I don't want to go to that school anymore," I said.

I tried to explain as accurately as possible what had happened. My mother listened to my side of the story and cut up the cabbages and put them into five-gallon crocks and poured salt over them and put a piece of apple-box wood on top of the cabbage, and on top of the wood she put rocks the size of eggplants. She said nothing until I was finished, and then she said, "Go back to the school and mind the teacher. Hereafter when there is garlic in your lunch, eat a sprig of parsley. Do not be so eager to defend the honor of Armenian cooking."

This attitude infuriated me.

I went to my room and put some things together—a pair of socks, a slingshot, three pebbles, a key I had found, a magnifying glass, and a copy of the New Testament I had won at Sunday School—and tied them into a bundle, to run away. I walked two blocks and then went back to the house and threw the bundle on the front porch and went back to the school and reported to the principal.

He gave me a strapping with a heavy leather belt. After this greatest insult of all, I dried my eyes and went back to my class and sat at my desk.

After school Hawk said, "See what I mean? You're a foreigner and don't ever forget it. A smart foreigner keeps his feelings to himself and his mouth shut. You can't change teachers. You can't change principals. You can't change people. You can laugh at them, that's all. Americans make me laugh. I wouldn't fool with them if I were you. I just laugh at them."

What happens to a man like Hawk Harrap as the years go by?

Well, I had been out of the Army about a month when I decided to drive from San Francisco to my hometown before summer ended, and try to find out. It was mid-October, and I wanted to eat some grapes and figs and melons and pomegranates and new raisins, too.

I reached Fresno early Saturday evening and telephoned Roy Coulpa and my second cousin Mug Muggerditchian and took them to dinner at El Rancho on Highway 99, just past Roeding Park.

It was 1945, and it was good to be breathing the air of the San Joaquin Valley again, and to be talking to fellows I had known most of my life, who had just come home from the war.

Mug mentioned two of his cousins who had been killed, and how it had affected their mothers and fathers; and Roy mentioned some Italian boys I had known long ago who had been killed, and a boy who was a mess from injuries to his head and spine, who probably wouldn't ever escape from the Army hospitals.

One thing led to another and then Roy Coulpa remembered Hawk Harrap.

"Hawk beat the draft," Roy said, "and as far as I'm concerned I'm glad he did. It would have been silly for a guy like Hawk to go through all that chicken, or get himself messed up by a lot of complicated injuries. He's got a half interest in The Wink, a little bar on Broadway, but he's not there very much. He drives to Hollywood or Frisco or Reno or Las Vegas and has fun the same as ever. I ran into him in the bar about a month ago. Well, you know Hawk. He winks and takes care of himself. He was behind the bar but not in a white coat. He came out and sat down and we threw the bull a couple of hours. When I asked him how he had managed to beat the draft, a professional fighter three years, six feet one, two hundred pounds—well, maybe you remember the way he always was, even if you haven't seen him in ten or fifteen years. Swift and serious, but you always know he's laughing inside.

" 'Roy,' Hawk said, 'you know the time to make money is when there's a war going on. That's no time to be saying yes sir and no sir.'

"Well, *somebody* made a lot of money out of the war," Roy went on. "I know Hawk didn't make it *all*, but I'm glad he made *some* of it."

Roy Coulpa told a half dozen little stories about Hawk Harrap, and then he told this one which he got from Hawk himself:

Immediately after the war, Hawk took to walking around Hollywood with a cane, a discharge button in his lapel, and a gentle, thankful look in his eyes. He limped into the best places and reluctantly told stories to beautiful girls about his fighting in the Solomon Islands, in Casablanca, in Anzio, in Normandy—in the infantry, in the engineers, in the Navy, in the Marines.

Sometimes he would limp with his right leg, sometimes with his left. Sometimes he would shake all over and apologize and ask somebody for atabrine and accept another scotch-over-ice instead and calm down and apologize some more and say he would be all right soon—sixty or seventy more attacks and he would be finished with malaria.

Sometimes he would have twitches in his face and ask a beautiful girl who had just mentioned her brother, named Jim, to please never, never mention that name in his presence again, and twitch some more and shake his head and shut up like a clam, trying to be mysterious; and then he would try to control himself enough to hint to her why he could not bear to hear that name, what had happened to his best pal, Jim Sooney, in the breakthrough at Bastogne.

Well, Jim Sooney and Hawk were old friends from O Street. Jim was Assyrian, not Syrian, but they were good friends just the same.

Jim and Hawk bought a hundred acres of good land in Reedley during the war and made a lot of money growing and shipping fruit and vegetables.

There was a pretty good farmhouse on the land to which Hawk sometimes invited friends for an all-night game of stud, and one Saturday night after the war he was there at sundown, waiting for the boys to arrive. All over the land watermelons were ripening, and he enjoyed seeing them. When it was night, around eight, Hawk was sitting in the rocking chair on the front porch of the farmhouse breathing the good air when three cars stopped on the road beside his watermelon patch, and out of the automobiles eleven boys and men fell on Hawk's watermelons. Hawk watched them a few minutes and then went into the shack and got the rifle off the wall. He strolled down the dirt road of his land and took everybody by surprise.

MY NAME IS SAROYAN

He said he was just back from Germany where he had almost lost his respect for mankind, and now that he'd come home and was trying to earn an honest dollar, here they were, showing their appreciation for all the private sacrifices he had made in helping to win the war and save civilization. Here they were, stealing his watermelons, taking bread out of the mouths of his children. He warned everybody to follow his instructions and not try to run, or he would shoot to kill. He had gone through a lot in Germany. He had been taught to kill, and he could easily kill every one of them. He counted the watermelon stealers over and over again, saying in a kind of madness, "One, two, three, four, five, six, seven, eight, nine, ten, eleven—almost a dozen. I killed twenty-seven Germans with a machine gun once, and they hadn't done anything to me at all. Now, every one of you, lie down according to size, on this road."

A number of the watermelon stealers had recently been discharged from the Army and told Hawk so. He asked them not to provoke him. He hadn't made up his mind what he was going to do with them just yet, and he didn't want to be provoked into making an unfair decision.

Everybody stretched out in the road, and Hawk asked them to count off, which they did, or tried to do. The younger boys, twelve years old or so, were crying now.

Hawk said, "I wish I knew what to do. I must ask God for guidance. I don't want blood on my hands if it's not His will."

Somebody said, "It's not His will."

"We're not sure about that yet," Hawk said. "We're only poor ignorant misguided human beings. God brought me home from Germany. He will answer my prayer."

So then Hawk prayed.

"O God," he said, "these boys and men have come to steal my watermelons and I've caught them with their pants down. As you know, I served faithfully at Anzio, Normandy and Bastogne, suffering terrible embarrassment and being underpaid. Now that I have come home at last to my wife and five children, these men have come to take the bread out of their mouths. I have caught them, and I must do my duty. O God, please tell me what my duty is. Amen."

After a minute of silence Hawk said, "I thank you, O God."

A man lying on his belly in the dirt turned his head and said, "What did God say?"

"He said my duty is to kill every one of you, and I'm sorry, but I must do my duty. I expect you to die like men and boys. Let the first volunteer stand at attention. I promise him a painless death."

Nobody moved to volunteer and the smaller boys wept harder than ever and begged for mercy. Finally, the boldest man got to his knees so that Hawk wouldn't take him for a volunteer and said, "For God's sake, man, I was at Bastogne myself. We'll pay for the watermelons, but don't do this crazy thing."

"Don't provoke me," Hawk said, "or I'll shoot you on your knees."

Now, Jim Sooney and four others stopped their car in the road and got out to see what foolishness Hawk was up to this time.

The man on his knees appealed to Jimmy Sooney and the others, but Hawk ordered the man to fall to his belly, which he did.

Hawk badgered the watermelon stealers a half hour, asking each of them to recite his name, his age, his address, his birthplace, his nearest of kin, his religion, blood type, race, amount of insurance carried, favorite movie actress, combat decorations, secret ambitions, and whether they liked apple pie for dessert better than Jell-O. If a man said apple pie, Hawk said he was sorry for the man; if a man said Jell-O, Hawk said he was afraid the man had made a poor choice. He asked the men to change their religions, and they were all glad to do it.

Finally, because he wanted to go in and start the poker game, Hawk struck a bargain with the watermelon stealers. He said he wanted to hear some good choral singing of hymns. If the group sang well enough to bring tears to his eyes, he would turn them free. He ordered everybody to kneel and sing, but the men couldn't think of one single hymn to sing. At last one of the small boys began to sing "Nearer, My God, to Thee," and the others tried to join in.

"It's not that the hymn isn't heartbreaking," Hawk said. "It's your lousy singing. Try another hymn."

The boy who seemed to know a hymn or two began to sing "I Love Life," but Hawk cut him short, saying that that was not a hymn at all but a dirty semiclassical number. The boy thought a moment and tried again. "When the Roll is Called Up Yonder," he sang, and the others tried to join in, but when the choral singing broke to pieces and the little boy tried to save them all by sobbing through the whole song alone and looked eagerly into Hawk's face, Hawk was still unmoved.

"One last chance," Hawk said. "I can give you only one last chance. I shall name a song and you must shout it out with all your might. If you hear me singing with you, then you shall know that I want you all to live. I want you all to go home and live decent, Christian lives. I want you all to sing "God Bless America."

The watermelon stealers began to sing, but Hawk remained silent through three choruses.

At last Hawk began to sing, too, and the men and boys jumped up and ran off to their cars, slipping and falling and slamming doors and driving off.

Then Hawk Harrap and Jim Sooney and their friends went into the farmhouse and started the all-night poker game.

Nobody laughed while Roy Coulpa told the story, and there were tears in his eyes when he stopped talking.

"What's the matter?" Mug Muggerditchian said.

"Nothing," Roy said. "I just feel sorry for all those guys."

"Hawk was only having a little fun," Mug said.

"I don't mean the watermelon stealers," Roy said. "I mean the guys in the war."

The Plot

The plot was as follows:

The L Street Boys would dig the three-feet-deep, six-feet-long, three-feet-wide hole in the middle of the shortcut across Kazakian's empty lot that ran from M Street to the alley between L and M. They would dig the hole at midnight, after everybody in the neighborhood had gone to bed, so that Apkar Popcorn, as he was called, who was the first to use the path in the morning, would not suspect anything. They would cover the hole with plaster laths, newspaper and dirt.

At half-past five in the morning they would hide behind Kazakian's house and watch Apkar Popcorn fall into the hole.

The L Street Boys were the Shimshamian brothers, Husik and Jaziyire, called Fussy and Jazz; the Melkonian brothers, Arsen and Ardash; Fat Kishmish; Shag Barekomian; Haig or Ike Ardzrooni; and George Vrej. But it was Fussy and Jazz Shimshamian who were the creators of the plot. The backyard of their house on L Street faced the backyard of Apkar Popcorn's house on M Street. Two of their chickens had wandered across the alley into Apkar Popcorn's garden and Apkar Popcorn had captured them, but he had denied it, so the boys wanted to get even.

The other L Street Boys didn't know about the chickens, they just liked the idea of making a hole for Apkar Popcorn to fall into, so they dug the hole and covered it precisely as planned, and at half-past five in the morning they gathered together behind Kazakian's house. Apkar Popcorn left his house on M Street every morning at exactly a quarter to six, and he always used Kazakian's shortcut on his way to town, so the boys knew they would see something unusual in a few minutes.

At twenty minutes to six a tiny woman entered the shortcut on M Street and began to move upon the hidden hole. This was not what the L Street Boys had had in mind, but the woman had appeared so suddenly and was moving with such speed upon the trap that everyone became speechless.

At last Fat Kishmish said to Fussy Shimshamian, "That looks like your mother, Fussy."

"No," Fussy said, "my mother's home baking bread."

"Isn't that your mother, Jazz?" Fat Kishmish said to Fussy's brother.

"Yes, it is," Jazz Shimshamian said. "What's she doing on M Street?"

"That's Jazz and Fussy's mother," the L Street Boys said to one another.

"Well, aren't you going to stop her?" Ike Ardzrooni said.

"How can I stop her?" Fussy said. "She'd kill me."

"You've *got* to stop her," George Vrej said. "One of you has got to stop her. You just can't let your mother fall into a hole. We dug the hole for Apkar Popcorn, not for your mother."

"Jazz," Shag Barekomian said, "you've got to stop your mother from falling into the hole."

"It's too late now," Fussy Shimshamian said.

The L Street Boys stopped breathing to watch Mrs. Shockey Shimshamian fall into the hole they had dug for Apkar Popcorn. The woman had only two or three more steps to take. They saw her left foot go through the false surface, and then every bit of her plunged forward onto the surface, and then into the hole. They heard a scream.

The trap had been perfectly set and concealed, and it had worked perfectly.

After the woman had disappeared into it, the L Street Boys turned and ran. They ran straight down San Benito Avenue across the Southern Pacific tracks to the outskirts of Chinatown, and there, outside Chong Jan's Wholesale Produce House, they stopped to think and talk things over.

It was agreed that no member of the organization would confess knowing anything about how the hole came into being, and there the matter ended.

Mrs. Shimshamian was not seriously injured, but she did go to bed for a week.

The open hole remained in Kazakian's empty lot for several years and was finally filled with garbage from Mr. Kazakian's home.

Every morning at a quarter to six, on his way to town, Apkar Popcorn glanced at the hole. It broke up the monotony of his walk very nicely.

A Saroyan Trilogy

SAROYAN'S NOTE

In 1933 my writing had not yet appeared in a national magazine, but during that year I worked rather well and steadily.

I wrote many short stories, each of them experimental in the sense that I hoped to find out from the writing of many kinds of stories which kind suited me best, only to discover in the end that I could not settle for *any* specific kind, as such.

Early in the year I began a long novel which I soon abandoned for two reasons: first, because the Armenian newspaper published in Boston, *Hairenik Daily*, which had invited me to be a contributor, was unable to bring out the novel in daily installments; and second, because quite frankly, I became bored with the whole idea, which was to trace the lives and fortunes of three kinds of Armenians, beginning in three different cities in Armenia and ending in three different cities in America: Markar, as I remember it, was a peasant farmer who was transplanted (or transplanted himself) from the city of Moush to the city of Fresno; a merchant in Van became a merchant in New York; and a poet preacher (probably my father) of Bitlis died an early death, amidst failure, poverty and sorrow, in San Francisco.

Novels that take eight or nine hundred pages in which to trace something or other are all right now and then, I suppose, but I just couldn't be bothered in 1933.

During the month of October I wrote a "novel" to which I gave the high-flying title of *Trapeze Over the Universe*, and out of which came, I should say, my first accepted short story. "The Daring Young Man On the Flying Trapeze," which was written only several days after the novel had been finished.

I took what I believed to be a thousand-to-one chance and sent the story to the editors of *Story* magazine, recently transferred from various places of Europe to New York. My note to the editors was belligerent. I dared them not to accept the story and still pretend they were interested in new writing and new writers. I had become sick and tired of rejection slips, or patronizing letters (telling me how to write) from unknown editors of insignificant magazines; and I had decided late in 1932 not to send any more stories to any more editors, but to go on writing until I was thirty, at which time I planned to examine my work and decide if I wanted to continue in the profession of writing.

The reason I broke the rule was simple: I believed the story had a chance.

Waiting for word from editors when a writer has hopes, or is willing to pretend he has, is a special kind of joy and anxiety I suppose only unpublished writers know.

But then the whole business of being a writer, let alone an unpublished one, is a little mad, and I mean in the clinical sense.

To begin with, the aspiration to write is not recognized by anybody as a real one with real possibilities. A man can decide to be a doctor, for instance, and he can go to school, and study, and meet all the requirements, and eventually *become* a doctor. And thereafter there is never an organized critical fraternity which reports publicly on the effectiveness or non-effectiveness of his work. Any doctor may make mistakes and continue to be a doctor, and even to enjoy the protection of his fellow professionals. On the other hand, there is no formal procedure to the business of becoming a writer of any kind. There is no such thing as going to school, turning out so much work, and then being taken in by a magazine or a publishing house, as a doctor is taken in by a hospital.

Thus, the first requirement for the would-be writer would appear to be a willingness to work very hard for ten or fifteen or even twenty very important years of his life, without any guarantee that all of the time and effort shall not have been in vain.

In short, the would-be writer must be impractical at the outset, and a very wild gambler.

This tends to increase his loneliness, to point up his isolation, and to make of him something at best midway between a harmless eccentric and a sorrowfully comic character.

After the age of twenty, society (one's family and friends, at any rate) expects a man to fit into a proper order of things, to find a place in an acceptable pattern, to work, to keep regular hours, and to be able to pay his way to respectability, a proper social life, a wife, a home, children, promotions, plans for retirement.

Nobody is willing to believe in the would-be writer's writing, least of all the experts. (The very term Rejection Slip is insulting and the text of each of them is painful for the would-be writer even to *behold*—for there is no point in reading it. It is meaningless and is meant to be.)

Nobody says of the would-be writer, "He is going to become a writer." It is assumed that he is not, and the assumption is powerful. The would-be writer must be a little crazy to dispute the assumption and to hold fast to the theory that even against such overwhelming odds he is in fact going to become a writer someday—and of course the sooner the better: perhaps today, perhaps tomorrow.

In any case, while I waited for word from the editors of *Story*, I did a great deal of walking all over San Francisco. I lived at that time on Carl Street, next door to the Polytechnic High School, about five miles from the heart of town. I am not going to go into the importance to the would-be writer of doing a lot of walking during his apprenticeship, because he never knows where he stands in his apprenticeship; and if he walks a lot it's not because he has reasoned that it is important for him to do so, but because he hasn't carfare.

My shoes were important to me, there is no doubt about that. I needed them more than I needed anything else except a place to sleep and something to eat.

I believe (although I am not sure) that it was while I was waiting for word from the editors of *Story* that I lived and wrote "My Shoes," which is a deliberately facetious story about an unpublished writer.

Now, it goes without saying that the material could have been worked into another kind of story entirely, but this happens to be the story into which the material came together.

I shall not pretend that twenty years later I have not cut a great deal out of the story, or that I have not revised most of the rest of it, for I *have* done both. I have done so on behalf of the reader, if it turns out that there shall be one. As a writer I have no obligation to myself after material has been put to use in one way or another; my obligation is to the stranger I hope shall someday take the time to read what I have written.

Now, I did not in 1933 believe that I had any such obligation to any such stranger, and as right as I may be today, I may have been then, too. I certainly refused to revise my writing in those days. I even believed that revising was cheating, but of course I wasn't willing at that time to accept the probability that all art is purposeful cheating. The point isn't worth laboring.

At last, a few days before Christmas, I saw the mailman of my neighborhood come up the street, stop at my door, and drop something in the mailbox. Among the mail I found a letter from the editors of *Story*. Yes, they wanted the story. Furthermore, they said I could expect a check for fifteen dollars sometime soon. It would be difficult—certainly time-taking—to make known now what this meant to me then, so I shall only say that if I had been a little bats before the letter arrived I went clean off my nut after it did, only now there seemed to be quality to my madness, and I may say quality of a high order.

I was both delirious with astonishment, and altogether matter-of-fact about this new circumstance in my career as a writer, and in my life as a personality which preferred not to remain forever anonymous.

I began to make plans for the immediate future, and for the practical use of the fifteen dollars. When the money reached me I spent eleven dollars for an overcoat, and the rest of the money for paper, envelopes, clips, and postage stamps.

It is not my intention at this time to imply that "My Shoes" is a kind of lost-and-found masterpiece by an unpublished writer who, as luck would have it, turned out to be great. If anything, I was probably as great when I was unpublished as I shall ever be, although I am willing to acknowledge that I hadn't at that time learned as much as I have since learned about the art and business of writing.

I am not implying, either, that after twenty years of professional writing I am an expert in the profession, or that it is at last a profession in which a reasonable predictability exists concerning the quality of work I may do in a year, or the amount of income this work may bring me.

Both the profession and I myself remain a little impractical and unpredictable to this day.

Shoes are still very important in my life, and while I have half a dozen pairs, including a brand-new pair in a box where they have already remained six years, I stay with a particular pair until it is virtually unwearable. I also polish all of my shoes myself—first, because the saving is great, second, because I can do a better job than any bootblack I ever saw, and finally, because the business of polishing my shoes satisfies my soul.

I walk on my feet, and my feet are put into shoes whenever I am ready to walk, that's all.

1.

MY SHOES

The job of writing a novel while a writer's feet are in worn-out shoes is difficult, as such a circumstance not only affects his circulation, but also his style. A good pair of shoes establishes a security between a writer and the world that is most desirable.

It is unfortunate therefore that my only pair of shoes has approximated, from long walking, a state very near total disintegration: the ball of each foot is exposed, so that on all my walks I go partly barefooted, and in the heart of town where lighted cigarettes fall thickest I may be seen almost any day leaping suddenly; as in church I dare not cross my legs. That is the price I pay (and gladly) for the honor of being a great, if unknown, writer.

The novel I am writing moves forward slowly; a paragraph a day, sometimes a single sentence, and not rarely only one word. Yesterday the word was *cold*, and so was the climate. (I address myself for the remainder of this paragraph to those who simply read and do not know—cannot imagine—the daily ordeal of an honest writer: to you, ladies, and to you, gentlemen, and to all of my cousins, my daily production may seem meager, but I am prepared to offer a polite explanation to the ladies and gentlemen, and to swear at my cousins: I take pride in the enormous amount of bad writing I have had the skill not to put to paper. Furthermore, my integrity is sustained by the fact that although I have been writing for almost ten years I am not responsible for one bad novel. It is a pity, in my opinion, that no prize exists for the writer who best refrains from adding to the world's bad books.)

How have I managed this marvelous achievement?

Well, it is quite simple.

Until I am sure that I am ready to write greatly, I don't write at all. I *walk*.

For such a technique it is better to own a pair of good shoes than a typewriter, although two pair would be better.

And so, in my life, walking is a very important business. As I walk on my own two feet, vanity, ambition, and other absurdities fall away from me, and I view the world with the clear eye of art, truth, wit, and humility.

My plans as I walked to town this morning were precise and pleasant: I would enter a shoe shop and have my worn-out shoes repaired.

At the first shop I was amazed to learn (since I had been able to borrow only a dollar and a half from my brother-in-law Joe) that the cost for the repairs would be a dollar and seventy cents, ten cents additional for sewing.

"I will return this evening," I said. "I am late for work."

At several other shops the cost proved very nearly the same, now a bit less, now a bit more.

All morning, on top of everything else, I hadn't had a cigarette, and I wanted one badly.

At last I found a shop that advertised a rate for repairs that I could afford: sixty-five cents for half-soles, thirty-five for heels, and, the clerk said, twenty-five cents to take care of the rips, since there were five of them. This came to a total of a dollar and a quarter, leaving enough to cover the cost of a package of cigarettes and seventy sheets of writing paper from Woolworth's.

I felt grateful, and immediately removed my shoes.

"To avail yourself of these bargain prices," the clerk said, "it is necessary to leave your shoes at our shop twenty-four hours. There is an additional charge for work done while you wait."

"How much will it cost, to have the work done immediately?"

"A dollar and *sixty* cents," the clerk said.

I put on my shoes and said I would return later. I walked home, a distance of five miles, and tried on a pair of my brother-in-law Joe's discarded shoes. They were altogether out of shape, in worse condition than my own, and although I felt uncomfortable in them, I was determined that they would do until my own shoes were repaired.

I walked back to the shop, and the clerk announced that my shoes would be ready to wear the same hour the next day. He handed me a slip of paper with my name written on it.

"Shall I pay now or tomorrow?" I asked.

"Tomorrow," the clerk said.

It was now two o'clock in the afternoon, and since I had not yet smoked a cigarette I bought a pack and smoked one, then another, and another, so that in half an hour two fingers of my right hand were stained, and the corner of my mouth was scorched.

It was difficult to walk in Joe's shoes, so I went to the Public Library to sit down. I took Chekhov's Letters to a table in the great Reading Room, but all of a sudden a pretty girl sat at the table immediately across from me, and there went the letters right out the window. In an hour I read forty pages without understanding one word.

When the girl got up to go, I remembered that I needed a breath of fresh air myself. In the hallway she opened her handbag, and from it fell a slip of paper, which I picked up quickly and handed to her. On the slip of paper was written: two cans tomato sauce, two bars soap, one box matches.

"Are you a stranger here?" I said.

"No," the girl said. "I was born in San Francisco."

"I'm a stranger here," I said.

"Oh," the girl said. "Where are you from?"

"Russia," I said. "I've been here only four years. I've been living in New York."

"You speak good English," the girl said.

"My father," I said, "was English. He was a mechanic in Moscow. My mother was Polish. Are you Spanish?"

"No," the girl said. "I'm Roumanian."

"Well, it's practically the same thing," I said.

We left the building and walked across the street to the Civic Center Park. An old man stood near the fountain feeding pigeons crumbled pieces of stale bread. He tossed the crumbs to the birds with the gesture of one sowing wheat.

We took a bench and watched the man. I began to smoke cigarettes quickly.

"My name is Charles Dilkins," I said. "What yours?"

"Esther Bercovitz," the girl said.

"Yes, that's Bulgarian," I said. "You look Spanish all right."

"Roumanian," the girl said.

"Well, it's all the same," I said. "What were you reading at the library? I'm a writer."

"Are you, *really?*" the girl said.

"Yes," I said. "I use a pen name. You've probably read some of my stories."

"Are you *really* a writer?"

"Yes, of course," I said. "I'm working on a novel now."

"What name do you write under?" the girl said. "Maybe I've read one of your books. I do a lot of reading. But you don't *look* like a writer."

"I know," I said. "I look more like a reader, I guess."

"What name do you use?"

"Sherwood Anderson."

"Are *you* Sherwood Anderson?"

"That's *one* of my pen names," I said. "I have several others. Ever hear of Theodore Dreiser?"

"I *saw* him last year," the girl said. "He was walking on Powell Street, and a friend of mine said, that's Theodore Dreiser, the writer. He's sort of fat."

"Well," I said, "I never use the name Theodore Dreiser. I use other names, mainly Sherwood Anderson."

"I've heard of you all right," the girl said. "But I'm afraid I've never read any of your books."

"That's all right," I said. "I'll dedicate my next novel to you."

"That's very kind of you."

"Not at all. I was looking for somebody suitable to dedicate it to."

"But you hardly know me," the girl said.

"I know you well enough," I said. "A writer knows more about people than they do themselves. You'll like my novel."

"What's it called?"

The Merry Money of Beggars."

"Oh, you *are* a writer!" the girl said.

I lit another cigarette quickly.

"The novel," I said, "is about a young man who has no money."

"I see," the girl said.

"Of course," I went on, "in order to *write* about such a young man it is necessary for me to live the part. I have all the money I need, but I must pretend to be poor while I'm writing the novel."

"Is that the way books are written?"

"Yes."

"Do you make a lot of money writing?"

"Yes. I have a Cadillac."

"I thought all young writers are poor."

"They used to be," I said, "but these days things are different. Last year a friend of mine showed a net profit of fifty-seven thousand dollars."

"He must have done a lot of writing," the girl said. "When do you writers find the time to write so much?"

"Oh," I said, "it's easy. A writer is always on the job. His hours are all hours."

"I didn't know that," the girl said.

"Oh, yes," I went on, "a good writer is *always* alert for new material. Last Christmas, for instance, when the rest of the world was being happy, I sat in my room in a sweat working on a story called 'Joy to the World.' And what did I get for it?"

"What?"

"Influenza."

"Did you have a fever?"

"One hundred and four, but I got a good story out of the *fever*, too. Did you know that during the two weeks in which Voltaire was ill with typhoid fever he wrote an opera, six essays denouncing Catholicism, four against the French government, a six-act play, and seventy-two letters?"

"No," the girl said. "I'm a Catholic."

"That's all right," I said. "Now, in the novel I'm writing the young man who has no money meets a beautiful girl in an art gallery. They take a fancy to one another."

"They do?"

"Yes. Would you like to see a movie?"

"All right," the girl said, so we got up and walked together to the Golden Gate Theatre on Market Street.

Matinee admission was thirty-five cents. As for my shoes, that was tomorrow.

We entered the great cathedral of darkness and secrecy on tiptoe.

Movies are all right in their place, I guess, but it is the comfort of the plush seats in the movie mansions that I cherish most, and I was pleased to sink contentedly beside my companion with not the faintest regret that the recovery of my shoes was now an uncertainty of the future. Tomorrow if I wished to walk to the zoo it would have to be in Joe's shoes, but no matter. One thing at a time is a good policy.

"Now they're married," the girl said suddenly.

"Who?"

"Martin and Helen Hayes."

"Who's Martin?"

"Ronald Colman."

"What picture is this?"

"*Arrowsmith*," the girl said, "from the novel of the same name by Sinclair Lewis."

I sat up and watched carefully.

"A nice picture," I whispered at the end.

"Yes," the girl said. "She died."

"Helen Hayes?"

"Yes, I don't see why they couldn't let her live."

"Yes," I said. "Live and let live. On the other hand, don't you see that Mr. Lewis wished to impress us that life is sad?"

The vaudeville overture fortunately silenced us. It was a medley of classical compositions by Irving Berlin, Walter Donaldson, Lew Pollack, and Franz Schubert. Next a curtain was parted, another raised, and the first act began.

The lady of a song-and-dance team, performing the role of a racketeer's moll, said, "I love him," and then added, "but I hate him," so that my companion said, "What's she mean?"

"She hasn't made up her mind yet," I said, and added to myself: "Write an essay and send it to *Harper's* magazine on 'The Influence of D. H. Lawrence on the Song-and-Dance Teams of American Vaudeville.' Say, the influence of D. H. Lawrence on the song-and-dance teams of American vaudeville is inestimable. Then start estimating."

At the end of the show we left the theater refreshed and inspired, and went to a restaurant where I impressed my friend with the generosity of those who engage in writing.

"Eat all you like," I said.

"I'm glad I'm helping you with your novel," the girl said.

"It's a pleasure to be helped by you," I said.

"I love children," the girl said. "Do you?"

"Yes," I said.

I escorted the girl to her home, and then, since I no longer had the price of a streetcar ride, I began the long walk home. When I got there it was a few minutes after eight and I found Joe sitting in my room pretending to be reading Ouspensky's *Tertium Organum*. He was beginning to nod from having been up since four in the morning to get to his job at Jack Isola's in the produce market.

"It says here," Joe said, "'If rationality exists in the world, then it must permeate everything, although manifesting itself variously.' What does *that* mean?"

"The hell with it," I said. "I been talking all afternoon myself, and I got a headache. Any mail for me?"

"Yes," Joe said. "This bill."

I dropped the bill in the wastebasket and removed Joe's shoes.

"Where'd you find those shoes?" Joe said.

"Joe," I said, "my shoes are in the shop, and I've spent the dollar and a half I borrowed from you this morning."

"What for?"

"I met a pretty girl."

"Just a millionaire on the loose, is that it?"

"Yes," I said. "I began telling lies and showing off, and couldn't stop until the money was all gone. I told her I was Sherwood Anderson, I took her to a movie, and then I took her to a restaurant. Now I'm broke."

"Who's Sherwood Anderson?"

"He's a writer, too."

"Is she a nice girl?"

"Yes, she is."

"I wish you'd write a best seller," Joe said, "so you could live like a millionaire all the time."

"So do I."

"Well," Joe said, "I can't lend you any more money unless I win a prize on a lottery ticket or something."

"I hope you do," I said.

Joe went home and I sat down to work on my novel.

For two hours I worked very hard and wrote two sentences I feel I shall never have occasion to regret.

I then opened the windows of my room, and prayed.

"Our Father," I said, "who art in Heaven, hallowed be Thy name. If I have been a fool this day, it has been to Thy glory. If I have uttered one lie after another, it has been for Thy amusement. Lord, there are enough who groan lamentations, which I presume must bore you; as for me, I have no gift for it. I cannot worship except with a joyous heart. Although I am ill-clothed, although my stomach groans from fasting, and my body shivers with cold, I have nothing for Thee save gratitude. Thy kingdom come: there is no better school of writing. Amen."

Hushed by the enormity of space, the endlessness of time, and grateful to God for the solemnity of the night, and the benediction of sleep, I went to bed; but in the midst of sleep I sat up with a start to write down one last idea: "Write a story about your shoes."

2.

THE FIRE-PREVENTION MAN AND HIS SISTER

the fire-prevention man
ten years old at ten at night
speech pitched deep
in grand falsetto baritone
throws his weight around the house
looking for loopholes and hazards
followed in admiration by his sister
asleep on her feet:

now look here mister
you've got to be more neat
those newspapers on the floor
get them out as quick as you can
they'll burn your house down
before you can get to the door
and that junk in the corner
I give you fair warning
has got to go:

that junk's my writing
it's getting late:

against the law:

what is?

to write
paper burns you know:

well anyhow
to bed:
watch that cigarette
don't forget it there
don't set those books on fire
who wrote those books?

I did
you two had better get to bed:

against the law
don't write any more
let somebody else write
and set *himself* on fire:

to bed I said:

never mind to bed
I've got a fire to prevent:

prevent it then
and get to bed:

takes time mister
all night sometimes:

not tonight:

look here will you
inside this refrigerator:

something wrong?

(deep thought: what's the loophole here?)
not enough food in there:

what's that got to do with fire?

burns you up:

all right
to bed:

the grand falsetto ends
let's set fire to the house, he says:

yes, his sister says:
what for?

fire, fire, they cry together:

nothing doing
now off to bed

and so they go
looking at one another
for being only children again
and brother and sister

3.

THE STOLEN SECRET (A Short Play)

Man.
Woman.
Boy.
Girl.
Animal.

MAN: Well, here we are, then—come to the latest moment of time—time, a thing we do not understand. What's a century? A hundred years. What's an hour? Sixty minutes. What's an hour a century ago? Us. What's an hour a century from now. Us. We are time, such as it is, and such as we are.

WOMAN: So we are, but what about tea? Do you want tea, or would you rather have coffee?

MAN: Coffee, thank you. I'm trying to restore order, and you want me to choose between tea and coffee. Coffee, then, I hate them both, I may say.

WOMAN: I'm sorry. Most people are quite fond of them. Sugar? Cream?

MAN: Sugar. Cream. Anything else?

WOMAN: You're getting awfully old.

MAN: Yes, I know. My time is running out, no doubt—so coffee, sugar, cream, and so on. Is that right? Keep eating? Keep busy with cups and saucers and—?

BOY: Saucers? The flying ones, I mean. From Mars, or wherever it is they're supposed to be coming from. Isn't there a little cold meat to go with the coffee?

MAN: Yes, get the young man a little cold meat—beef, or lamb, or pork, I suppose. Whatever creature it was that was slaughtered not long ago so that we might have something more to eat. Something more. *(To Man representing Animal)* Fish? Or bird? Salmon? Or stork?

ANIMAL: Stork? Are storks being eaten, too?

GIRL: Perhaps not, but it might be a good idea. After all, too much is more than enough. The stork delivers a child to its parents, and stays for dinner. That is their dinner. The child's dinner. One stork to a child. That's enough.

ANIMAL: As you say. We've never complained.

GIRL: That's your trouble, and we always have. That's what makes us so superior. Look at our clothes, for instance. Look at the things we wear.

MAN: Look at the things *they* don't.

ANIMAL: You are ashamed, and we aren't. You do everything we do, and a million things more, but you deny what you have done and we don't *know* what we have done.

BOY: You don't?

ANIMAL: Dog eat dog, I mean, as you say, only dogs don't eat dogs. Animals eat other animals, though, and that's all there is to it. Neither the eater nor the eatee regrets it. Beef, lamb, or pork, as you say, a cow, a sheep, a pig. Why should you be ashamed of eating them? Why should you deny *being* animals, too?

WOMAN: Tea or coffee?

ANIMAL: Neither, thanks.

WOMAN: A glass of water?

ANIMAL: A stone of any kind—to look at, not to eat. I have noticed lately that my hunger is satisfied by looking at a stone. I don't quite know why. But please go on. This meeting is not for me.

MAN: On the contrary, it is for you as much as it is for us. You are the representative from the Animal Family. *(Suddenly)* What does the cat actually think? Can you tell me that?

ANIMAL: The house cat?

MAN: Yes, precisely. Inside the house, living with the Human Family. That is to say, what does the *cat*, for instance, think?

ANIMAL: Well, I can't say I think anything, for I don't, and I never have. I look, I see.

MAN: You have feelings. What do you feel, walking on carpets inside the house, moving on four soft feet, far below the heads of the members of the Human Family, moving on two feet? What do you feel?

ANIMAL: Nothing, I suppose I'm waiting.

BOY: For what?

ANIMAL: I don't quite know. I don't suppose I need to know.

WOMAN: A dog, then. Surely a dog thinks *something*.

ANIMAL: No, I don't. I really don't.

BOY: Then what's all the barking about?

ANIMAL: Bow-wow?

BOY: Yes, bow-wow.

ANIMAL: Bow-wow. What does bow-wow mean? Doesn't mean anything. Bow-wow means bow-wow. What would you have it mean? Hurrah?

GIRL: A horse, then. Surely you will not pretend a horse doesn't think.

ANIMAL: I tell you I have never had a thought in my head, or for that matter in my foot. I just haven't, that's all. What does a man think? What does a woman think? What does a boy? A girl?

WOMAN: I think we'd better have some coffee. It's no good starting the meeting with everybody annoyed with everybody else. We're all in the same boat.

GIRL: And the boat's sinking, is that it?

BOY: Or the boat's on fire. As the saying is, "The boy stood on the burning deck." So he did, I suppose.

WOMAN: *(To Animal)* Do you have a cup of coffee?

ANIMAL: *(Takes a cup from tray)* Thank you. *(He sips.)*

WOMAN: Now, isn't that better?

ANIMAL: Thank you.

WOMAN: Now, can all of us just drink our coffee and for heaven's sake not be so glum because we've got it into our heads that it is the end of the world all of a sudden?

BOY: I don't mind if it *is* the end of the world. I never have.

WOMAN: But at the same time let's not be cynical, either. Just drink this coffee and wait a moment.

GIRL: Now, you know perfectly well I want to get married, and it just isn't happening, that's all.

WOMAN: The coffee, please. Just the coffee now for a moment.

MAN: And very good coffee it is, too.

WOMAN: Do you actually believe we've come to the end of our rope?

BOY: But you yourself just said coffee for a moment.

WOMAN: Oh, well, we've had a sip or two, and I speak of the whole matter without excitement. I don't believe we've come to the end of our rope at all. That's what I mean. As far as I'm concerned everything is the same as ever. Now, isn't that so?

MAN: Not quite.

WOMAN: What is it that's happened? What is it that's different?

MAN: Well, now you're a woman, and I may say a woman who is both beautiful and clever.

WOMAN: I'm so glad that you're able to speak that way again.

MAN: But the fact is that either you can't think at all or you've decided thinking is useless, because I've explained to you precisely what it is that has happened, and what it is that is different. Many times. Perhaps *too* many times.

GIRL: Oh, well, then, once more won't do any harm.

MAN: We are, here, the Human Family.

BOY: So we are.

MAN: We are safe at home, only our home isn't safe anymore.

BOY: But we know that.

MAN: We are two thousand million men and women of all ages at home in every part of the earth. With us are a thousand times as many animals of all kinds on the surface of the earth, under it, in the sky, and in the sea.

GIRL: We know that, too.

MAN: This morning the sun came up. Last night the moon came up, and the sky was filled with stars. All far away, and all very near, millions of miles away, and millions of years, but right here, and right now, too— as we are.

ANIMAL: I wish I had a stone to look at. A small rock. A pebble.

WOMAN: Would the diamond in this ring do?

ANIMAL: I'm afraid not. I can't see a diamond.

WOMAN: I just don't happen to have a pebble.

ANIMAL: It's all right.

BOY: Can't you *remember* one?

ANIMAL: Of course I can. That's why I want to look at one. What's the good of just remembering a rock? I want to look at one. *(To Man)* I'm sorry.

MAN: Not at all. But to go on. I have been asked to state once again what it is that has happened, and what it is that is different. Well, it's this. *(He holds something small in his fingers.)*

WOMAN: What is that?

MAN: This, as I have told you again and again, is a secret. The Ninety-ninth Secret, the smallest, the most astonishing, wonderful, powerful, and dangerous.

BOY: Why don't we just give back the secrets to the Indians?

MAN: Because we didn't get them from the Indians, because *we* are the Indians, because we can't give anything back to anybody.

WOMAN: All well and good. The Ninety-ninth Secret. We certainly can just put it aside and go about our business, can't we?

MAN: Not quite. The Ninety-eighth Secret, only a little less powerful than the Ninety-ninth, has been removed from its proper place by one of us here, and until it has been returned everybody and everything is in grave danger—of coming to an end.

BOY: Isn't everybody in danger of coming to an end anyway?

MAN: Everybody is *promised* a proper end, and entitled to it, but the end we are worried about is not a proper end.

BOY: What's the difference? An end is an end, isn't it?

MAN: A proper end is also a beginning, but an improper end is entirely an end, and that's no fun at all.

GIRL: What can the Ninety-ninth Secret do?

MAN: Well, it can cancel us—all of us. Once and for all.

WOMAN: Whoever has the Ninety-eighth Secret must put it back, that's all.

MAN: Not quite. The Ninety-seventh and a good many others have been stolen and put back any number of times, and that is the thing that makes everything different. That continuous business of back and forth, anxiety and relief and then new anxiety, has made us quite sick. This time the Secret must be put back and left there—forever. Otherwise I am afraid we *have* come to the end of our rope.

BOY: Forever? That would be a dictatorship, wouldn't it? As free creatures, we must always have a right to lie or steal or kill, and pay the consequences, mustn't we?

MAN: I'm tired, I'm tired. I can't talk to my own wife and children anymore. I give up. It's too much. I can't be bothered anymore.

WOMAN: I'm glad. Really, I am. Why don't you lie down and have a nap?

GIRL: Yes, it's such a nice afternoon for a nap.

BOY: You *ought* to take a nap.

ANIMAL: The nearest thing to a stone I've ever seen is the head of a man who is asleep.

WOMAN: Lie down and sleep. We'll all be very quiet.

MAN: Have you lost your wits, to ask me to lie down? *(Angry)* You know that's what I *want* to do. Well, I'm not going to—for *you!* Now, each of you listen to me carefully. It's very simple. I'll explain the whole thing again, and whoever has stolen the Secret must put it back, and this time let it stay put until we can find a sensible and proper use for it. Now, listen very carefully, please.

The Rearward Dog

The Rearward Dog had been his mother's name in Armenian for anybody who kept him company.

"Why do you have a man for a dog?" she had said. "Why do you have to have a dog trotting along behind you all the time? You walk too fast, you talk too fast, why don't you let them be?"

Now, years later, the Rearward Dog sat behind the wheel of the 1939 Oldsmobile he had just bought, in 1950. for $500 cash, and he remembered her saying of this one, "My sister thinks well of him, he's her son, that's how it must be with mothers. Every now and then I find that I almost believe you yourself are as much as you seem to think, as much as you have always thought, but let my sister and myself own up to the truth, he is a fool and you are crazy. I will give you the truth about yourself as I see it. A mother is supposed to follow a pattern in this business, but let us put aside such foolishness. Why do you go to so much trouble to make money, putting yourself into solitary confinement, sitting at that table for weeks, writing your stories, and then when you have earned the money, when you have earned your freedom at last, when it is time to live a little in the world instead of in that lonely place where you live, why do you call one of the rearward dogs and go off night after night, carousing, gambling, taking airplanes, driving automobiles, drinking, shouting, and laughing? Why do you go berserk after you have worked so hard, the rearward dog trotting along behind you? I get letters from strangers telling me how proud I must be to be your mother, but what do they know about anything?"

The car swung around the corner and began to climb the hill. The Rearward Dog shifted to pick up the necessary power for the climb, the motor coughed, choked, began to hiccup, the Rearward Dog trying to act as if the motor were doing fine, for the other one had already kidded him half to death about the bargain he had made.

"It's a good car."

"I think the mechanic forgot to adjust the carburetor."

"It's doing fine."

The car was stopped in the middle of the hill. They were sitting far back because the hill was steep. The owner of the car stepped on the starter, hoping the motor would start again, trying not to show how mad he was about his bad luck all his life, even a little thing like the buying of a used car had him coming up with the worst one in the world—whoever heard of anybody buying a 1939 Oldsmobile?

"That was the year I went to Europe for the second time."

"What was?"

"Nineteen thirty-nine."

"She'll start in a minute. She's only got ninety-seven thousand miles on her."

The car wanted to roll back. The foot brake wasn't enough, so the driver dragged the hand brake out as far as it would go. The car began to groan.

"Let's smoke a cigarette," he said. "Let's talk about poetry a minute. After that it'll start, I know."

"You'll be late," the driver said. "I told you I'd get you there. I insisted on it. Hell, I *wanted* to, with my big mouth. I know you'd rather take a taxi to the depot when you're going on a trip, but I don't know, I thought we'd have some laughs on the way there. I mean, across the bridge to the Oakland side, and now this car won't even get up the hill to your house."

"I've never been late in my life," he said. "I won't be late this time."

The other tried the starter again, once, twice, three times, and then it was too many times to keep count.

"You see?" he said, his voice filled with pain. "That's my luck. I can't even buy a car that'll act like a car. I wanted to show off. A man with no money wanting to show off. It looked pretty good. I dreamed last night that I'd get a real bargain, something fine—but *this* is what I got."

"It's only six blocks. I'll get out and walk the rest of the way. My bags are packed. I'll get a taxi at my house and pick you up here. We'll ride together, after all." He got out of the car. "Ease her back down the hill and let her rest somewhere."

"I think she's going to start now," the other said, but the walker was already at the top of the hill, going around the corner.

The driver eased the car back down the hill, got out and stood beside it, waiting for the taxi to show up, already waiting, even though the walker couldn't be more than a block away. Why was he waiting? Was it more of his stupor, for God's sake? He could leap up the hill and catch up with him, after putting him through a rigmarole like that, insisting on driving him to the depot instead of letting him go any way he wanted to go. He began to run suddenly, but when he got to the top of the hill he saw no one climbing any one of the three blocks that went up to the street where his cousin's house was.

He turned and ran back down the hill to the car, saying, "I've got to drive him in, the way I said I would, that's all. Once in a while in my life I've got to be able to do something the way I planned to do it." He jumped into the car, pressed on the starter, and sure enough the motor started. He backed away from the curb, swung the car around, raced the motor to warm it up for the climb, then let her go. She made it this time, but when he got to the top of the hill and was on his way to the first of the three blocks that would bring the car to the street he wanted, the coughing and hiccuping started again. He fought it out with the motor, cursing bitterly, then heard metal fall from the car to the asphalt of the street. The car stopped. He eased it back to the curb, to get it parked, out of the way, and as he drew back he saw the metal—stuff he didn't recognize, but it *was* parts of the motor. He got out of the car, picked up the stuff, and flung it, because each piece was hot, under the car. Then he brought out a cigar—his best comfort—lighted it, and began to wait for the taxi.

When the taxi came the door swung open.

"How'd you get it up *here?*"

"Drove it," the driver said. "Will you make it?"

"Easily."

The taxi moved smoothly and swiftly.

"The motor fell to pieces," the driver said, "or I would have come up and driven you over to the Oakland side, like I'd planned." He began to laugh to himself, hysterical about his bad luck.

"Just before the motor fell out," he said, "I remembered what your mother used to call me, and I was so ashamed I wanted to prove to myself that I could catch up with you, get there before you called a taxi, and drive you across to the Oakland side. I felt sure I'd make it and I felt pretty good. I figured to myself that *you* made the motor nervous, that's why it couldn't make the hill the last time." He was laughing silently, trying to talk and trying to smoke the cigar at the same time. "You made the car ashamed of itself, I thought, and here it was going along just fine—well, it was coughing a little—and I was sure the whole thing would turn out all right." He couldn't go on. He could barely breathe. His face was red, and he was trying to gather himself together.

"O.K. Let's have it."

"That's when the motor fell out," he said. "Your mother was right. The Rearward Dog. That's me, all right."

"She called everybody that."

"The difference is, it fits me."

"This is fine," he said. "An easy ride to the Ferry Building. If you want to ride the boat with me to the Oakland side, good. Otherwise get on back to your car and find out what's the matter with it."

"I'll ride to the Oakland side," his cousin said. "I haven't done that in years. How long will you be gone?"

"Well," he said, "if I don't like the university I'll stay only a day or two. If I like it I'll stay three weeks. Then I'll go to New York for a couple of days, by way of Montreal. I just want to walk through the streets there. I've never been there. Then I'll come back by way of New Orleans. I'll see you about the end of July."

"You going to teach at the university?"

The taxi was hurtling up the steep curves of Sutro Forest now.

"There'll be little new houses in Sutro Forest pretty soon," he said. "Each house with a little new family in it. I'm going to find out if I want to stay at the university at all."

"You may run into a nice girl there."

"It's a thought."

"Clean mountain girls."

"They stink," he said. "I didn't half-accept the offer from the university because I want to teach anybody how to write plays. I half-accepted it because I'm looking. Write a play if you can. *The Cocktail Party's* a big hit in New York. It's about people drinking cocktails. Write a play about people drinking water. But don't let the work get so important that you don't know how lucky you are. Don't let it make you give your wife a bad time. She's pregnant and she's got two kids to take care of without any help, so give her a break. Take it easy and if the writing of the play doesn't go well, know it isn't important for the writing of the play to go well. It's important for the pregnancy to go well."

"Go and see them in New York," his cousin said. "Go and see your kids."

"No, I won't see them," he said. "Why should I give *them* a bad time? I'll attend to a little business, and then hurry back and go to work again."

"You're turning the stuff out."

"You wouldn't do it if you didn't have to. I have to. I've always had to. I've always had to get the money."

"I've always *needed* the money," the other said, "but I've *never* gotten it. My luck stinks."

"You're lucky enough," he said. "When you get home Maud's there, supper's there, the two boys are there. What do you want?"

"I want to be famous," the other said, giggling at himself, hiding his face in mock shame. "I'm bald-headed. Your hair won't fall out. You can turn the stuff out. You can get money for it every time. Big money. You can get up and ramble all over. You don't give a damn about any of it. I do. I want it so bad I'll never get it, I guess."

"You've *got* it," he said. "When you get home you'll see *how* you've got it. The two boys, the girl coming, supper on the table—what are you having for supper?"

"Fridays," he said. "I try to have her cook fish of some kind. She can cook anything. It'll be a small baked salmon with boiled potatoes, pie and coffee. She makes some kind of dessert every night. That's why I'm getting to be such a slob." He began to laugh silently again.

"What's the secret now?"

"Getting to be," he said. "Getting to be a slob. I always was. Take care of your health. You work too hard. You've lost a lot of weight."

"It wasn't from work."

"Don't worry about the kids. They're all right."

"Sure they are. What are you doing tomorrow?"

"I never work Saturdays. I'll take them to the park." He began to laugh silently again, and then he said, "In my car. In my car with the motor in the street."

"You've got a good safety valve," he said. "That laughing. If you run out of work, try writing a play, but don't let it throw you. Just be glad about Maud and the baked salmon."

"She asks me every morning what I want for supper. She asked me this morning and I didn't know what else to say, so I said salmon. We love to eat. You ought to eat more."

"It's an escape I don't enjoy," he said. "I used to think I did, but I don't. I like whiskey, but it never kicks me around too much. My proper escape is the family."

"I hope you run into somebody real nice at the university."

"I won't, but I want to go to the university just the same."

"Yes, you will," the other said. "It's only the middle of the year. Before the year's over you'll have everything in order again. Wait and see. I told you last November this year was going to be a great year for you."

"Didn't I say it was going to be a great year for *you*, too?"

The other one laughed again, moving inwardly to his secret.

"All of my years," he said, "are the same. All failure. I can't even buy a used car that won't turn out to be a gyp. I've got to work like a dog to pick up sixty or seventy dollars a week. Everything I write is childish. I keep running after fame and I keep falling on my face." He laughed silently again.

"You've got Maud and the boys."

"Yes, I've got them. You better see your kids when you get to New York. Take them somewhere and spend three or four hours with them. Hold them and let them smell you. It's not good for your own kids to forget how you smell."

"I know," he said. "It's not good to forget how they smell, either. Or how they walk, or how they look out of their eyes."

When they came to the Ferry Building his cousin—the Rearward Dog, as his mother had always put it—took both of the bags while he took care of the taxi, but when he was free he took the heaviest one away to carry himself.

"We'd better run," his cousin said. "They're closing the door."

"No," he said, "let them close it." He walked slowly to the door. When they were past the gate the man slid the door shut.

They got aboard the ferry, and the cousin said, "What would you have done if he had shut the door before we'd gotten in?"

"I would have taken a taxi to the airport," he said. "I would have taken an airplane to New York. I would have taken another airplane to Paris. I would have taken a taxi to Enghien. There I would have sat down and played baccarat."

"Honest?"

"That was my plan."

"What about the university?"

"What about it?"

"What about the girl you might run into there?"

"What about the one I might run into at the casino in Enghien?"

They went to the top deck of the boat just as it began to draw out of the slip.

"Well," the Rearward Dog said, "you can't say it hasn't been a good year so far."

"No," he said, "I can't say that. Because it could have been worse, although I can't imagine how."

They watched San Francisco loom up, grow small, and then disappear, the sun going down over it. At the proper time they went to the other end of the boat and got off. The train was waiting and the porter took him to his compartment.

"I hope the ferry doesn't sink when I go back," his cousin said.

"Have them all drinking water."

"Who?"

"The people in the play. Thanks for riding with me. Take good care of Maud and the boys."

They got off the train together until starting time. When the train began to go he swung onto the platform of his car and watched his cousin standing there, laughing silently, almost unable to lift his arm and wave goodbye from a sense of frustration and failure, but the most truly successful man he had ever met just the same.

Notes

In addition to the publication history of each piece, the following notes include commentary, excerpts from Saroyan's letters and certain biographical details pertaining to the work. A complete catalogue of Saroyan pieces as they appeared in the Haireniks was published in the *Saroyan Memorial Issue* of *The Armenian Review* (September 1981). The SMI catalogue includes twelve Saroyan pieces of a miscellaneous nature not reprinted in this volume; these include all but two of Tashjian Listings 98 through 111 (see brief citations, page 387 below).

Abbreviations:
  HD = *Hairenik Daily.*
  HW = *Hairenik Weekly.*
  SMI = *Saroyan Memorial Issue* of *The Armenian Review*
    (*TAR* vol. xxxiv, 3–135, September 1981).
  TAR = *The Armenian Review.*
  T.L. = Tashjian Listing of Saroyan works in *HD, HW* and *TAR*
  WS = William Saroyan.

PREFACE
  1. *The Armenian Review (TAR),* vol. xxxiv (3–133), 1981, p. 327, the *Saroyan Memorial Issue* (SMI), titled "104 Unpublished Letters of William Saroyan: Ethnic Motivations of an American Writer." Bardizian first met Saroyan in late 1932, not in 1933. Saroyan's memory here is faulty. It should be noted that Saroyan's first published piece was his "Preface to a Book Not Yet Written" *(Overland Monthly and Out West Magazine,* August 1928, vol. 86:8), followed in the December 1928, issue of the same publication (vol. 86:12) by his short story "Portrait of a Bum."
  2. Ibid.
  3. Saroyan was last extensively interviewed by this writer on June 29, 1975, over dinner and in his lodgings at the Ritz-Carlton Hotel, Boston, following his visit to the Hairenik, 212 Stuart Street, Boston. Notes on this five-hour exchange were sedulously made by this writer but, at Saroyan's request, no dictaphone

record was kept. A typed transcript of the Tashjian notes was mailed to Saroyan who, a few days later, called to report the transcript "in good shape," but he asked that it not be published in all or in part "until I am dead, if that is ever to happen." He said he was "troubled by my [Saroyan's] unusual candidity . . . but what the hell, after I'm gone, who cares?" Saroyan insisted that the present version of his "discovery" was "correct as far as I can remember," despite minor variances with his introductory note to his "The Broken Wheel" as it appeared in his anthology *The Man With the Heart in the Highlands and Other Stories* (1968).

4. The O'Brien-*Story* phase of this oral testimony does not conform in all instances with what we read in his story "Yvor Winters and His Poetry Students at Stanford" (see his *Sons Come and Go, Mothers Hang In Forever*, [New York: McGraw-Hill, 1976]). In the latter, Saroyan says O'Brien published a virginal story by Saroyan entitled "Resurrection of a Life" which, Saroyan swears, "had its first appearance in the Armenian English-language Weekly Hairenik, published in Boston." Saroyan here is confused. "Resurrection of a Life" was never published in Hairenik; it was rather Saroyan's lead piece in his *Inhale and Exhale* (1936) which bore a number of other Hairenik-based stories. Saroyan of course meant "The Broken Wheel" as the story O'Brien picked up. In the same work, Saroyan explains why he adopted "Sirak Goryan" as his early pen name (see note to "A Fist Fight for America"); but his recollection of how Burnett-Foley of *Story* found him must bow to the version Saroyan told me, which agrees generally with his opening note to "The Broken Wheel," as republished in *The Man With the Heart in the Highlands* (1968).

5. "Conversation with Tashjian" (fn. 3, above). See also SMI, Letter 90, Rue Taitbout, Paris. [General] Antranik [Ozanian] was a celebrated Armenian World War I officer who toured the United States in 1919. Saroyan, then eleven years old, saw the general at his uncle Aram's office in Fresno, an incident which he later formed into his story "Antranik of Armenia," as originally published in *Inhale and Exhale* (1936). The Asbarez was an Armenian publishing house and adjoining coffeeshop and reading room in Fresno which Saroyan often visited. His father had briefly (1910) worked at Asbarez. Later, Saroyan met Bardizian in San Francisco where, again, Bardizian urged him to write for the Haireniks. Saroyan's earliest contributions to Haireniks were mailed from San Francisco.

6. "Conversation with Tashjian."

7. On the history of the Haireniks, see the Preface to the *Saroyan Memorial Issue* of *The Armenian Review*, 1981.

8. Ibid.

9. The Saroyan children spent five years in the Finch Orphanage, Oakland (1911–1916) not four years, as Saroyan himself had early believed. See his "An Orphanage Far Far Away," in his *Sons Come and Go, Mothers Hang In Forever* (1976).

10. Page 316 of the Fresno City Directory, 1908–1909, lists "Armanoc Saroyan" [Armenak Saroyan] as a "laborer" residing at "621 I Street," Fresno, as per courtesy of John K. Kallenberg, The Librarian, Fresno County Library. Of course, this means that the Saroyans were residing at this address when William was born.

11. See Note to T.L. 96, this work, "Hayastan and Charentz."

12. In his story "Armenak and Takoohi," about Saroyan's parents (in *Sons Come and Go, Mothers Hang In Forever*, 1976), Saroyan, as the child, imagines his

dead father as a crude, coarse, heavily sensuous man, in order, ostensibly, to convince himself that he had lost a brute of a father—and was the better for it; but then, as the adult, he reverts to his cherished image of a taciturn, imaginative sire. He says that as a child "I refused to believe in his death, and permitted myself to believe that he would come back, somehow come back to me—the hell with the others, the rest of the kith and kin . . . I loved and admired him most [although] I had never known him, for he was a perfect man." WS then admits that in fact his father did not fit the vulgar, animal image, "fit for anything else gross and stupid and real and shitty like that, at all." In the same story, Saroyan reveals that his father died in San Jose, California, "in the heat of a grand July afternoon in 1911 . . . of a ruptured appendix." His story "Armenak of Bitlis" (*Letters from 74 rue Taitbout or Don't Go But If You Must Say Hello to Everybody*, 1969), describes his second visit, when he was fifty-eight years of age, to his father's grave "in a cemetery by the railroad tracks in San Jose," where he brings to mind his first visit there as a youth, and contemplates his lack of rapport with his own son, Aram, which he illustrates with a poignant account of a chance meeting with Aram on a New York street and the polite conversation that takes place, as if casual acquaintances were passing the time of day. Saroyan laments that to his son he is all but dead—as dead as his own father, lying here, is really dead, but *mourned* for it. For Aram Saroyan's interpretation of the difficulties between father and son, and daughter, read his *Last Rites: The Death of William Saroyan* (New York: William Morrow, 1982).

13. On Darbinian's life and career, see *The Armenian Review*, vol. xxxii (3–131), September 1980, "Two Newly Discovered English-Language Journals, or Workbooks, of Reuben Darbinian. . . ."

14. SMI.

JAMES H. TASHJIAN

TO THE VOICE OF SHAH-MOURADIAN (Poem)

By "William Saroyan." In *HD*, January 14, 1933. Two verses. Not republished. Armenak Shah-Mouradian was the charismatic Armenian tenor. Saroyan (*Here Comes/There Goes You Know Who*, 1961) comments:

When I was seventeen [1925] the songs of Armenia, sung on discs by Shah-Mouradian of Moush [Armenia], became profoundly important in my life. I played them on the phonograph and sang them with the great singer. Hearing his singing for the first time I thought, "So *that's* what it means to be an Armenian. That open voice, field voice, wind-voice, voice of the plains."

"Mayr Araksie" (*Mother Araxes*) is an Armenian folk song which idealizes the Araxes (Aras, Arpa Chai), the Armenian goddess-river. See SMI, p. 233. *T.L.I.*

TO THE RIVER EUPHRATES (Poem)

By "William Saroyan." In *HD*, January 21, 1933. Not republished. The Euphrates is the Armenian Danube. *T.L. 2.*

To Lake Van (Poem)

By "William Saroyan." In *HD*, April 7, 1933. Not republished. The Lake of Van is the celebrated Armenian salt sea in Eastern ("Turkish") historical Armenia, around which many legends have been woven. This is the third and last of Saroyan's old country verses. *T.L. 3*

A Fist Fight for Armenia

By "Sirak Goryan." In *HD*, May 9, 10, 1933. For pen name see SMI, p. 233, fn. 1, and Saroyan's *Sons Come and Go, Mothers Hang In Forever* (1976), p. 73. "Goryan" = "Goriun," a fifth-century (not "eighth" as Saroyan pretends) Armenian writer; "Sirak" = the name of several of Saroyan's cousins. Certainly this is one of WS's most artful stories, but it was never republished in more popular media. At the time of the story, the 1915 Turkish massacres of the Armenians was a recent event. Caspar is the more militant Armenian, the overmatched Armenian "enforcer." Reuben Paul is the aesthetic Armenian—the Armenian intellectual, who eschews confrontation until he too has had his bellyful. Sommers, the school bully, is of course the hostile Turk. It is Saroyan's version of David and Goliath, but here the Armenian loses the battle but wins the war. In Saroyan's youthful days in Fresno, there existed a good deal of antipathy toward the newcomer Armenians. See Saroyan's letter dated May 14, 1956, from Malibu (SMI Letter 84, p. 321). The story was written in San Francisco. *T.L. 4*

The Broken Wheel

By "Sirak Goryan." In *HD*, three installments, June 2, 4, 6, 1933. One of WS's favorites. After its original appearance in *HD*, it was first republished in Edward J. O'Brien's *Best Short Stories of 1934*. See Preface to the present work. Later republished in at least four WS anthologies: *Inhale and Exhale* (1936); *31 Selected Stories from Inhale and Exhale* (1943); *The Saroyan Special* (1948); and *The Man With the Heart in the Highlands* (1968), which see for Saroyan's own introductory comment. This is without doubt the first identifiable "Aram Garoghlanian" story (*viz., My Name is Aram*, 1940), as betrayed by Saroyan's reference to his brother "Krikor," in real life Henry Saroyan. *T.L. 5*

The Barber's Apprentice

By "Sirak Goryan." In *HD*, October 5, 6, 1933. Republished in *HW*, March 1, 1935. (SMI, in error, reports it as having been printed in *HW* in 1934.) For comment on this and the next four stories, see SMI, Letter 84, May 14, 1956, p. 321. Not otherwise republished, but it received honorable mention in Edward J. O'Brien's *Best Short Stories of 1934* and in the *Year Book of the American Story*, published August 28, 1934. *T.L. 6* and *T.L. 16*

THE MOMENT OF LIFE

By "Sirak Goryan." In *HD*, November 26, 28, 1933. Never republished. In this sensitive story, WS's father Armenak becomes "Aram"; it is nevertheless an "Aram Garoghlanian" story inasmuch as WS's brother is referred to as "Krikor," a cartouche of the "Aram" tales. *T.L. 7*

NONEH

By "Sirak Goryan." In *HD*, November 26, 28, 1933. Never republished. This piece is about WS's maternal grandmother Lucy (née Garoghlanian). It too falls into the "Aram" category. Saroyan could speak Armenian, but never learned to read or write it, and his transliterations, accordingly, were "à la Saroyan" and conformed phonetically to the spoken dialect of the city of Bitlis, of which Saroyan's parents were natives. Thus *Noneh*, which is an endearment for "grandmother" (compare "nanny"), is more generally rendered *Nanah* by Western Armenians, but it is often converted to other localized forms in the various provincial dialects—*Noneh* in Bitlis. Unrepublished. *T.L. 8.*

PRINT

By "Sirak Goryan." In *HD*, December 12, 13, 1933. All the hallmarks of the "Aram" series are found in this story. Republished in *Inhale and Exhale* (1936) under title "Daily News." *T.L. 9.*

HATE

By "Sirak Goryan." In *HD*, two installments, December 3, 1933; January 3, 1934. Clearly, an "Aram" story. An elaborate critical essay can be written about this story, in which Saroyan suggests allegorically that he hates the Turks altogether for their national misdeeds rather than individually . . . and is aghast at violence and war. This story was republished in *My Kind of Crazy, Wonderful People: Seventeen Stories and a Play* (1964) under the title "The War," with certain adjustments and restructuring. Earlier republished as "The War" in *Inhale and Exhale* (1936). *T.L. 10.*

SUMMER LAUGHTER

By "Sirak Goryan." In *HD*, January 12, 1934. Not republished. The site of this story is probably Fresno, and it represents the first of two WS stories (the second is "Explosion") about "Uncle Aslan," a tailor and would-be farmer. In a later conversation, Saroyan revealed that he had intended to do a sort of "My Name is Aslan" series for book publication, but "I got caught up in other work, and nothing came of it." *T.L. 11.*

THE DEATH OF CHILDREN

By "Sirak Goryan." In *HD*, two installments, Jan. 20, 21, 1934. Apparently an early story written in Fresno. Saroyan was a pupil at the

Emerson School, L and San Benito, Fresno, at least in 1918 (see his *Places Where I Have Done Time*, 1972, p. 33). The passage describing the little Armenian survivor of the 1915 massacres ranks among Saroyan's most memorable lines. To our knowledge, the story was twice reprinted, in *Inhale and Exhale* (1936) and in *The Saroyan Special* (1948). *T.L. 12*.

RAISINS

By "Sirak Goryan." In *HD*, three installments, January 30, 31; February 1, 1934, and later reprinted "by William Saroyan" in *Inhale and Exhale* (1936) and in *31 Selected Stories from Inhale and Exhale* (1943). *T.L. 13*.

EXPLOSION

By "Sirak Goryan." In *HD*, May 18, 1934. The second of Saroyan's "Uncle Aslan" stories. Not republished. Saroyan ("Conversation with Tashjian"): "I especially like this story, but never selected it for reprint, as I recall, because I wanted someday to put out a book on my uncle. You ask if the family ever really knew if Aslan, the consumptive, had tried to blow himself up. If they did, they never told me. Look, rank it with Edwin Drood among unfinished mysteries. . . ." The reference is of course to Charles Dickens' novel. *T.L. 14*.

JAZZ

By "Sirak Goryan." In *HD*, June 2, 1934. Not republished. *T.L. 15*

YEA AND AMEN

By "Sirak Goryan." In *HW*, March 22, 29, 1934. Received three stars in O'Brien's 1935 anthology. An "Aram" tale, it was republished in *Inhale and Exhale* (1936). *T.L. 17*.

THE BARBER WHOSE UNCLE HAD HIS HEAD BITTEN OFF BY A CIRCUS TIGER

By "William Saroyan." Republished in *Inhale and Exhale* (1936) and *The Saroyan Special* (1948). The first of the "by William Saroyan" pieces to appear in *HW*. In a letter dated November 19, 1935 (SMI, Letter 4), Saroyan says of it: "My story is an Armenian story, a Sirak Goryan story, by William Saroyan. It is all the same." (SMI incorrectly titles this story "The Barber Who Had His Head Bitten Off by a Circus Tiger.") An "Aram" story, it is reminiscent of Saroyan's little play "The Haircut," published in *The Dogs, or The Paris Comedy* (New York, 1969). *T.L. 18*

HOME

By "William Saroyan." In *HW*, July 24, 1936. Written after Saroyan's first trip (1928) to New York, it reveals Saroyan's knowledge of early Armenian history, literature and revolutionary figures. Gregory the Illuminator was the clerical founder of the Armenian Apostolic Church

(A.D. 301); Bedros Tourian (Saroyan's "Dourian") was the revered Armenian poet (1851–1872); Antranik, Khetcho and Mourad were titans of the Armenian liberationalist struggle. Not republished. *T.L. 19*

THE INSURANCE SALESMAN, THE PEASANT, THE RUG MERCHANT AND THE POTTED PLANT

From T.L. 20 on, all pieces are by "William Saroyan." In *HW*, April 15, 1938 (*sic*). One of Saroyan's favorite stories, as evidenced by its republishing history: *Peace, It's Wonderful* (1939); *The Saroyan Special* (1948); *The William Saroyan Reader* (1958); and *The Man With the Heart in the Highlands and Other Stories* (1968), in the latter of which (p. 155) he notes, "Ralph Moradian, who lived across the alley from me on San Benito Avenue in Fresno in 1918, told me this story in 1938 and I wrote it immediately. Insurance salesmen have always seemed interesting to me. I especially enjoy their recitations about life expectancy." Mailed from Carl Street, San Francisco. In a letter dated March 26, 1938 (SMI Letter 8, pp. 253–254), he says, "The little story attached is appearing soon in *The New Statesman and Nation* of London and will be included in my next book of stories . . . ," that is, The *Trouble with Tigers* (late 1938). Saroyan's interest in Armenian insurance salesmen, although here indicated as a purely literary concern, reflected nonetheless the unique position such agents enjoyed in the early twentieth-century Armenian American community. In the usually English-deficient Armenian community, insurance salesmen served as community factotums through their quasi-legal training and knowledge of English. They acted as scribes, interpreters, advisers and, in some instances, as real estate agents or brokers to their soul brothers—all in return for signing them up to life and other insurance policies. Moradian, who told Saroyan this story, later became a Fresno County judge. The original publication of this story was accompanied by a linoleum cut done by Boston artist Dertad Boyajian. *T.L. 20*

THE RUSSIAN WRITER

In *HW*, April 20, 1938. Republished in *Peace, It's Wonderful* (1939) and *The Saroyan Special* (1948). According to Saroyan ("Conversation with Tashjian"): "This happened in Moscow, yes, in Moscow, during my 1935 trip abroad. For obvious reasons, let's say, I have 'forgotten' the name of the Russian writer who thought my stuff was awful, but not as awful as the stuff being written in Russia. I must accept his judgment; I don't read Russian." Republished too in *Three Worlds* (1939), the Hairenik anthology, and mentioned by O'Brien in his 1940 *Best Stories*. *T.L. 21*

THE TWO THIEVES

In *HW*, May 6, 1938. Never republished. In a letter of April 25, 1938 (SMI pp. 254–255), WS notes: "I am herewith sending a story of some social significance . . . It was to have been in *Inhale and Exhale* [1936] and was taken out at my suggestion because there were too many stories in the book; about twenty other stories were similarly taken out. . . ." *T.L.* 22

THE POET

In *HW*, May 13, 1938. Not republished. The scene is obviously WS's room at Carl Street, a productive living room-office which, for some reason, WS chose not to describe in his *Places Where I've Done Time*. Saroyan had a lifelong interest in graphic art, which was later to announce itself in his original line drawings, which illustrated a number of his later books and led to a posthumous "one-man-show" of his art at Fresno State University late in 1981. This story was obviously written under the inspiration of William Blake, one of whose works, WS reveals in this story, he was reading. Like Blake, Saroyan was fascinated by the qualities of the tiger, as manifested by his book *The Trouble With Tigers* (1938), the same year of the composition of "The Poet"; his 1951 *Tracy's Tiger* and, of course, his short story "The Barber Whose Uncle Had His Head Bitten Off by a Circus Tiger." We might add that in the latter, Saroyan's tiger was meant to illustrate metaphorically the crushing impact of the dispersion on Armenian migrants, a theme which continues to occupy Armenian intellectuals. When this was suggested to Saroyan ("Conversation with Tashjian"), Saroyan reflected, "That's it! That's the whole meaning of the story." In the story, WS reveals that as early as 1938 he had toyed with the idea of writing a full-length work devoted simply to vital human statistics, a project he was not to fulfill until 1979 when his last bound work, *Obituaries*, appeared. "Amiel" was the Swiss philosopher and critic Henri Frédéric Amiel (1821–1881). Saroyan means he was at that time reading Amiel's best-known work *Journal Intime*, which existed in an English translation, a writing which "interpreted many lonely souls to themselves." *T.L.* 23

THE MONUMENTAL ARENA

In *HW*, May 20, 1938. In a letter dated August 22, 1938, Carl Street, (SMI pp. 263–264), WS says, "It may interest you to know that 'Monumental Arena' has been republished in the *London Evening Standard*." The story was also to appear in *Peace, It's Wonderful* (1939). Palpably, the scene is San Francisco. It is possible that Saroyan heard this story in some form at the Palace Bar, which he frequented in his Carl Street days. Originally published with a linoleum cut by Dertad Boyajian. *T.L.* 24

SEVEN FRAGMENTS

In *HW*, May 27, 1938. This is also one of Saroyan's "San Francisco" stories. Not republished. *T.L.* 25

NOW IS THE TIME: A SIDESHOW OF THE WORLD TODAY (A Play)

In *HW*, June 3, 1938. This is the first Saroyan play—"experimental" though Saroyan termed it—ever published anywhere, a fact which has escaped Saroyan's biographers. Never republished and of course never produced. The first Saroyan play to receive formal performance was *My Heart's in the Highlands*, which opened on Broadway in April 1939, with the author's cousin, Ross Bagdasarian, in the lead role. Saroyan's more celebrated *The Time of Your Life* was to hit Broadway in October 1939, after a tumultuous trial run in Boston overseen by the playwright. It won him the Pulitzer and New York Drama Critics Award, but he turned the Pulitzer down. See Preface to SMI. *T.L. 26*

THE RUSSIAN SINGER

In *HW*, June 10, 1938. Not republished. *T.L. 27*

DEATH

In *HW*, June 17, 1938. The story appeared with a linoleum cut by Boston artist Dertad Boyajian. Saroyan ("Conversation with Tashjian"): "This story was told to me not by the painter, but by a close friend. It is a totally real story . . . death is very real." Not republished. *T.L. 28*

THE YOUNG HUSBAND AND FATHER

In *HW*, June 24, 1938. This is an "Aram" story, not an "Uncle Aslan" tale, despite the occurrence of that name. Saroyan ("Conversation with Tashjian"): "I recall I wrote that one as an Aram Garoghlanian story after something that happened in Fresno to another Armenian, not related to us. It's all the same." Not republished. *T.L. 29*

THE HOURS OF DAY AND THE HOURS OF NIGHT

In *HW*, July 1, 1938. His submission letter of May 3, (SMI, pp. 255, 257) refers to this piece as having a subdesignation "A Prose Poem," but *HW*, for some reason today unknown, did not add this under the principal title. Not republished. *T.L. 30*

THE BODY

In *HW*, July 1, 1938. In his submission letter of May 16, 1938, (SMI, Letter 12), Saroyan notes this as one of twelve stories submitted to *HW*: "I sincerely trust that you will not be displeased with my sending a large batch of pieces, some recent, some rather old. I feel myself that each piece is definitely worthy of publication, and that some of the pieces are very important . . ." Not republished. *T.L. 31*

THE COMIC PAGE AND VITAL STATISTICS

In *HW*, August 12, 1938. One of twelve pieces mentioned above. The "comical men" of course were Franklin Delano Roosevelt ("the great

Democrat"), Hitler ("the great German with the small moustache"), Mussolini ("the stark-faced Italian"), Stalin ("the bovine-eyed Russian"), and Kemal Ataturk ("the dissipated Turk"), who was to die Nov. 10, 1938. Not republished. *T.L. 32*

WHAT YOU GET FOR TRYING YOUR BEST, IF ANYTHING

In *HW*, August 19, 1938. (SMI, Letter 12, as above.) Another of the twelve pieces, and a specimen from Saroyan's "philosophical period," at its height in 1938. Note his reference to "a manufacturer of movies": in 1936 Saroyan had been employed by producer B. P. Schulberg, for whom he did scriptwriting. Not republished. *T.L. 33*

A NICE OLD-FASHIONED ROMANCE WITH LOVE LYRICS AND EVERYTHING

In *HW*, August 26, 1938. In a letter dated August 22, 1938, (SMI, Letter 19, p. 263) Saroyan reports that this story was to be published in his *A Native American* (1938), "a limited edition book. This will be only 450 copies, each signed. . . . All stories are about Aram Garoghlanian and his family . . ." The story was republished in the above-mentioned work, now a rarity, and appeared again later in *My Name is Aram* (1940). *T.L. 34*

1924 CADILLAC FOR SALE

In *HW*, September 2, 1938. Republished in *Peace, It's Wonderful* (1939) and *The Saroyan Special* (1948). Saroyan ("Conversation with Tashjian"): "It's an easy story written easily and pleasantly. I often reread it, and it brings many smiles to my face . . . and memories." *T.L. 35*

THE FIRST DAY OF SUMMER

In *HW*, September 16, 1938. Among the twelve stories sent to *HW* May 16, 1938. The writer "Joe" is of course Saroyan himself, and the story is palpably an outlet for WS to get some things off his chest in relation to his 1935 tour of Europe and, especially, the Soviet Union. It points east and west—for instance, it emerges that Saroyan has no love for Edmund Wilson, in his day a top American Marxist critic, whom he had met in Moscow in 1935 deep in his game of cops and robbers, a game in which "Joe" refused to take part. Wilson often commented on Saroyan's writings. See Howard Floan, *William Saroyan* (New York: Twayne, 1966, pp. 32, 36, 156, 163, 167; also see Saroyan's *Obituaries* (1979), p. 321. Not republished. *T.L. 36*

OF LOVE AND TIME

In *HW*, September 23, 1938. Not republished. *T.L. 37*

PIANO

In *HW*, September 30, 1938. (SMI, Letter 12, as above.) Letter 12 bears a couple of puzzlements. Its listing of twelve new pieces being sent to *HW* has, as Number 6, a short story titled "Advertisment" but a search of the *HW* files has yielded no story bearing this title; and, similarly, Number 9—"Of Love and Money"—cannot be found in *HW*. It may be that these lost stories were in fact never received at *HW*. Saroyan was a notoriously poor clerk, and it's possible he simply neglected to include the stories in the package. He never inquired of the editor as to the disposition of these two pieces. "Piano" was republished in *Peace, It's Wonderful* (1939), *The Saroyan Special* (1948), and in *The Man With the Heart in the Highlands and Other Stories* (1968), in which (p. 207) Saroyan notes: "I have always considered the piano as one of the greatest pieces of architecture and sculpture devised by man, forgetting its usage and what it's for and can be made to do. Everybody has unfulfilled ambitions; one of the best of an assortment I have always had was to be able to sit at a piano and play great music—my own. And I have never been able to do any such thing. But the very sight of a piano pleases me deeply, and the knowledge that a funny-looking concert pianist named de Pachman [*sic*] used to talk to the audience about the music he was playing and the superb manner in which he was playing it has always made me feel a special admiration for the influence of the piano on the human race. Wherever I have lived, even for a short time, I have tried to have a piano or a pianola in the place—to see, if nothing else. And I have had in mind doing the book of a musical comedy called *Piano*, because I know it would have to be something great." Saroyan's first piece in Haireniks was his verse on the subject of the Armenian folk song "Mayr Araksie" (*T.L. 1*) as sung by Armenak Shah-Mouradian, a magnificent Armenian tenor, whose art is still revered by Armenians through the agency of now scratchy represses of his original discs which, however, still effectively—and nostalgically— project the folk and patriotic music of the Armenian nation. Of course, Saroyan is not talking exclusively of the piano and its products, but is indicating the influence of folk and other music on him and his work. Perhaps one of the more memorable moments in Saroyan theater was Walter Huston's raspy rendition of Saroyan lyrics and tunes in *Love's Old Sweet Song* (1940), a work which Saroyan characterized as "a song from beginning to end." His less successful play *Sam the Highest Jumper of Them All* (1960) had four Saroyan lyrics and tunes. His first popularly read story, *The Daring Young Man on the Flying Trapeze* (1934) was of course a reflection of the ballad bearing the same title. Saroyan was a popular-music addict, but he admired equally the classical genre as manifested, for example, by his interpolation of Gabriel Fauré's "Impromptu for Harp" into his *Across the Board on Tomorrow Morning* (1942). Saroyan ("Conversation with Tashjian"): "One of the first things I bought when I sewed up the holes in my pockets was a victrola and, naturally, I needed records so I started buying, without any discipline, works of Beethoven (especially his piano music), Mozart, Grieg, Sibelius, Rimsky-Korsakov, Janáček, Rossini (I wore out his anthem 'O Italia, Italia, Beloved'—do you know that one?), and then discovered Smetana's 'The Moldau,' which has always spun me back to our own Armenia and our own Araxes river. Was it composed by a Czech? The guy must have had something Armenian in him, or is it that I discovered from him and the others that the theme of love for the fatherland is universal to man? [Here Saroyan leaped to his feet, raised his arms and, to my amazement, assumed the stance of a conductor leading an orchestra. Waving his arms wildly, he began "conducting" and bellowing "The Moldau"—"da-da-da-da-da-de-de/ da—da, da, de/ da—"—and without altering the 4/4 cadence, or key, struck out into "Mayr Araksie aperov. . . ." Saroyan's affection for the musical idiom of the Armenian people often as spontaneously asserted itself elsewhere. We are told that once, while delivering a "lecture" before an Armenian group, Saroyan suddenly blurted out, "To hell with all this. Let us sing and let us dance . . . ," breaking out in his boisterous Bitlis baritone in the bucolic "Khntsorin dzarin daguh" (Under the Apple Tree), and spiritedly, if not wildly, leading a sinuous queue of delighted but astonished Armenians, joined together at their pinkies, in the traditional Armenian 1–2, 1–2 . . . and, of course, end of "lecture." The best-known Saroyan foray into music was, however, the 1951 hit song "Come On-a My House," which bore Saroyan's famous "easter-egg" lyrics to music composed by his actor-musician cousin Ross Bagdasarian. In his *Obituaries* (1979, p. 129 *et seq.*), Saroyan regrets the passing of Betty Clooney and then proceeds to give us his kind-of-history of the origins of the ditty:

Her [Betty's older] sister Rosemary Clooney belted out a song I wrote with my cousin Ross Bagdasarian, and the song became an instant hit. The year was 1951, I believe. My kid cousin and I had written the song in 1939 . . . on a drive from New York to Fresno in November of 1939 we put words to half-forgotten Armenian folk songs, and found that some of these fittings were amusing enough to think about not forgetting forever . . . The one that I insisted we must not forget was based upon an Armenian immigrant's invitation to a non-Armenian girl he had fallen in love with: "Come on-a my house," which approximated the accent of the man who, in the song, enumerated the good things he would give the girl. The music is not unlike a yelp of longing, consequently the words are haphazard, helpless, and a little wild: "I'm a-gonna give you candy" to begin with, and then a few other things: peach, pear, Easter Egg, Christmas Tree, pomegranate, phonograph, and then finally he

says, "Come on-a my house, I'm a-gonna give you my house." In
short, marriage . . .

The recording sold three-quarters of a million copies, had fifteen different pressings, was cut in Spanish, French, Armenian and Yiddish
versions, and was widely used by other vocalists of the day. Saroyan's
"de Pachman" (sic) was of course the prominent but eccentric pianist
Vladimir de Pachmann, known in his day not only for his virtuosity but
for his habit of audibly commenting on his music and performance, to
the delight, or fury, of his concert audience—i.e., "Akh, Pachmann, that
was brilliant"! In HW, May 10, 1940, Saroyan is reported to have told an
interviewer, "I wanted to be a pianist but became a teletype operator
before I succeeded as a writer," and still later ("Conversation with
Tashjian"), he noted, "I'm really a musician, just listen to my prose.
When I was a kid living on I Street, in Fresno, I believe, I used to sit at our
piano and talk to it, as if I were playing it . . . I remember that big black
piano fondly. I can't say how it was that we had it, but it is true that an
Armenian will go without his bread to feed his culture—or something
like that. We were poor, but we still had our piano and our Gramophone
which I would wind up to grind out those old 'O-d-e-o-n Rekkords' . . ."
T.L. 38

THE JOB
    In HW, October 21, 1938. Republished in The Trouble With Tigers [1938],
and in The Saroyan Special (1948) without however any acknowledgment
of its earliest publication in HW. It received still another republication in
Saroyan's My Kind of Crazy, Wonderful People: Seventeen Stories and a Play
(1966), with certain adjustments and resettings into scenes. The scene of
the story is of course San Francisco. T.L. 39

AT THE CHOP SUEY JOINT ON LARKIN
STREET AT TWO-THIRTY IN THE MORNING
    In HW, October 28, 1938. Listed as story Number 11 in that group of
twelve pieces (SMI, Letter 12). Republished in Peace, It's Wonderful (1939).
A "Frisco" jobless story. T.L. 40

A FLASH OF THE FLASHLIGHT AND THE
WORLD-SHAKING QUESTION: "JOE?"
    In HW, November 4, 1938. This beautiful piece may be regarded as an
"Aram" tale. Not republished. T.L. 41

THE RIDE ON THE GREAT HIGHWAY IN THE
SKY OF THE SINKING SUN
    In HW, November 11, 1938. SMI, p. 342, erroneously lists its title as "A
Ride . . ." rather than "The Ride . . .", as borne by the published story.

As noted, this descriptive piece was written at Carl Street, October 17, 1938. Not republished. *T.L. 42*

Seven Easy Ways to Make a Million Dollars

In *HW*, November 18, 1938. Not republished. *T.L. 43*

Genesis

In *HW*, November 25, 1938. This story is first mentioned in the letter of May 16 (SMI, Letter 12, p. 258), as among twelve stories sent to *HW* that date, but there the title is rendered "Genesis: Or: God's Only Begotten Son." But in a later letter Saroyan asked that the story title be reduced simply to "Genesis," which it was on publication. This somewhat uncharacteristic story is of course a spoof of the scientific theory of the creation of man, which amused WS. Not republished. *T.L. 44*

Problems of Writing

In *HW*, December 2, 1938. In a letter dated November 21, 1938, Carl Street, SMI, Letter 31, pp. 275–76, WS says: "Lately, I want to say a few words to the new writers [of *HW*] on the technical problems of writing; but most of all I want to stress simplicity and brevity. As they grow, and as they master the technical problems of writing, they will know how to do effectively the things which if they attempt to do now usually prove unsuccessful. I may even write a few words for them just as soon as I close this letter; in which case I will send it along." Originally catalogued (SMI, p. 344) as Number 103 under "Miscellaneous Writings." Benchley and Nathan, whom Saroyan admired, could not have done this better. Not republished. *T.L. 44a*

The Empty House

In *HW*, December 2, 1938. Not republished. *T.L. 45*

Notes

In *HW*, December 9, 1938. WS had a habit of jotting down thoughts and impressions as he raced through his turbulent life, storing them away for possible use in works to come, in conformity with the advice he gave young writers. On the evidence of his reference to the final days of the year, Saroyan probably wrote this just shortly before submitting it. Not republished. *T.L. 46*

The Mouse

In *HW*, December 16, 1938. SMI, Letter 12 included this story among the twelve sent on that date, but at Saroyan's request later submissions were published ahead of it. Saroyan ("Conversation with Tashjian"): "I've always loved this story. It's real. It happened during those days I was broke in San Francisco. I was broke because of my crazy choices of horses at the race track—and I saw this thing happen to The Mouse. I didn't like it, but I was not the Harry of the story who avenged The Mouse. I should have been, but I chickened out. The guy was bigger than me, and this was simply another occasion of my playing the wrong odds. I needed a winner those days, but I blew it again. By the way, this Harry, the hero, was an Armenian. I have forgotten his name, but he was a guy from Moush, and Moushetsi's don't take any crap from anyone, as you know." Republished in *Peace, It's Wonderful* (1939). *T.L. 47*

California

In *HW*, December 30, 1938. In 1938 Saroyan published twenty-nine pieces in *HW*; his second most productive year with *HW* was 1939, when twenty-seven Saroyans appeared there. Saroyan ("Conversation with Tashjian"): "In San Francisco, sometime around the early thirties, I actually thought of selling pianos, but nothing came of it since dealers quickly discovered I couldn't play a note, so how could I demonstrate them? So I continued to admire them, that's all." Unrepublished. *T.L. 48*

A Moment of Prose in Kansas

In *HW*, January 6, 1939. SMI, Letter 14, dated May 18, 1939, Carl Street, pp. 259–260. Among the twelve stories sent on that date. The story is based at least somewhat on a true-life experience. Saroyan (*Here Comes/There Goes You Know Who*, p. 21): "In 1928 I was obliged to go from San Francisco to New York . . . When I say I was obliged to go from San Francisco to New York, you may imagine that I was sent on a matter of great importance. No such thing. I didn't even have the bus fare, which was $38 in those days, but my father's younger brother Mihran loaned me the money. As a matter of fact he loaned me $200 . . . The bus bounced in a ditch in Kansas and fell on its side . . .", etc. As he says, the incident occurred in August of 1928, while Saroyan was bound for New York "to interest someone, anyone in my work" and to seek employment to support his ambition. We will probably never know if "the girl" of this story really existed. If she did, Saroyan wrote of her twelve years after the bus mishap—belatedly fulfilling his promise to "the girl." See "A Holy Silence," where Saroyan refers to a girl named "Maud, who was a child in a field of Kansas wheat," perhaps ["the girl"] of this story. Not republished, but twice asterisked by O'Brien in 1940. This is the second of a "Kansas series" of three stories, the third being "A Holy Silence." The first, "Two Days Wasted in Kansas City," appeared in *Inhale and Exhale* (1936) and was built around "a little girl," a streetwalker, Saroyan saw while shooting craps in Kansas City. It too dates to August 1928. *T.L. 49*

A Holy Silence

In *HW*, January 13, 1939. Not republished, but cited with three asterisks (highest honors) in the 1940 O'Brien anthology. *T.L. 50*

The Europa Club

In *HW*, January 20, 1939. Republished later in the same year in *Peace, It's Wonderful*. Received one asterisk in the 1940 O'Brien anthology. *T.L. 51*

The Unpublished Writer, Rain, and His Daughter

In *HW*, January 27, 1939. Not republished. *T.L. 52*

The Word

In *HW*, February 3, 1939. Saroyan here expresses his penchant to act the maverick, the freethinker, which leads him, against his will, to suppress the conventional, if not conservative, traits he knows reside deep within him. Saroyan ("Conversation with Tashjian"): "Now, I am different, and that is the way it must be. Each person must be different from all others. What a helluva gray world this would be if we all thought alike—a world of homogenized Milquetoasts! Why don't we all *look* alike that we are asked to *think* alike? But my difference has never been understood, and I'm not sure I understand it myself. I've done many mad things in my life, but something in me drives me to do such things. I regret my *having* to do them. It isn't easy for me to be me. I have always been in full rebellion against the world, *and* myself, But—and this is something crucial about me—there are *convictions* and *beliefs* within me which, were I to allow myself to express them, would type me as more of a conservative, a religious man, than anything else. Is it because I am Armenian . . . haven't the Armenians always been believers . . . ? Say, do you know anything about atavism? Tell me what you know!" Saroyan usually acted the stereotypical intellectual liberal. He was fervently opposed to war and violence, although when his own toes were stepped on, he would drop Gandhi's "passive resistance," which he so admired, and would raise Cain, which is a typical practice among most men, even those of non-belligerent principles, when personally affronted. He deplored poverty and want, which he himself had experienced, and scorned the affluent; and yet he readily sought and accepted enormous fees for his works, banked very little of his earnings and sank a good deal into the pleasures of the rich. He buffooned the so-called "qualities of greatness," and he was cynical of society in general, although he firmly believed that, individually, people were essentially good. He would bridle, however, when anyone tried to characterize him as a "humanist." Saroyan ("Conversation with Tashjian"): "In the first place, I'm not sure what the word [humanist] means. Are you? I looked it up in the *Collegiate* once and found the word absurd. Sure, I deal with humans, but so did Stalin, Hitler, Mussolini, Tamerlane and Cromwell. Were they 'humanists' because they swore that the evil they were doing was after all for the good of the human race? Didn't Talaat [the Turkish immolator] argue that in exterminating the Armenians he was benefiting both the Turks and other humans? Now, this man said he was a 'humanist,' so why place me in such company? I ask no one to define what I am. The fact is I am simply William Saroyan, I represent only what *I* am, there may be no other like me, and if I am a 'humanist,' it is only in terms of *my* understanding of myself—and the term. Classifications are usually meaningless, anyway, and nobody is an expert on anybody else, just as nobody is an expert on himself. I've never understood myself, so how can anyone else understand me? If I have a philosophy, it has to be sought for in my writings; but such a search will usually get the seeker nowhere. But no harm done; let people class me anyway they wish. Let them have their fun. The only thing I won't stand for is they're forgetting that Bill Saroyan is Armenian. I guess I'm not a typical Armenian in the way I live, but you've got to admit that I always come out an Armenian." This unrepublished piece must not of course be confused with Chapter VII of his *Here Comes/There Goes Your Know Who,* similarly titled "The Word." *T.L. 53*

1933

In *HW,* February 24, 1939. This story represents a Saroyan memory of his trying years before the appearance in *HD,* in May 1933, of his first short stories—before, that is, Foley and Burnett saw his work and projected him into prominence. The scene is Fresno in April 1933. Not republished. *T.L. 54*

THE NEW ARRIVALS (A PLAY)

In *HW,* March 3, 1939. Clearly, the *second* Saroyan play to be published anywhere (the first being "Now Is the Time: A Sideshow of the World Today," in *HW,* June 3, 1938). Saroyan's first *produced* play, *My Heart's in the Highlands,* was not to be performed until April 1939. Saroyan ("Conversation with Tashjian"): "The *Weekly* [*HW*] published this play as a straight short story, but it was my fault, I didn't indicate it on the manuscript as a little play, but no matter." The Melikians of Fresno were Saroyan kin, and Saroyan's cousin, John Melikian, wrote a number of short stories for *HW.* Not republished.

THE SONG

In *HW,* March 10, 1939. Obviously, an "Aram" story. The scene is Armenian Town, Fresno. Not republished, but received one asterisk in O'Brien's 1940 anthology. *T.L. 56*

LIFE, THE MAGAZINE, AND HARRY, THE POLO MAN WHO DIDN'T
MAKE THE TEAM
   In *HW*, March 17, 1939. Not republished. *T.L. 57*

THE FABLE OF THE WAR BETWEEN THE OLD COMPLEX AND THE
NEW CULTURE
   In *HW*, March 24, 1939. Saroyan was of course an almost totally self-
educated man, his highest degree of formal education being his two
years of high school where (Saroyan: "Conversation with Tashjian") "I
majored in typing and minored in boredom, a condition which I soon
bettered by simply leaving school. I had discovered the Fresno library,
and it seemed to me there was more there to interest me than at McLane
(high school). I first saw the Harvard Classics there and when, on
Sundays, I would note in the papers that the Harvard football team had
lost another one, I would say to myself, 'Well, at least they have the
Classics.' " Saroyan's terminating credo—"it's no use kidding [our-
selves] any more: culture and poverty and years of democratic slavery
just naturally don't mix, that's all"—is echoed in many of his other
works. Not republished. *T.L. 58*

THE LONG WAY TO TIPPERARY
   In *HW*, April 7, 1939. This story had its genesis in 1919 (*viz.*, "twenty
years ago") when Saroyan was eleven years of age and is obviously a
memory of those Fresno days. Saroyan ("Conversation with Tashjian"):
"I've always had good luck with the Irish—and the song 'The Long Way
to Tipperary' is one of my whistling songs. Reminds me of the war years
in Fresno—which was far enough from the front to warrant people
whistling. Ireland I have always admired because it has somehow
produced a colorful, and often happy, culture in the face of years of
oppression—much like Armenia and the Armenians. Anyway, I've
always liked green, and I have been told that anciently green was the
color of Armenian culture, which probably explains somewhat my
partiality to the Irish. I remember some years ago reading in some issue
of the *Weekly* [*HW*] a story which suggested racial and cultural affinities
between the Irish and the Armenians. That's it. I said, that's why we are
alike. It's all to the good." Saroyan's 1939 ambition to see Erin was
fulfilled later in the same year. Alas, we don't know if he was uplifted or
disappointed by what he saw. Not republished. *T.L. 59*

THE LIFE
   In *HW*, April 14, 1939. At Saroyan's request, this brief piece was
republished in *TAR* (see T.L. 119) in 1963, his last creative contribution to
the Haireniks. No other republication. *T.L. 60 and T.L. 119*

Cuba Libre

In *HW*, August 18, 1939. A letter dated August 8, 1939, from his new address, 1821 Fifteenth Avenue, San Francisco (SMI Letter 40, p. 289) reports enclosure of this story. The piece appears to have been written in San Francisco before Saroyan's return from a summer trip abroad [1939], which had taken him to London, Dublin and Paris, or before Saroyan became an international rage through the Broadway production of his play (in October 1939), the Pulitzer Prize-winning *The Time of Your Life*. In his letter Saroyan reported, "I am in a new house, which I am buying for my mother and sister [Zabel] and myself too of course. F.H.A. I am not settled yet, but everything is getting a little closer to what it should be every day. Anyway, in getting my manuscripts in order I have come across some fairly new, and some old but good stories which I feel you might like to publish in Hairenik." He then lists the stories being submitted, which include the next two entries. "Cuba Libre" was never republished. *T.L. 61*

The Last Supper

In *HW*, August 25, 1939. The second story sent in under cover of SMI, Letter 40. An allegorical story probably written in the late 1920s, during Saroyan's days of struggle in San Francisco. Not republished, but O'Brien, in the 1940 anthology, gives this story three asterisks. *T.L. 62*

The Three Instructions; and the Evil Step-Mother and the Beautiful Step-Daughter

In *HW*, September 8, 1939. See SMI, Letter 40, as above. This leads us into the matter of a number of Saroyan "fables" which were originally published in *HW*, as will be shown as we go along, and later collected and republished, along with a few others, in *Saroyan's Fables* (1941), a work which represents a veritable anthology of *HW* materials. This book bears the sub-legend "with illustrations by Warren Chappell" (New York: Harcourt, Brace and Company, 1941, 90 pp.). It is dedicated to "My Uncle Aram Saroyan" (obviously at a time when WS was on good terms with his uncle). *Saroyan's Fables* contains twenty-seven fables. Its flyleaf carries this notice: "Being a Handful of Old Armenian Stories Remembered by His Relatives From the Old Country, Set Down in Very Simple English, as Well as Several Stories About a Number of Young and Old Armenians of His Home Town, Fresno, California, Set to Paper for the First Time in Any Language"—in the best traditions, of course, of Aesop, Chaucer and Boccaccio. It terminates in this fashion: "This First Edition [there were no others—JHT] of SAROYAN'S FABLES, embellished by five wood engravings by Warren Chappell has been set in 18 point Caslon Old Face. One thousand copies have been printed from type by Huxley House, in New York City, in the year ONE HUNDRED AND

FORTY-ONE A.D. and signed by the author." Of the twenty-seven pieces in this now coveted autograph edition, nineteen were fables originally published in *HW* as seven units (only two *HW* fables were not used). "The Three Instructions . . ." appeared in *Saroyan's Fables* (p. 81, *et seq.*) under the title: "XXVI. My Grandmother Lucy's Magnificent Parable of the Three Instructions, and How They Brought the Half-wit Husband Home to His Utterly Unattractive Wife After Eighteen Long Years and How I Think He Could Have Used a Fourth Instruction." It is one of three "Lucy tales" in the volume. The only other fable published in *HW* and later republished in *Saroyan's Fables* ascribed to a personal source was one told WS by his uncle Aram (*viz.*, Fable II., p. 3). But Saroyan's ascription of his sources was simplistic; he elides over the assistance given him in the compilation of his *Fables* by the editors of *HW*. In SMI, Letter 22, dated September 8, 1938, Carl Street, p. 268, Saroyan reveals earliest that he is toying with the idea of writing some pieces akin to "fables": ". . . Let me ask a favor; will you send me any Armenian (or Kurdish) proverbs you know? translate them literally; and ask old-timers you know, and others as Hairenik to do the same; I want to collect as many of these proverbs as possible; put them in living English [in the book, Saroyan says "Simple English"] (American) and ultimately to use them in a small book: a special book." Obviously, *HW* complied, for, in Letter 27, dated October 12, 1938, Carl Street, p. 271, Saroyan writes: "Thanks very much for sending me the booklet [of fables]. I think eventually a collection of all available (or remembered) Armenian proverbs should be published in English. (Keep this in mind for a later date.) The German book of Kurdish proverbs should also be kept in mind. . . ." The reference here to an edition of *Armenian* and Kurdish fables compiled in German by the Armenian-German scholar Professor Manoog Abeghian of Leipzig University, a copy of which the *HW* editors also provided WS. Identification of all *HW* materials found in *Saroyan's Fables* will be made as we go along. The terminating portion of "The Three Instructions . . .," beginning with the line "My grandmother told me this story . . .," to the end, was omitted in the book; this portion was however republished as an independent fable (*Saroyan's Fables*, p. 89) under the title "XXVII. The Lovely Thing That Happened to the Beautiful Step-Daughter Who was Cemented into the Tower by the Bad Step-Mother." While we are at it, something more ought to be said about WS's relations with his uncle Aram, who related one of Saroyan's "fables," and who undoubtedly had a curiously two-edged influence on Saroyan—a relationship at one time widely discussed in Armenian circles. In *Here Comes/There Goes You Know Who* (p. 51), Saroyan comments:

> My mother's kid brother, Aram, the success, or Aram the Successful, the Criminal Lawyer, the Grape Shipper, the Vineyardist, the

Orator, the National Patriot, was quite simply the greatest man in my family insofar as making out in the world was concerned, and on the other the most arrogant, impatient, irritable, unreasonable, unpredictable, and generally preposterous man I had ever met. All the same I liked him, and died laughing (as we used to say) at the stories he told . . . it was probably inevitable that Aram and I would have a lot of laughs together, and so of course it came to pass . . . we had fallings out, and sometimes they were loud and unintentionally funny.

Elsewhere (p. 56), WS adds that when he was fifteen years of age (1923), he went to work at one of Aram's vineyards, and adds (pp. 62, 64):

It was June, 1926. Soon I'd be eighteen years old, but still I was in Fresno, which I now hated . . . [He goes to work in Uncle Aram's law office, but when he tells his uncle he wants to get out of town, Aram tells him], You're a disgrace to my family. To my sister. To the Saroyan family. Now get out of here . . .

And so it was that WS left for Los Angeles, worked three days at Bullock's department store, moved on to San Francisco, occasionally visited Fresno, and found work at the Postal Telegraph office in Frisco (ibid, pp. 61, 64, 77), carrying on the while a long-distance duel with Uncle Aram, who accepted him warmly (and readily) only after Saroyan was "no longer a disgrace to my family . . ." that is, when Saroyan had become a successful writer. *T.L. 63*

THE THEATER OF WAR

In *HW*, September 15, 1939. In a letter dated September 8, 1939, place not designated (SMI Letter 42, p. 286) Saroyan urgently asks that *HW* "publish this story as soon as possible." Saroyan's play *The Time of Your Life* was written about this time, in six days, at the Great Northern Hotel, New York. Saroyan ("Conversation with Tashjian") was not sure if "The Theater of War" had been the inspiration for his play, or had been inspired by it: "Those were bang-bang days, and I can't get the sequence straight in my mind." Republished (November 27, 1939) in *The Time of Your Life and Miscellaneous Essays*. Saroyan opens this story with the line "This is a play," but the writing is not in conventional play form. *T.L. 64*

OLD COUNTRY STORIES, PART I

In *HW*, September 22, 1939. A series of three "fables." The first—"The Poor Man"—was republished in *Saroyan's Fables* (1941), p. 63, as: "XX. The Severe but Instructive Words that were Said to the Poor Man Who was Under the Impression that Being Poor Entitled Him Also to be Slovenly, Which Even a Couple of Centuries Ago was Regarded as Nonsense"; Number 3—"The Socially Ambitious Wife and the Simple Cobbler"—was republished in the same work (p. 67) as: "XXII. How Difficult it is for a Man to Enjoy Living if His Wife is Socially Ambitious and Goes Around Telling Fantastic Lies About His Clairvoyant Powers, and How One Poor Cobbler Got Out of the Awful Mess"; Number 2— "The Watermelon Eater"—is one of the only two *HW* fables not republished in *Saroyan's Fables*. *T.L. 65*

Two Old Country Armenian Stories, and One New One

In *HW*, September 29, 1939. See SMI, Letter 44, dated September 18, 1939, Fifteenth Avenue; p. 288. Number 1—"The Dishonest Traders"— was republished in *Saroyan's Fables* (1941), p. 51, as: "XVII. How the Dishonest Traders Outwitted Each Other but Died in the End Nevertheless and Unwittingly Caused Little Children to Thank God for Flowers"; Number 2—"The Man Who always Said Praise The Wisdom of God"— republished in *Saroyan's Fables*, p. 55, as: "XVIII. What Happened to the Wise Guys Who Scoffed at the Family Man Whose Faith was so Great that even in Tragedy He said, Praise God, He Knows What He is Doing"; Number 3—"The Man Who Prayed Confidentially"—republished in *Saroyan's Fables*, p. 58, as: "XIX. One of the Long and Confidential Prayers the Religious Old Armenian of Fresno Used to Make Every Wednesday Night at the First Presbyterian Church About Twenty Years Ago, and How Empty the World is Without Him." *T.L. 66*

Axis

In *HW*, October 6, 1939. The word "maniagg" is certainly a Saroyanesque dialectical play on "maniac." Armenian, Turkish and Arabic words sounding like this patently do not describe the characteristics of Mr. Pragg, "the slave-driver" boss. Not republished, but cited with one asterisk in the 1940 O'Brien anthology. *T.L. 67*

Four Little Armenian Stories

In *HW*, October 13, 1939. Number I was reprinted in *Saroyan's Fables* (1941), p. 75, as: "XXIII. What the Priest Said to the Assassin Who Had Broken the Standard Rules for Inhuman Behavior"; Number II (ibid, p. 76), as: "XXIV. How the Hair of Women is Long, the Understanding Short, and What a Ghastly Lack of Appreciation There is in Them for Genius" (reprinted still later in Karen Kennedy, *Hesitant Wolf and Scrupulous Fox: Fables Selected from World Literature*, New York: Random House, 1973, p. 52); Number IV (ibid, p. 77), as: "XXV. The Problem of the Unhappy Little Boy Whose Father Regarded Him as a Child, Instead of a Personality, Little Suspecting that Anyone Capable of Knowing Sorrow is Ageless and Will Therefore Refuse to Have a Wounded Heart Healed by a Kewpie Doll." Number 3—"When the Cow Came . . ."—was not republished in *Saroyan's Fables*, or anywhere else. *T.L. 68*

THE GREAT DAY COMING (A PLAY)

In *HW*, October 20, 1939. Bears subtitle, "A Fragment of a Play." This early play was written by WS in his San Francisco period and was dug out by Saroyan during his reassessment of his manuscripts when he moved to his Fifteenth Avenue address in San Francisco. The *HW* published it about the time *The Time of Your Life* was appearing on Broadway, and after it had had its trial run in Boston in early October 1939, on which see SMI, Letter 47, dated Oct. 2, 1939, Fifteenth Avenue, p. 280. On the historical sequence of Saroyan's pre–*Time of Your Life* plays, see T.L. 26 and 55. Not republished and, as far as is known, never produced. *T.L. 69*

TWO LONG NOVELS, CONDENSED

In *HW*, October 27, 1939. Undoubtedly one of "two more pieces attached" cited without titles (the other probably "Lauri"). A letter dated October 2, 1939, (SMI, Letter 47, p. 289). *T.L. 70*

LAURI

In *HW*, November 3, 1939. Page datings of this *HW* issue read "October 27, 1939," but the masthead dating of November 3 is correct. This is a sort of "Aram" story. To our knowledge, Saroyan never fulfilled his inclination to tell us something more about this "simple" but "immortal" man, his "cousin Lauri." ("Lori" is the name of a celebrated environment in historical Armenia.) Not republished, but given two asterisks by O'Brien in 1940. *T.L. 91*

THE BOY FROM KINGSBURG

In *HW*, November 24, 1939, which in error titles this story "The Boy from Kingsbury." Submitted with a letter dated June 14, 1939, from Hotel Great Northern, New York City (SMI, Letter 41, p. 286). This story must have been written during the six days WS spent composing *The Time of Your Life* at the same hotel. Letter 41 says: "I am sending you herewith one more story, to be published after the material with you is disposed of . . ." Saroyan apparently transposed the scene of this autobiographical story to Kingsburg, a small California town of important Armenian context, from his own native Fresno. Saroyan ("Conversation with Tashjian"): "I've always cared for that story. It mostly happened. I can't recall the girl's name but, no harm done, she existed— and I hope she still exists and has a dozen kids, and a half-dozen grand-kids. She deserves it. In San Francisco, I tried selling books at a place in the Powell Street area before I hooked on with Postal Telegraph [1927], but I thought it was absurd selling books by others and not me, so I quit. Another stroke of good fortune was not finding a job with a newspaper, although I had enjoyed thoughts of becoming another Richard Harding Davis—is that right? Writing newspaper stuff would have destroyed me; I would have had to use the newspaper jargon—'Observers say the firemen got there late and twelve people were incinerated because the firemen were shooting craps in the firehouse'—that sort of immortal stuff." Not republished, but cited with two asterisks in the 1940 O'Brien. *T.L. 72*

OLD COUNTRY STORIES, PART II
In *HW*, December 1, 1939. Four more Saroyan fables. Number 1 was republished in *Saroyan's Fables*, p. 38, as "XIII. The Lies the Bald-Headed Man and the Man with the Running Nose told the Man with the Crooked Leg, in a Small Contest, and What he Said in Reply"; Number 2, in *Saroyan's Fables*, p. 41, as "XIV. How the King Who Wanted to Believe the Blind of His Realm Were Nice People Got Back His Gold Coin from the Blind Thief Who looked Like a Saint but Acted Human Just the Same"; Number 3, in *Saroyan's Fables*, p. 44, as: "XVI. How the Mohammedan Period of Fasting Was Brought to an Official End Because Now and Then Even a Handful of Deaf People are Thrown Together by Humanity for the Purpose of Sending a Little Laughter Down the Ages." *T.L. 73*

MY WITNESS WITNESSETH
In *HW*, December 29, 1939. In SMI (p. 343), this is incorrectly titled "*The* Witness Witnesseth." This is a spirited, if not savage, defense of Saroyan's "experience" writings, then under broad fire by critics. Republished in *Dear Baby* (1944) and *The Saroyan Special* (1948). *T.L. 74*

OLD COUNTRY STORIES, PART III
In *HW*, January 5, 1940. More Saroyan fables, Number 1 of the present set was republished in *Saroyan's Fables*, p. 25, as "X. How the City Slicker Made a Monkey Out of the King Who Thought He Was Too Smart to be Fooled by Anybody, Let Alone a Common Old-Time Pitchman"; Number 2, in *Saroyan's Fables*, p. 28, as "XI. What the Armenian Butcher Said to the Armenian Barber Without Speaking, in the Presence of the Astounded King and the Astounded King's Unastounded but Very Suspicious Spy"; Number 3, in *Saroyan's Fables*, p. 31, as "XII. How the Devil Was Humiliated Three Times by the Young Native of Bitlis Who Never So Much as Went to School." *T.L. 75*

A WORD TO SCOFFERS
In *HW*, February 16, 1940. Republished later in *My Name is Aram* (1940) and, consequently, an "Aram" story—but of Aram (WS) at twenty years

of age, that is when WS visited New York (1928) to try to make his mark. "Gyko" is a term of endearment for "Krikor," which in turn is the English "Gregory"; but it was Saroyan's uncle Mihran who lent him $200 to get out of town and try New York. *T.L. 76*

THE SMALL TROUBLE THAT STARTS AT HOME

In *HW*, March 8, 1940. One of his "Sam the Bartender" stories. The scene is probably San Francisco. Not republished. *T.L. 77*

THE MAN WHO WAS BORN UNDER THE SIGN OF SCORPIO

In *HW*, March 22, 1940. The title over the original *HW* printing of this story had "Scorpia" for "Scorpio", here corrected. The second "Sam the Bartender" piece. Saroyan himself was born under the zodiacal sign of Virgo (August 23–September 22)—on August 31, 1908. Not republished.

OLD COUNTRY STORIES, PART IV

In *HW*, May 10, 1940. "The Scoundrel from Odessa . . ." was republished in *Saroyan's Fables*, p. 15, as "VIII. The Embarrassment that Came to the Crook from Odessa Who Tried to Swindle the Bright Boy of Bitlis"; "The Simple Husband . . .," in *Saroyan's Fables*, p. 17, as "IX. The Tribulations of the Simple Husband Who Wanted Nothing More than to Eat Goose but Was Denied This Delight by his Unfaithful Wife and her Arrogant but Probably Handsome Lover." *The Saroyan Special* (1948) also reprinted this fable (IX) as simply "Saroyan's Fables, IX," as did *The William Saroyan Reader* (1958), there as "Fable IX, from *Saroyan's Fables*. *T.L. 79*

HOW IT IS TO BE

In *HW*, June 21, 1940. Not covered by any WS letter in the *HW* files. Gershwin died in 1937; thus, this story must have been written in San Francisco after that date. Saroyan ("Conversation with Tashjian"): "I met Gershwin, sure enough, at a big party given by some muck-a-muck during one of my trips to New York. Was it 1935? He's the only one I remember at that party, and what I remember of him was his playing his show-tunes on the piano—yes, I remember his playing and his melodies but, alas, I have difficulty in bringing *him* to mind, but no matter, he *was* great. Sibelius? I met him too. In Helsingfors, I believe, some years ago [Sibelius died in 1957]. A *great* man, too. He gave me some recordings of his work, which I cherished." In Saroyan's story "Finlandia" (in *Inhale and Exhale*, 1936) Saroyan talks about meeting Sibelius at the latter's home in Järvenpää, Finland (not Helsingfors), during his first trip abroad. See also T.L. 82, where he reports his possession of a "signed photograph" of Sibelius. Republished in *Dear Baby* (1944) and again in *The Saroyan Special* (1948). *T.L. 80*

A COUPLE OF MISCELLANEOUS PROPHECIES, MORE OR LESS GUARANTEED TO COME TRUE

In *HW*, July 5, 1940. SMI, Letter 52. In his letter dated June 25, 1940 (SMI, Letter 52 from Fifteenth Avenue, pp. 292–293) WS said "At the end of [this] piece be sure the date it was written is published: Oct. 19, 1938. Purely for the record. Most of the pieces I shall send you might require similar dating. . . ." In October 1938, WS was residing on Carl Street where, then, this story was written. Not republished. *T.L. 81*

ANOTHER DAY, ANOTHER DREAM

In *HW*, July 12, 1940. Letter 53, dated June 25, 1940 (SMI, p. 293): "Here are six more pieces. Being old, they have something in common, which I do not feel is a disadvantage. One or two are very good, but there is no use in my going into that, or into one or two of them not being very good. . . . The date of composition should be published after every piece, excepting the first [this "Another Day . . ."]. which begins with the date. . . ." In October 1937, Saroyan was in San Francisco. Not republished. *T.L. 82*

LIBERTY, 5¢

In *HW*, July 26, 1940. One of the six stories sent on June 25 (see above), but date of composition, as such, does not appear in the published story, although we glean from its context that it was written in 1938, obviously in San Francisco. A sort of allegory, its autobiographical "vital facts" are "all screwed up," as Saroyan would have put it. He was however born on "I" Street, Fresno (and not on "H" Street, as some pretend) and, in 1938, was in San Francisco. Not republished. *T.L. 83*

I'M RIGHT. THE WORLD'S WRONG

In *HW*, August 9, 1940. One of the six stories submitted in June. It bears as date of composition August 9, 1938, which means it was done at Carl Street, San Francisco, when WS was indeed thirty years of age. Not republished. *T.L. 84*

MY FINANCIAL EMBARRASSMENT

In *HW*, August 16, 1940. Number four of six stories (see above). It is notable for a few important revelations. WS recalls that his "first short story," entitled "How I Earned My First Dollar," was written when he was "eight years old," which would make it 1916. It was of course nothing more than a school essay and, certainly, was lauded by his teacher, a "Miss Eulalia Pinkerton Washoe," whom WS fondly remembers as opposed to some of his teachers, whom he does not fondly remember in other works. His grandmother was of course Lucy Garoghlanian. The "Paramount Distributing Company," which he reports he and his brother founded when WS was seventeen years old, was launched on its brilliantly brief career in 1925. The reference is to his brother Henry, to whom Saroyan refers in his story as "Krikor." WS never really got over his "financial embarrassment." Not republished. *T.L. 85*

THE WONDERFUL WORLD OF GENIUSES

In *HW*, August 23, 1940. Another of the six T.L. 82 stories. Its date of composition makes it one of his Carl Street, San Francisco, writings. Not republished. *T.L. 86*

HOW THEY GOT RID OF THE UNWELCOME
AND GREEDY VISITOR

In *HW*, August 30, 1940. In his submission letter Saroyan listed this as one of some "old pieces" from his files, but there is no date of composition. Another of the Saroyan fables. Not republished. *T.L. 87*

THE PARACHUTE JUMP

In *HW*, September 13, 1940. Not covered by Saroyan's correspondence in the *HW* files. It bears no date of composition, but was probably done in San Francisco in 1937 or 1938. Not republished. *T.L. 88*

A SURVIVOR OF THE INFLUENZA EPIDEMIC OF 1918

In *HW*, September 20, 1940. More than likely written in 1937 or 1938 during WS's days at Carl Street in San Francisco. In terms of pure narration, I believe it is one of Saroyan's finest efforts. Not republished. *T.L. 89*

THE FRIENDS OF THE MONKEYS

In *HW*, October 11, 1940. Not republished. *T.L. 90*

NOTES OF DAYS GONE BY

In *HW*, November 22, 1940. The last of the six stories sent in with the June 25 letter (see above). "The Eyes and Ears of the World" was written in San Francisco, as noted, on November 23, 1935, after Saroyan's second trip to New York on business. "After the Last War and Before the Next," which bears the May 24, 1936, dating, was putatively written in Hollywood, while he was there employed by producer B. P. Schulberg; the same may be true of "I Thank You." "Memoirs of a Friend of My Father," dated June 11, 1937, seems to have been written during the days when Saroyan was working on his *Little Children* (1937); ditto, "A Life," "Moscow in Tears," "AHF Wien," "Every Last One of Them Was a Fool," and "The Young Man with the Brilliant Imagination." All not republished. *T.L. 91*

MY GRANDMOTHER LUCY TELLS A STORY WITHOUT A BEGINNING, A MIDDLE OR AN END

In *HW*, January 14, 1942. SMI, Letter 59, dedicated December 30, 1941, Fifteenth Avenue, pp. 296–297: "I am at home for a short time before going on to what I hope will be some fresh work; therefore, as it is almost New Year here, it will be the New Year when you get this letter. I am sending you herewith a little story—with many corrections . . . ," a reference to this piece. Much water was at that time washing over Saroyan's dam. In January 1940, his *A Theme in the Life of the Great America Goof* (later to be adapted to American television) opened in New York. In the same year, he received, but rejected, the Pulitzer Prize for the best play of the 1939–40 season and was awarded the New York Drama Critics Circle Award for the same play—*The Time of Your Life*—the first play in American theatrical history awarded both recognitions. In April 1940, his *Love's Old Sweet Song* debuted on Broadway, the same year that *My Name is Aram* saw the first of its many printings. The year 1941 had been just as hectic for Saroyan. In April, he directed and produced on Broadway his play *The Beautiful People* and later, in December, went to Hollywood to do a movie scenario, *The Human Comedy*, which appeared in 1943 in the form of a novel. Saroyan ("Conversation with Tashjian"): "Metro made me an offer—without a beginning, a middle or an end—to do a book for a movie on any idea I chose. My previous experience with Hollywood [1935] had been absurd and I should have turned them down, but I was short of cash, as is customary with me. Well, I decided to give the movies another try. The idea was, apparently, that they were doing me a favor in putting me to work—they had cleverly discovered that I was broke; so they gave me a crib of a room, a typewriter, a cell of a window, and told me to bang away—which I did for a couple of days without getting anything done. Finally, I saw that I wouldn't get anywhere at all if I were to remain in that city and that dungeon, and that I ought to return to civilization as soon as possible. So, I just got up and left, not a word to anyone, and went directly to San Francisco, where I hired a room in a hotel on Powell Street, and went to work. One day a fast-talking lawyer representing Metro came and said I had broken an oral contract with his Hollywood people and that I was about to be sued. For what, I asked? Now, I can't make a long story short, or a short story long. A story is a story, there are so many words in it, and that is that. I told the lawyer that I couldn't do anything but smoke cigarettes down there, and the costs of maintaining the habit in Hollywood had proved prohibitive; but I told him I would meet my 'oral contract' and would have a script ready very shortly. I said, you'll have to get a bailiff to get me out of San Francisco at this time. So he went, and, finally, I produced the scenario of *The Human Comedy*, a tough piece of work, that later became the lousiest movie ever done, in three weeks, between visits to the Kentucky Club [a favorite Saroyan pub]. In examining the finished script, I knew that what we had here was a fine piece of work—one of my best—so I decided that I would break my oath never to visit Hollywood again so that I could take the manuscript to Metro personally and ask $50,000 for it—or nothing. But at this point, something happened, and I raised the ante to $60,000. . . . You are now supposed to ask me the earthshaking question, 'Well, *what* happened'? . . . I had fallen in with this interesting little man who ran a little frame and print shop where I would often find things that would interest me. Just about the time I was ready to take my script to Hollywood, I dropped in on him and found the place all in boxes. I asked, what in hell are you doing? I'm broke, he said, busted, bankrupt and got to close up. Now, I had an obligation to this man. I had been buying prints from him on IOU's and he had been happy to take my word in place of my money—although he had a neat sign over his counter which read 'no credit.' I'm no big giver, as you know, probably because I've never had the ready money to give big, although I always contribute generously to the horse tracks. I asked him, how much do you need? He said, $10,000. Don't close this place, I said, keep it open. Get your junk out of those boxes. Go back to business, I'll be back. That's what happened. When I left him, the price for my script had gone up to $60,000. I took the manuscript to Metro and they read it without talking about money. A couple of days later, one of Hollywood's greatest authorities called me in and said, 'Saroyan, we'll give you $25,000 for that ream of junk, even though we don't know what we'll do with it; we're doing you this favor since we called you, you didn't call us.' I was not impressed at all at his generosity. I asked, 'what's your next best offer?' Not a *sou* more, he said (educated Hollywood people always use 'sou' for 'cent'). When I turned to leave, he said, well, how about 40? Well, he finally went up to 50, that figure I had decided to ask for *before* my visit to my friend's shop, and I said to him, make it 60, I'll *have* to have 60. He said, Why do you have to *have* 60? I said, Never mind why . . . I'll *have* to have 60. Wait a minute, he said, taking my manuscript and starting out. I said, wait a minute, now wait a minute: you're a free man, although I don't know *how free* you are, but leave my script right here on this desk. He finally came back shaking his head, and I said to myself, Well, William, you blew it again. All right, he said, we'll give you 60 but it's a holdup. All right, I said, I'll take the 60, put it on paper. The 'junk' is yours. I'll take my check now. So I left Hollywood as fast as I could, got back to San Francisco, deposited the check, withdrew $10,000, in cash I believe, took the bundle to my friend, handed it over to him and walked out when he told me he would pay me back. Now, there's more to the story, if you're not already bored. I am; but I guess this is what they call biographics for the biographer. Well, the war was on, and I had been classified deferred because I had dependents—

although how I managed to provide for my dependents is a mystery. One day, I got scared by the thought of the $50,000 wasting away in the bank—actually, there were $60,000 through my royalties on *Razzle Dazzle* [published in the spring of 1942], so I thought it would be wise to turn all this money over to my mother, grandmother, and sister [Zabel], rather than to leave it there tempting me to the racetrack and other associated activities, and I did; after which I went to my draft board and told them I was now a dependent of my former dependents, and what were they going to do about it? They did. In July I was reclassified 1-A and was told to stand by for induction. I was called up October 29, 1942, and that is the end of the story. I have referred to these matters in one of my books, but as it often happens, that account may vary here or there with this account, but I'm sure *this* is how it really happened." Investigation proved that the book in question was his *Here Comes/There Goes You Know Who* (1961), where on pp. 199–200, Saroyan gives a tolerably similar account of the story relating to his scenario of *The Human Comedy*. Certain elements of this episode in Saroyan's life were published in the *Philadelphia Evening Bulletin* (March 30, 1942), *The Boston Globe* (July 22, 1942), and the *San Francisco Chronicle* (October 29, 1942), but Saroyan's verbal statement here brings the whole thing together. "My Grandmother Lucy . . ." remains unrepublished.

In his *Letters from rue Taitbout . . .* (1969, p. 159), Saroyan records a sequel to this whole business. He identifies the "movie mogul" with whom he became entangled as the redoubtable L. B. Mayer, of Metro-Goldwyn-Mayer. After returning from the Army, Saroyan recalls, he approached Mayer and offered to pay back to him the $60,000 Saroyan had received for *The Human Comedy* script in order to buy it back. He was turned down:

> I said, "Keep the millions of dollars in profit you made from the phony movie you made of my story. Keep the print. Just let me pay back every cent you paid me, so I can own my own writing again and do what I please with it. No sir," your assistant said, "drop dead, foolish writer."

And Saroyan bitterly adds that Mayer got money too from the television version of *The Human Comedy*.

THE MAN WHO KNEW MY FATHER AS A BOY IN BITLIS

In *HW*, February 25, 1942. No *HW* correspondence on this story. The printing seems correctly to terminate itself, although a continuation is indicated. In fact, the story ends perfectly à la Saroyan. In August 1942, Saroyan both directed and produced on Broadway two plays, *Across the Board on Tomorrow Morning* and *Talking to You*, while his *Hello Out There* opened in New York city in September, almost immediately followed by

Saroyan's induction into military service on October 29, 1942. Saroyan was not again to publish a story in *HW* until May 13, 1954, but he resumed his collaboration with the Haireniks in the winter of 1948 with the inaugural issue of *The Armenian Review*. (In fact WS's role was somewhat more than that of an *amicus familiae* in the conception of *TAR*.) On Saroyan's wartime trials, see SMI, pp. 297–298. Briefly, he married Carol Marcus, of the Bendix fortune, in Ohio in February 1943, while he was a private in the Signal Corps. His immensely popular novel *The Human Comedy* was published in 1943, and his play *Get Away Old Man* was performed on Broadway in November of the same year. His son Aram was born in 1943. *Dear Baby* and *The Adventures of Wesley Jackson* were written and published during Saroyan's army stint, in 1944, which ended with his discharge in September 1945. Saroyan did not resume his correspondence with the Haireniks until March 29, 1946 (SMI, Letter 60 [p. 298], from 2727 Taraval Street, San Francisco, Saroyan's new home), and his daughter Lucy was born in that year. In 1957, WS's new play, *Jim Dandy; Fat Man in a Famine*, was published to the indifference of critics, and Saroyan moved his family to a leased home, a former admiral's mansion in fashionable Mill Neck, near Oyster Bay, Long Island, New York. There his wife and his mother-in-law took over, much to WS's distress—on which see Saroyan's *Places Where I've Done Time* (1972), part 15, "House in Millneck, Long Island, 1947," pp. 45–47, where WS describes, in some wistful prose, his anachronistic presence in a court of high society, ending, "I had six months of high society and then the lease ran out." He published no book-length work in 1948, the year *The Armenian Review* first appeared. Not republished. *T.L. 93*

One Hello and One Goodbye

In *HW*, May 13, 1954. This is the first of four WS stories representing his return to *HW*, from which he had been absent for twelve years. Submitted April 21, 1954, from 24848 Malibu Road, Malibu, California, where the now divorced WS lived in a beach cottage built on stilts (see his *Places Where I've Done Time*, pp. 137–138, and T.L. 112). The boy of the story is his son Aram, the girl, his daughter Lucy. Not republished. *T.L. 94*

A Moment of Freedom and Fun

In *HW*, May 27, 1954. A letter dated April 26, 1954, from Malibu (SMI Letter 74, p. 413) forwards this "slight sketch." Saroyan's children Lucy and Aram are his passengers,.conversants and companions.

Hayastan and Charentz

In *HW*, June 10, 1954 (later republished as T.L. 118, in *TAR*, vol. vii (4–28), December 1954, q.v.) In his letter of May 29, 1954, Malibu (SMI Letter 80, pp. 318–319), which forwards this story, Saroyan writes: "Here

. . . is a very-much revised item for the *Weekly*," that was written on the request of Vahan Navassardian, a Cairo, Egypt, Armenian intellectual, so that it might appear, in translation, in the latter's projected work on the life and career of Yeghishe Charentz, an outstanding Armenian poet who, during the Soviet Armenian phase of the Stalinian purges of 1937–38, lost his life on charges of writing "formalistic" [read "nationalistic"] materials. Saroyan commented in Letter 80: " . . . If I am to write for the Armenian press it is likely to be for Hairenik on general principles, but I prefer my personal politics to be kept out of it, since in the nature of things they must remain pretty much undefined . . . and the world is very small these days, so that more than anything else I am eager not to bring difficulties upon others, unwittingly. Charentz, for instance, had a small son, but in my piece, I have deliberately refrained from mentioning him. And of course many other things as well. I'm sure you understand. . . ." The *HW-TAR* editors understood full well, and "Hayastan and Charentz" ("Armenia and Charentz") was printed without commentary or extrinsics. In 1969, of course, the Khruschevian "rehabilitation of Stalin's victims" was underway in the USSR, and Saroyan felt it safe to dedicate his *Letters from 74 rue Taitbout* . . . to "Yeghishe Charentz, Vahan Totoventz and Gourken Mahari, poets, novelists, and playwrights of Armenia, and to their children and grandchildren." Totoventz had also been executed. In his "Yeghishe Charentz" (ibid., p. 117, *et seq.*), Saroyan deals with unusual candor on the subject of Charentz. See SMI, Preface, on Saroyan's "personal politics." "Hayastan and Charentz" was widely translated and republished in the Armenian press abroad. *T.L. 96 and T.L. 118*

The Gambled Coat

In *HW*, July 1, 1954. This is the *last* Saroyan *story* to appear in *HW*. One of his "Kentucky Club" pieces. The scene is San Francisco, and it represents a memory of his days before he made his mark; it was perhaps written in the early 1930s. Saroyan was inveterately addicted to gambling on horses. From "Conversation with Tashjian": "I guess I'm an Armenian in more than one way. I love horses, my father Armenak, I am told, loved horses, and everyone in Bitlis loved horses . . . [singing] 'Crazy about horses, horses, horses'—you know the ditty. If I had the money I've lost at the horse track I'd be a millionaire now. I once lost $50,000 in two days of God damned madness at a track, and I was wiped out so badly that I tried to get a couple of Armenian millionaires to lend me some cash, but they had become millionaires because they were good businessmen, and they turned me down. I don't blame them. . . ." Reuben Darbinian, the Haireniks editor in chief, and Saroyan's "surrogate father," was advised by the "millionaires" of Saroyan's request to borrow from them, and he concurred with their decision to turn Saroyan down "as a lesson to William to stop throwing his money after the horses." Darbinian identified the millionaires as Arpaxat Setrakian, a San Francisco raisin shipper, Alex Pilibos and Harry Carian, Indio, California, ranchers. Not republished. *T.L. 97*

T.L. 98 Through T.L. 111
Twelve miscellaneous pieces not reprinted here are briefly cited below:

T.L. 98. "My Armenia," in *HW*, November 16, 1934. A Saroyan credo.

T.L. 99. "In Answer to 'An Answer' to William Saroyan," in *HW*, December 21, 1934. On debate engendered by T.L. 98.

T.L. 100. "DeMaupassant, Saroyan and Bezzerides," in *HW*, May 13, 1938. Saroyan "reviews" his friend I.O. Bezzerides' novel *Long Haul*, based on the struggle of the Seropian brothers of Fresno against the railroad barons. Bezzerides too was an *HW* writer, his father Greek, his mother Armenian.

T.L. 101. "Every Armenian Should read [Hairenik] Weekly," in *HW*, July 8, 1938. Saroyan urges more *HW* subscribers.

T.L. 102. "Saroyan Invites Armenian Young People to Write a Story a Week for the Hairenik Weekly," in *HW.*, October 28, 1938.

T.L. 103. See "Problems of Writing," *(T.L. 44a)*.

T.L. 104. "Speech of Saroyan at ARF Press Day, March 19, 1939, in Fresno," in *HW*, March 31, 1939. The ARF is the Armenian Revolutionary Federation, sponsors of the Haireniks. T.L. 104, SMI, p. 344, erroneously dates this speech as having been given on March 31, rather than March 19.

T.L. 105. "(Poem) A Note on Contemporary Poetry," in *HW*, August 16, 1940, reprinted in the present work as T.L. 105, ahead.

T.L. 106. "A Book About American Writing," in *HW*, October 18, 1940. Saroyan "reviews" C. John McCole's *Lucifer at Large* (New York, 1937).

T.L. 107. "An Interview with Veradzin," in *HW*, December 10, 1941. Saroyan interviewed by Minas Veradzin, then editor of *Asbarez*, of Fresno.

T.L. 108. "Saroyan on the 40th Anniversary of the Hairenik Weekly," in *HW*, March 8, 1953.

T.L. 109. "Saroyan Congratulates Hairenik Weekly on 1000th Issue," in *HW*, May 7, 1953.

T.L. 110. "Saroyan's Wire on the Decease of Reuben Darbinian," in *HW*, May 9, 1968.

T.L. 111. "William Saroyan on James G. Mandalian," in *HW*, May 9, 1974. On passing of Mandalian, former *HW* editor. Autobiographically revealing. Reprinted in *TAR*, vol. xxvii (4–108), April 1975.

The Theological Student
In *TAR*, vol. i(1), Winter 1948. Saroyan's contribution to the inaugural issue of *The Armenian Review*, on the inception of which see Preface, SMI,

and Letter 64, dated March 23, 1948. This "Aram" story is built around an episode, or episodes occurring in Fresno when Saroyan was fourteen, that is, in 1922. This outstanding piece of writing was later (1949) republished in *The Assyrian and Other Stories. T.L. 112*

THE FOREIGNER

In *TAR*, vol. 1(2), June 1948. In his letter of March 29, 1948, (SMI, Letter 65, pp. 305–306), Saroyan comments: " . . . I have been having a bitter struggle with this story, and I am not sure even now that I have worked out all the elements which do not satisfy me. Please ask that pains be taken with this work and that the title of the story is changed to The Foreigner [from "The Veteran of Foreign Wars"] . . . I discovered while working on this story that part of its failure is its unnatural effort to be an 'Aram' story for it does not have the bland, casual, humorous and kindly tone of the Aram stories, and I have found it absolutely impossible to give it that tone; hence I have removed it from the 'Aram' group and put it into the looser and broader group of all my stories, in general . . ." Nevertheless, the piece is set in Fresno and refers to Saroyan's eighth year (1916), and the European war. Republished in *The Assyrian and Other Stories* (1949). *T.L. 113*

THE PLOT

In *TAR*, vol. ii(6), May, 1949. Not covered by any known letter to Haireniks. Obviously an "Aram" story. Republished in *The Assyrian and Other Stories* (1949). *T.L. 114*

A SAROYAN TRILOGY

In *TAR*, vol. vii (2–26), June 1954. A unitarian publication of three Saroyan contributions:
"My Shoes: a Short Story from 1933." *T.L. 115*
"The Fire-Prevention Man and His Sister." *T.L. 116*
"The Stolen Secret." *T.L. 117*
Letter 72, dated April 17, 1954, Malibu (SMI, pp. 312–313): "Now at last, I send a story (with introductory note) for the Review, if you find that you want it." Obviously, the reference here is to "My Shoes . . ." not, as proposed by the editor, to "The Rearward Dog" (T.L. 117a). In Letter 73, dated April 21, (SMI p. 313) WS writes: "This is how the title of the story should appear, I think: 'My Shoes: A Short Story from 1933.' This is followed by: Note [i.e. an 'introductory note']." On later arrangements with Saroyan, this Note appeared in *HW over* the body of the story proper, as herewith published.

In a latter dated May 1, (SMI p. 314) Saroyan submitted " 'The End of Our Rope? A Very Short Play.' It is also quite revised, I wonder if it is for the *Review*? If so, could it be got in the same issue as 'My Shoes'?" SMI, page 314, erroneously reports that "The End of Our Rope . . . ?" never appeared in the *Review*, or for that matter in the *HW*, but it turns out that "The End of Our Rope . . . ?" and "The Stolen Secret," the third of this trilogy, were one and the same—Saroyan had obviously requested that the title be changed, perhaps earliest via phone.

On May 4 (SMI p. 316) Saroyan wrote: "Here is something half-presuming to be a poem called The Fire-Prevention Man and His Sister: My thought is this, if it is at all possible: since I have not been in the *Review* for such a long time, to return with a group namely: 'My Shoes'; 'The Fire-Prevention Man and His Sister'; 'The End of Our Rope'—that is to say, a short story, a short play, and a little verse."

And on May 10 (SMI pp. 315–316): "Thank you very much for gathering the three items together for appearance in the *Review*; yes, I think trilogy will cover the situation nicely . . . the story has been attended to [revised and proofread], and is in order. Here then, is the play, and the verse. The play: you will notice the name has been changed to 'The Stolen Secret, A Short Play.' I have revised it considerably . . . The verse is also revised . . ." None of the three items has been republished, and the short play has never been performed. All unre-published. *T.L. 115–117*

The Rearward Dog

In *TAR*, vol. vii (3–27), Autumn 1954. WS's letter of May 4, from Malibu (SMI p. 316) discloses that this story was sent to *TAR* as "Baccarat at the Casino in Enghien": " . . . here's [a new story] right now, by all odds the best story I've sent you: Baccarat at the Casino in Enghien . . ." Then in a letter of June 21 (SMI p. 319): "I have forgotten the full title of the Baccarat story: in any case the important thing is that I don't like the title, so for the time being let's call that story 'The Rearward Dog,' as it was in the first place—when in fact the item was the beginning of a full novel. . . ." Republished in *The Whole Voyald, and Other Stories* (1956). Through printer's mishap, this story was not listed in the original T.L. compilation; here it is given the catalogue number T.L. 117a.

EDITOR'S NOTE

In accordance with William Saroyan's last will and testament, a funerary urn bearing half of his ashes was borne to the Armenian Soviet Socialist Republic where, on May 29, 1982, it was ceremoniously deposited in the Armenian Pantheon, a quadrangle reserved for the Armenian great in the Komitas Public Gardens. Top-level Armenian political and cultural dignitaries were elegists, eulogists and addressants, among them Karen Demirchyan, the first secretary of the Armenian Communist Party who, according to international press reports, "depicted Saroyan as a fervent supporter of Soviet rule in Armenia." This was, of course, predictable nonsense.

In order to avoid political polemics, which Saroyan himself carefully shunned during his lifetime, scarce reference has been made in the present work to Saroyan's many visits to Soviet Armenia; nor has there been any substantial discussion of what this might mean, or of what attitude Saroyan held on the issue of Soviet hegemony over that little corner of the ancient territorial patrimony represented today by the ASSR, although his writings give some insight into how he felt about all this.

Quite understandably, Soviet Armenian publications made quite a fuss over Saroyan's visits to the ASSR and, invariably, cast inferences that he was an admirer of the prevailing political order. This both distressed and amused Saroyan. In "Conversation with Tashjian" he said:

My visits to present Armenia are a compulsion. I want to see my people there, to speak to them, to hear Armenian spoken in the streets, to sing with them, to dance with them, to view the glories of our race. I want to see their print, to breathe their air, to sit in the Madenataran [Scriptorium] and touch the works of our ancient Masters. I want to enter the University and see the bright faces of our young students and pass the time of day with our scholars. I must spend an evening at the Spendiarian [music hall] hearing Komitas and Khatchaturyan as only Armenian musicians can know them. I must climb our hills to Ambert ["The Monastery Built in the Clouds"] and visit our museums to marvel at the artifacts of our past . . . say, do you know that the use of the wheel for transport was an Armenian invention? I have seen with my own eyes the four-wheeled wagon found in a Sevan cave which some Englishman recently swore was the earliest example of wheeled transport. I must honor the genius of my *people;* for what they have accomplished in the past, and what they are accomplishing today, is the product of their own genius, despite the foreign presence, despite the difficulties our nation has suffered. I often ask myself what even greater wonders we might have done had we been left alone, had we been free to apply our genius freely to the exercise of the creative force that has led us, as an example, to create great works of literature while barbarians were burning our land. Now, I am aware that my visits to Soviet Armenia are often politically exploited. I have read statements attributed to me which I never said. But, hell, no harm done, let them have their fun. I return to my father's land and people to see my father's land and people, to learn, again and again, why we are a great although little people, to return refreshed in my inheritance. I'm no politician, and I detest political propaganda, although I understand why our politicians must make propaganda. But that is their problem, not mine. I am an Armenian, I am a writer, I am no politician, and if I don't pity politicians, I at least regard them perhaps as a necessary evil, although I often ask myself why. I am amused at some of the things they print about me. The important thing is that when I see my *people*, I breathe their air and I marvel that they have once again been able to lift themselves up by their own bootstraps. And I am assured that there will always be Armenians, Armenia, Armenian writing, Armenian art. It is important to the world that there are Armenians. Wherever it is that I will come to the end of the line, it will always be in my father's Armenia, our *Armenian* Armenia—and to hell with the others. James, my resting place will always be a little corner of Armenia. . . .

Reports of the rites held at the Komitas Gardens said that "thousands" of William Saroyan's *people*—the common folk of Armenia and their cultural leaders—gathered to honor his ashes. We are certain that William Saroyan was grateful.